Population and Food

Population and Food

Michel Cépède · François Houtart · Linus Grond

SHEED AND WARD · NEW YORK

Originally published as *Nourrir les hommes*
by Editions du Cep, Brussels.

Library of Congress Catalog Card Number 63–8546

Manufactured in the United States of America

Preface

HENRI LAUGIER is fond of repeating the following observation, attributed to an atomic physicist:

The man who knows all there is to be known about a subject goes into research. The man who knows something about it goes into teaching. And the man who doesn't know a thing about it—he co-ordinates the work of the others.

Well aware of which group we belong in, we have here limited our efforts to co-ordinating such knowledge as we may individually possess.

At the same time, to the degree that our investigations have advanced, we have considered ourselves in a position to teach others —to teach them, that is, the bit we do know of the matter, the bit that can be taught. As for research, it has become increasingly clear to us that there is still a great deal to be done if this vast problem is to be well and truly grasped. It is our joint hope that we shall have covered enough of the problem to bring the reader to the same opinion, and that we shall have stimulated him to undertake researches of his own. With St. John, we are convinced that the truth alone will save us, but we are not convinced that science can as yet claim to be in possession of it.

Like Karl Marx, we can see for ourselves that mankind addresses itself to a problem only when it is in a position to solve it. What this means to us is that the truth is disclosed to man within the limits of his needs and the resources of his knowledge. We find this yet another reason for trusting our own efforts to come closer to the truth—and for believing that the results of our own efforts cannot be a message of doom with respect to the future of mankind.

M. CÉPÈDE
F. HOUTART
L. GROND

Contents

Preface   v

PRELIMINARY CONSIDERATIONS   3

1 CURRENT TRENDS IN WORLD POPULATION GROWTH   5
    Some Historical Observations   5
    The Present Situation   16

2 HISTORICAL SURVEY OF POPULATION THEORY   37
    Before Malthus   39
    From Malthus to the Present   51

I HOW POPULATION DEVELOPS   69

3 THE BIOLOGICAL LAWS OF POPULATION   71

4 HOW ACTUAL POPULATIONS HAVE GROWN   98
    World Population   98
    Some Examples of Demographic Trends   104
    Population of Japan   114
    Population of the Maghrib   125
    Population of French Canada   131
    The "Baby Boom" after 1945 in the Western Countries   140

5 THE POPULATION FACTORS: MORTALITY AND NATALITY   151
    Changes in Life Expectancy   151
    The Effects of Medical Progress   166

Nutrition and Mortality   175
War and Disease   182
Natality: What Are the Facts?   184
Biological Causes of the Falling Birth Rate   192
Social and Cultural Influences on Fertility and Birth   201
Natality and Social Organization   208
Natality and Family Structures   216
Natality and Cultural Systems   219
General Conclusions   238

II THE MEANS OF SUBSISTENCE   247

6 HOW FOOD PRODUCTION HAS DEVELOPED   249
  Preliminary Considerations   249
      Methods of Measurement   249
      Vegetable Calories   258
      Man, Parasite and Predator   261
  The History of Food Production   262
      Food-Gathering, Hunting, and Fishing   262
      Pastoral Economy   269
      Agricultural Economy   273
      Production: True or False?   285
  The Paradox of Surpluses   309
      Looking Around the World   309
      What Was Learned in the Depression Years   317
  Examples of Increased Food Production   331
      The United States   331
      France   333

7 THE PROCESS OF FOOD PRODUCTION   338
  Economic and Technical Factors   338
      Advances in Technique   338
      Soils   343
      Labor   346

Social, Cultural, and Political Factors 357
  International Obstacles to Solving the
    Problem of Hunger 360
  Socio-Cultural Factors 369
  Institutional Obstacles: The Agrarian Question 389
  Political Factors 405
  First Priority: Education 410
Implementing Technical Progress 411
  Situating the Problem 412
  How to Hold on to the Factors for Progress 416
  Getting Two Different Technological
    Environments in Touch 418
  The Meaning of Values and Situations 430

III CONCLUSIONS 439

8 FEWER PEOPLE OR ENHANCED SUBSISTENCE? 441

9 WHAT CAN BE DONE 444

10 OBSTACLES AND ALIBIS 449

11 GENERAL CONCLUSIONS 454

List of Tables and Graphs

Table 1   China Proper: Emended Series of Population
Statistics, A.D. 2–1953   6

Table 2   Growth of World Population, 1650–1960 (estimates in millions)   10

Table 3   World Population by Continents, 1920 to 1960
(adjusted estimates of mid-year population, in
millions)   11

Table 4   Years Required for Doubling of World Population at Different Periods (population in millions)   12

Table 5   Estimated World Population, 1650–1960, by
Continent (in millions)   12

Table 6   World Population by Continents (percentage
distribution of total world population)   13

Table 7   World Population by Continents (decennial
percentage increase)   15

Table 7A   World Population by Sub-Continents (decennial percentage increase)   15

Table 8   Selected Countries of Rapid Population Growth,
1950–1960   16

Table 9   World Population by Sub-Continents, 1920 to
1960 (adjusted estimates of mid-year population, in millions)   18

Table 9A   World Population by Sub-Continents (percentage distribution of total world population)   18

Table 10   Average Population Density of Continents and Major Sub-Continents (inhabitants per square mile)   20

Table 11   Countries with Very High Population Density, c. 1960   21

Table 11A   Countries with Very Low Population Density, c. 1960   22

Table 12   Estimates of Urban and Metropolitan Population by Continents, c. 1960   25

Table 13   UN Estimates of Population in 1950 and 1980, Prepared in 1951 for Three Groups of World Regions (population in millions)   28

Table 14   Estimates of World Population, 1950–1975 (Two Assumptions)   30

Table 14A   Estimates of World Population, 1975–2000 (Three Assumptions)   31

Table 15   Increase of Population according to the "High" Projection, 1950–60 and 1960–70; Estimated Actual Increase, 1950–1960, for the World by Regions   32

Table 16   Anticipated Changes in Birth Rates, Death Rates, and Rates of Natural Increase of Continents and the World, 1950–1975   33

Table 17   Microbe Population in Closed Environment (non-sporuliferous species)   73

Table 18   Microbe Population in Closed Culture (sporuliferous species)   75

Table 19   World Population Growth: The Two Alternatives   95

Table 20   Urbanization and Occupational Structure, and Population Density in Western Europe, c. 1950   107

Table 21   Birth Rates in the United States by Statistical Region, 1960 (per 1,000)   110

Table 22   Recent Birth Rates and Urbanization in Canada (by Province)   111

Table 23	Birth Rates, Urban and Rural Switzerland, 1937–1959	113
Table 24	Populationof Japan and Rates of Increase over Five-Year Periods, 1920–1940	117
Table 25	Population of Japan—Birth Rate, Death Rate, and Rate of Natural Increase, 1933–1961 (per 1,000)	119
Table 26	Projected Japanese Population Growth, 1955–1975 (in millions): Three Projections	121
Table 27	Estimated Japanese Population Growth, 1975–2000 (in millions)	121
Table 28	Births and Legal Abortions in Japan, 1949–1961 (in thousands)	123
Table 29	Age Composition of Japanese Population, 1960 and 2000 (in percentages)	124
Table 30	Growth of Five Algerian Cities, 1900–1959 (in thousands)	126
Table 31	Population of Algeria, 1953 (crude figures rounded to nearest thousand)	127
Table 32	Comparative Age Structures, France and Algeria (in percentages of total population)	128
Table 33	Comparative Demographic Structure, Metropolitan France and Algeria, 1953 (per 1,000)	129
Table 34	Population of Canada and of Canadian Provinces, 1921–1957 (in thousands)	132
Table 35	Immigration to Canada, 1901–1951	135
Table 36	Growth of Ontario's Population, 1871–1951	136
Table 37	How Canada's Population Grew, 1911–1940 (in thousands)	137
Table 38	Birth Rates in Several European Countries before 1914	143
Table 39	Birth Rates in Some European Countries, before, during, and after World War I	144
Table 40	Lowest Pre-War Birth Rates Compared with Wartime Birth Rates	146

Table 41   Birth Rates in the Western Countries in Vari-
              ous Periods between 1910 and 1961   148

Table 42   Death Rates and Length of Life in Continents
              and Sub-Continents (estimates)   153

Table 43   Mortality in France, Actual and Potential,
              1958 (number of survivors per 1,000 births)   154

Table 44   Life Expectancy in Contrasting Countries,
              Recorded or Estimated 1955–1958 and c.
              1900–1920   155

Table 45   Recent Mortality Trends in Various Underde-
              veloped Countries Compared with the Secular
              Mortality Trend in Sweden   156

Table 46   Comparison of Birth and Death Rate in a
              European Population and in an Underdevel-
              oped Population, Placed One Century Back   160

Table 47   Trends in the Expectation of Life at Birth in
              Three Asian Countries; The Rapid Decline in
              Ceylonese Mortality since 1946   162

Table 48   Percentage of Total Deaths, 1936–1945, for
              Children Aged 0 and 1–5 Years   165

Table 49   Recent Crude Death Rates and Natural In-
              crease Rates for Selected Countries   172

Table 50   Correlation between Nutritional Level and
              Male Life Expectancy in Some Countries   176

Table 51   Correlation between Infant Mortality (per
              1,000 population) and the Nutritional Level in
              Certain Countries (in vegetable calories, as of
              1937–38)   178

Table 52   Correlation between Infant Mortality (per
              1,000 population) and Number of Inhabitants
              per Doctor   179

Table 53   Changing Birth Rates, 1871–1960   188

Table 54   Estimated World Population and Birth Rate,
              1937   189

Table 55   Estimated World Population Growth and Birth
              Rates, 1950–1975   190

Table 56   Relation between Protein Percentage in Diet and Fertility in Rats   194

Table 57   Birth Rates and Protein Consumption per Head   197

Table 58   Development of Family Disbursement Offices in France, 1931–1945   228

Table 59   How the Average Consumption (in calories) of the Principal Food Products Increases in Relation to Total Food Consumption (in calories) per Person and per Day   255

Table 59A   Transposition of the Consumption Curves in the Preceding Graph to Semi-Logarithmic Scale: (1) Cereal, Grains and Root Vegetables, (2) Dry Vegetables (pulses), (3) Sugar, (4) Oils and Fats, (5) Meat, (6) Milk   256

Table 60   Relationship between Nutritional Ration and Labor Ration and Productivity   265

Table 61   Mined Copper Production by Principal Producing Countries (in percentages)   295

Table 62   Estimated Harvests of Certain Food Commodities in Some Countries (averages for 1949–51 in 100 kilogram-hectares)   312

Table 63   Index of Agricultural Production (1934–38 = 100)   313

Table 64   Theoretical Development of Supply and Demand in Agricultural Products in View of Quantities and Prices   322

Table 65   Number of Tractors in Use in Agriculture (per 1,000 hectares) of European Countries, 1939–1955   341

Table 66   World Population Broken Down by Age Groups, c. 1950   348

Table 67   Life Expectancy at Ages 0–60 in an Advanced Country (type A) and in an Underdeveloped Country (type B)   350

Table 68   What Happen When a Program of Development Is Undertaken in an Underdeveloped
Country (type B) of Stable Population   352

Table 68A   What Happens When a Program of Development Is Undertaken in an Underdeveloped
Country (type B^1) of Growing Population   353

Population and Food

PRELIMINARY CONSIDERATIONS

Chapter 1

Current Trends in World Population Growth

SOME HISTORICAL OBSERVATIONS

THE MARKED INTEREST aroused in our time by quantitative increases in world population obviously derives from awareness of a threatening imbalance between current population growth and the means of subsistence.

Demographers and politicians who have addressed themselves to the problem of whether the earth may still be able, some years from now, to support mankind, are asking whether imbalances of the sort occurred before and, if so, what solutions men and nature worked out before now. Their questioning is based on the argument that knowledge of the world's population problems in the past may help us to grasp better various aspects of the present problem, especially if research might lead beyond information about historical events to fundamental reasons for the phenomenon which the twentieth century thinks of as "the population explosion."

Classical Times and the Middle Ages. Available data are scanty for the study of world population throughout antiquity and the early Christian era. Moreover, they refer only to one part of the world and, besides, their scientific value is highly relative.

We are told that, a few years before the birth of Christ, the population of the Roman Empire came to about 54 million.[1] This figure includes all territories of the Empire, in Asia and Africa as well as in Europe.[2] In TABLE 1 we can see the great fluctuations revealed by the best statistics available for China over the last two millennia. While there is no doubt that there has been an uptrend in

TABLE 1

China Proper: Emended Series of Population Statistics,
A.D. 2–1953

Dynasty and Year (A.D.)	Population (millions)	Dynasty and Year (A.D.)	Population (millions)
Western Han:		Sung-Ch'in:	
2	71	1193–1195 ...	123
Eastern Han:		Ming:	
88	43	1381	60
105	53	1393	61
125	56	Ching:	
140	56	1751	207
156	62	1781	270
Sui:		1791	294
606	54	1811	347
T'ang:		1821	344
705	37	1831	383
726	41	1841	400
732	45	1851	417
742	51	People's Republic:	
755	52	1953	518
Sung:			
1014	60		
1029	61		
1048	64		
1065	77		
1075	94		
1086	108		
1094	115		
1103	123		

China's population in the very long run, the absolute figures in this table cannot be taken at their face value. The only point that this table makes unequivocally is that China's population went down as well as up in various periods before the nineteenth century.[3] Two broad conclusions can be drawn within the perspectives of the 1960's:

1) The earth was sparsely populated at the beginning of the Christian era. The UN, which has access to data for widely scattered parts of the world (the Roman Empire, China, India, and other continents), estimates that the world was peopled by from 200 to 300 million individuals in the time of Christ.[4]

2) Century after century, the growth of world population was extremely slow. At the same time, the land was so sparsely peopled, with so many "wide-open spaces" beckoning mankind, that the phenomenon must seem strange to us today. We can only conclude that mankind was as little capable, in this remote epoch, of realizing the divine precept to increase and multiply and fill the earth, as it was incapable of subduing the earth to its purposes. We may suppose that the primary precept was so very imperfectly followed, because the latter was still beyond its powers. Face to face with nature and the universe, man found himself confronted with a great mystery he could not master, and which yet mastered him.

Ignorant of nature's powers, within his own body as well as outside it, he was a vessel too feeble to resist disease and death. The average expectation of life was no more than thirty years; one-fourth of all children died before the age of one. Nor did mankind have any greater knowledge of, greater control over, the world around it. In the nineteenth and the early twentieth centuries, the persistently underdeveloped countries typically experienced a death rate of some 30 or more per 1,000 inhabitants, and a birth rate above 40, and even up to 60, per 1,000. The preceding centuries since the decline of the Roman Empire were even less fortunate before the hand of death; yet their fertility rate cannot consistently have been over 70 per 1,000, and usually cannot have approached that figure. While the observer of today must be appalled by the death toll in the underdeveloped countries at the beginning of this century, their resultant rate of natural increase was not only positive, but often reached an annual average of 1 or 2 per cent. Before the first fruits of the industrial and agricultural revolutions were exported from the advanced countries, however, the population of the less developed countries scarcely increased at all, and frequently fell. This was the case also in the territories of the former Roman Empire before the agricultural and industrial revolutions, which, indeed, rarely produced fundamental benefits for the population at large in these countries until the last century. Sauvy has observed that, if the difference between the birth and death rates had averaged 1 or 2 per cent in that part of the world since the Dark Ages, they would now hold a population of 3 billion.[5] Actually the Roman Empire did not even enjoy such a moderate population growth, so that there are now 3 billion people in the whole world.

This spread between theoretical extrapolation and the actual growth that took place, constitutes, according to Sauvy, a constant feature of historical development over the centuries of our era. It is plain that man was not yet in a position of mastery over the various factors which acted as a brake upon his quantitative increase. He was helpless in the face of great natural disasters, such as the floods which periodically decimated the population of China, and epidemics like the Black Death of 1348 which may have killed off nearly half the population of Europe. Since there were years when the harvest was bad, he was obliged to accept periodic famine as an ineluctable result of disturbance in the balance between food supply and the numbers of people dependent upon it. Moreover, in every century history teaches us that wars have also had profound effects upon the demographic structure of the areas affected, and even more by their indirect repercussions (pillage, brigandage, destruction of the means of production, conditions favorable to the rise and spread of disease) than by the toll of dead and wounded on the battlefield.

Thus, many years after the peace of 1648 brought the Thirty Years War to an end, people throughout the Germanic countries were still feeling its deadly consequences. In a number of regions, the population was reduced to less than half of what it had been.

It can thus be said that, broadly speaking, the world did not for centuries know a direct imbalance between population and the means of subsistence. When the phenomenon did occur, it tended to be regional, and nature herself nearly always restored the balance, often very drastically. By and large the human mind gave little attention to this problem.

In classical times, it is true, a few thinkers had expressed concern over the growing numbers of human beings. McCormack begins his recent book *People, Space, Food* from Tertullian's *De anima*, 30, which is very much to the point.[6] On the one hand, he observes that "Now all lands are accessible, all are explored, all are open to traffic," and on the other hand that "The population is so great . . . we are now a burden on the world," and "There are barely enough of the essentials for us . . . for nature can no longer sustain us."

In our own day pessimistic attitudes like this are as common as they were rare in the ancient world. Strictly speaking, it was not until Malthus that the topic of imbalance between population and food began to be raised seriously and defined clearly. His treatment of it in the *Essay on the Principle of Population* shows that in his day the historical consequences of the great fifteenth-century discoveries were just beginning to make themselves felt, qualitatively and quantitatively. Man was beginning to get to know his world and to gain a degree of mastery over it. He was learning ways of freeing himself from his long helplessness before the mysterious, pitiless forces of nature.

In Malthus' day, the population of Great Britain, which had shown no greater growth between Roman times and the year 1675 than an increase from 1 million to something more than 5 million, was already past the 10 million mark. In other words, the population had grown more in one century than in all the preceding hundreds of years since the beginning of the Christian era.

The same phenomenon was making itself felt in every country of the civilized world, though the rate of increase was everywhere different, as were the precipitating factors. Reinhard concludes that we can hardly speak of any general trend even in modern times.[7]

Since 1650. Despite a number of reservations, the authors of this study agree in saying that our knowledge of world population trends is much more extensive and exact for the period after 1650. The UN has published a summary of the estimates of world population between 1650 and 1900 drawn up by Carr-Saunders and Willcox, adjusted to compare with the regional breakdown the UN supplies.[8] For 1920 and later, the UN's own estimates as of 1950 and 1960 are supplied along with the Carr-Saunders and Willcox estimates in TABLE 2.

TABLE 2
Growth of World Population, 1650–1960
(estimates in millions)

Year	1650	1750	1800	1850	1900	1920	1930	1940	1950	1960
Willcox	470	694	919	1,091	1,571					
Carr-Saunders	545	728	906	1,171	1,608					
UN 1950						1,834	2,008	2,216	2,406	
UN 1960						1,860	2,064	2,277	2,499	2,964

The relative value of these figures is clear, not just from the differing results of Willcox and Carr-Saunders, but also from the UN's first *Population Bulletin* (December, 1951), which gives different figures for the years 1850 and 1900 than Willcox gives. Sauvy gives still other figures,[9] though he also cites the UN study, *The Determinants and Consequences of Population Trends.* For the years 1800, 1850, 1900, and 1950, he gives (in millions) 907, 1,175, 1,620, and 2,476, respectively. The explanation for the discrepancies (and there are others besides those mentioned) is the general unreliability and inexactness of statistics for a great many countries, especially the newer and underdeveloped countries. One recent instance involves the population of China. According to the 1948 census, the figure was 463,493,000. However, the demographer Ta Chen is on record as stating that a little before 1950 China's total population came to 400 million at the most. Western demographers are generally agreed that in studies of

Chinese population, it is not too much to expect errors in the neighborhood of 100 million. . . . While the mainland government published a figure of 647 million for 1958, semi-official estimates also indicate a population of 670–680 million, so that no demographer would be surprised if the next census contradicted these figures.

And yet with all due reservations, there is no question but that world population has been increasing over the past three hundred years at a rate hitherto unknown in human history, and that it now stands at approximately 3 billion.

TABLE 3 gives the most recent UN statistics for the world's population, by continents.

TABLE 3

World Population by Continents, 1920 to 1960*
(adjusted estimates of mid-year population, in millions)

	1920	1930	1940	1950	1960
Africa	141	157	176	206	254
Americas	208	244	277	329	405
Asia	966	1,072	1,212	1,386	1,679
Europe	329	356	381	395	427
(excluding U.S.S.R.)					
Oceania	9	10	11	13	17
U.S.S.R.	158	176	192	181	214
World Total	1,811	2,015	2,249	2,510	2,996

* United Nations, 1963 *Report on the World Social Situation* (New York, 1964), Chap. II, Table 1.

Crude figures such as these, however, are not conclusive. We can only fully grasp the uniqueness of the situation today by studying what has been happening over the past three centuries, and on that basis forming some idea of prospects for the future.

There has been steady increase in the rate of world population growth over the past three hundred years. (See TABLE 4.) For a better understanding of present trends, it will be useful to analyze these data from two different points of view: first by parts of the world and then in terms of relative increase.

TABLE 4

Years Required for Doubling of World Population
at Different Periods
(population in millions)

Year	World Population	Doubling Period
1	250	
1650	500	1650 yrs.
1830	1,000	180 yrs.
1930	2,000	100 yrs.
1960	3,000	50 yrs.
1980	4,000	40 yrs.
2000	6,000	

Population Growth since 1650 in the Various Parts of the World. Although, as we have seen, the world's population has been steadily mounting over the past few hundred years, the rate of increase has not been the same in every part of the world. (See TABLE 5.)

TABLE 5

Estimated World Population, 1650–1960, by Continent*
(in millions)

YEAR:	1650	1700	1750	1800	1850	1900	1950	1960
Africa	100	98	95	90	95	120	206	254
Americas	13	13	12	25	59	144	329	405
Asia	330	400	479	602	749	937	1,386	1,679
Europe	100	110	140	187	266	401	576	641
Oceania	2	2	2	2	2	6	13	17
World Total	545	623	728	906	1,171	1,608	2,510	2,996

* UN, *1963 World Social Situation,* Chap. II, Table 1.

This anything but uniform development has consistently affected population distribution, as we can see in TABLE 6. Analysis of the above two tables brings out the following essential points:

1) The curve of African population cannot have risen appre-

TABLE 6

World Population by Continents*

(percentage distribution of total world population)

	1920	1950	1960
Africa	7.9	8.2	8.5
Americas	11.5	13.1	13.5
Asia	53.3	55.2	56.1
Europe	18.1	15.8	14.2
(excluding U.S.S.R.)			
Oceania	0.5	0.5	0.5
U.S.S.R.	8.7	7.2	7.1
World Total	100.0	100.0	100.0

* UN, *1963 World Social Situation*, Chap. II, Table 1.

ciably until the nineteenth century. Perhaps the subsaharan territories lost population in previous centuries, particularly during the
period of the slave trade to the Americas and the Middle East. Yet
the ravages of slavery may have been counteracted by the introduction of new food crops and the expansion of commerce. At any
rate, over the last fifty years, there has been a decided speeding up
of Africa's population growth. Previously Africa's population was
certainly declining as a percentage of the world's total.

2) Both in North America and in Latin America, population
growth was considerably enhanced by the great waves of immigration. Especially since the middle of the last century, North America
has grown relatively rapidly. Central and South America are still
in the early stages of population increase, though over the last fifty
years it has stepped up to the point where it deserves the term of
population explosion.

3) Asia, the most heavily populated of the continents, has
undergone a population decline with relation to world-wide population growth. Nonetheless, Asia has accounted for more than half
of the world's people since 1930, and will hold its own in the
coming decades. In crude figures, the Asian population is always
enormous. At present, the continent has reached some 1,700
million.

4) The history of Europe's population growth firmly substantiates the thesis that the factors governing population are not exclusively biological. Cradle of modern civilization and center of world industry, Europe has more than any other continent achieved mastery over the laws and forces of nature. Also, until quite recently, Europe's population has steadily increased, despite the emigration of several million inhabitants to other continents. Over the last few decades, European genius, along with that of other areas of Western civilization, has begun to achieve mastery and control over the natural laws of the human body and its creative powers. European population figures since 1900 are unmistakable evidence of this. In sum, the population of Europe and North America has expanded much more rapidly than the other continents over the last two centuries.

Rates of Population Increase. As we have seen, world population growth has been held back throughout human history. Indeed, down to the middle of the seventeenth century, the rate of increase was probably about zero on the average.

Such a low rate of increase has, of course, necessarily and substantially been raised by the prodigious growth of the world's population over the last few centuries. We ourselves confirm that the actual rate of increase of world population has been steadily climbing since the middle of the seventeenth century. Between 1650 and 1850, the world's population may have grown at one-half of one per cent each year. It accelerated in subsequent decades, reaching 1 per cent per annum by the 1920's. It had never approached 2 per cent per annum until the last decade. Should this upward trend persist, by simple extrapolation we might expect a rate of population growth of some 5 per cent. It seems more likely, however, that the world's population will not expand by much more than 2 per cent per annum before the end of this century.

We have also found that population growth is much more rapid in non-European regions than in countries of European civilization. This is clearly shown by the different rates of increase in the different parts of the world (TABLES 7, 7A).

TABLE 7
World Population by Continents*
(decennial percentage increase)

	1920/30	1930/40	1940/50	1950/60
Africa	11.3	12.1	17.0	23.3
Americas	17.3	13.5	18.8	23.1
Asia	11.0	13.1	14.4	21.1
Europe (excluding U.S.S.R.)	8.2	7.0	3.7	8.1
Oceania	18.2	8.7	15.0	26.9
U.S.S.R.	11.4	9.1	−5.7	18.2
World Total	11.3	11.6	11.6	19.3

* UN, *1963 World Social Situation*, Chap. II, Table 1.

TABLE 7A
World Population by Sub-Continents*
(decennial percentage increase)

	1920/30	1930/40	1940/50	1950/60
North Africa	12.8	15.1	16.4	23.9
Tropical & Southern Africa	10.6	10.6	17.0	23.0
Northern America	15.4	8.1	14.4	19.2
Middle America	13.3	20.6	24.4	29.4
South America	23.0	20.0	23.3	26.1
Southwest Asia	9.3	12.8	13.2	28.3
Southcentral Asia	11.0	13.3	15.1	18.4
Southeast Asia	16.4	21.1	12.9	22.3
East Asia	9.9	11.0	14.3	22.1
Northern & Western Europe	6.1	4.9	3.9	6.8
Central Europe	7.1	5.8	0.8	8.6
Southern Europe	11.8	10.5	6.3	9.0
Oceania	18.2	8.7	15.0	26.9
U.S.S.R.	11.4	9.1	−5.7	18.2
World Total	100.0	100.0	100.0	100.0

* UN, *1963 World Social Situation*, Chap. II, Table 1.

In the 1950's, as these tables show, Europe had the lowest continental population growth, 8 per cent. Northern and Western Europe had the world's lowest sub-continental growth rates, a mere 7 per cent. The populations of Middle America, South America,

Southwest Asia, and Oceania grew four times as fast as Northern and Western Europe's. In several countries, population grew by one-third or more over the last decade.

TABLE 8

Selected Countries of Rapid Population Growth, 1950–1960*

Country	Extremely Rapid % Increase	Country	Rapid % Increase
Canada	29.9	Algeria	25.9
Dominican Republic	41.4	Australia	25.6
Ghana	33.3	Brazil	26.5
Guatemala	34.2	Ceylon	28.9
Iraq	34.2	Colombia	24.7
Israel	68.0	Congo (Leopold.)	25.7
Mexico	35.5	Peru	27.4
Morocco	29.9	Thailand	27.6
Rhodesia & Nyasaland	31.6	U.A.R.	26.8
Philippines	33.7		
South Africa	31.6		
Turkey	32.9		
Venezuela	44.8		

* UN, *1963 World Social Situation,* Chap. II, Table 2.

Among the 13 countries with at least a 30 per cent population growth over the last decade, only Israel's rapid growth is due mainly to heavy immigration; 8 of these countries had practically no immigration at all on balance. Among the 9 countries with a 25 to 29 per cent increase, only Australia's gain has come largely from immigration. In other words, these high population growth rates in most cases are the result of a great excess of births over deaths, especially among the underdeveloped countries.

THE PRESENT SITUATION

As the preceding discussion has made clear, the growth of world population has been such as to bring it in our own time to an extremely high level, without precedent in human history.

Under the circumstances, it is hardly surprising that those who are responsible for the public welfare are demanding every assistance that science can give, in order on the one hand to be reliably informed as to the scope and character of these developments, and on the other hand to be able to take whatever measures may be necessary to eliminate the tensions and disasters already afflicting or threatening various parts of the world.

There is no doubt whatever that tensions of this sort already exist in large areas where there is imbalance between population and the means of subsistence. Two-thirds of the world's people are undernourished and lack the minimum comforts of life. And it is precisely among the peoples of these underdeveloped countries that the population increase is most pronounced.

Before trying to examine the relationship between population and the means of subsistence, it would seem in order to take a long look at the present world demographic situation, to sketch the typical characteristics of the various parts of the world, and to draw up an over-all view of their expected population development over the next forty years.

The World Population in 1962. The United Nations estimates world population at 2,854 million in 1962. In 1960, the year for which the most precise recent figures are available, the world's population was distributed by continent and by geographic area, as we see in TABLES 9, 9A.

When we compare these figures with the estimates for 1950, it can be seen that population increase was weakest throughout Europe (northwest, central, and southern) and in the U.S.S.R. (both European and Asiatic). It follows that, proportionately, the European continent has dropped still lower with relation to total world population. This was in line with existing trends. In 1920, Europe's population, including Asiatic U.S.S.R., came to 24.8 per cent of the world population. This figure went down to 23.0 per cent in 1950, and in 1960 was down to 21.3 per cent.

Every other continent, except Oceania, increased its proportion

TABLE 9

World Population by Sub-Continents, 1920 to 1960*
(adjusted estimates of mid-year population, in millions)

	1920	1930	1940	1950	1960
North Africa	47	53	61	71	88
Tropical & Southern Africa	94	104	115	135	166
Northern America	117	135	146	167	199
Middle America	30	34	41	51	66
South America	61	75	90	111	140
Southwest Asia	43	47	53	60	77
Southcentral Asia	326	362	410	472	559
Southeast Asia	110	128	155	175	214
East Asia	487	535	594	679	829
Northern & Western Europe	115	122	128	133	142
Central Europe	112	120	127	128	139
Southern Europe	102	114	126	134	146
Oceania	8.8	10.4	11.3	13.0	16.5
U.S.S.R.	158	176	192	181	214
World Total	1,811	2,015	2,249	2,510	2,995

* UN, *1963 World Social Situation,* Chap. II, Table 1.

TABLE 9A

World Population by Sub-Continents*
(percentage distribution of total world population)

	1920	1950	1960
North Africa	2.7	2.8	2.9
Tropical & Southern Africa	5.2	5.4	5.4
Northern America	6.5	6.7	6.6
Middle America	1.6	2.0	2.2
South America	3.4	4.4	4.7
Southwest Asia	2.4	2.4	2.6
Southcentral Asia	18.0	18.8	18.7
Southeast Asia	6.0	7.0	7.1
East Asia	26.9	27.0	27.7
Northern & Western Europe	6.3	5.3	4.7
Central Europe	6.2	5.1	4.6
Southern Europe	5.6	5.4	4.9
Oceania	0.5	0.5	0.5
U.S.S.R.	8.7	7.2	7.1
World Total	100.0	100.0	100.0

* UN, *1963 World Social Situation,* Chap. II, Table 1.

of the world's total. The greatest gains were found in Latin America and Asia. North America barely held its own.

Undoubtedly a change is taking place in the distribution of mankind over the earth's surface. The development has some good features. For example, in sparsely settled continents like Africa and, to a certain extent, South America and Southeast Asia, population increase is desirable in itself. North America's population is also growing. Similarly, from the point of view of population distribution, Europe's drop percentage-wise in relation to total world population may be deemed desirable. However, the present trends are not to be envisaged purely in quantitative terms. A better distribution of the world's people will only be possible and desirable when the conditions necessary to it have been realized—which will not be the case for many years to come. As long as great areas of the world remain underdeveloped in social, economic and technological senses, population increases can lead to disaster.

Under present conditions, Western Europe, though very densely populated, could support a population increase much better than Africa, which is relatively sparsely populated. In this connection, the population increase in South Asia gives cause for concern. To sum up, it is not enough just to know how many millions of people inhabit the different parts of the world. It is much more important to know:

1) The population density of each area.

2) The actual trends in world population. By studying population structure within different areas, on the basis of the demographic elements and factors at our disposal, it is possible to arrive at theoretical population models of those areas. Such constructs of "typical" countries can give clues to future population growth.

3) The economic potentialities of the various areas, from the point of view of living standards. In other words, are the means of subsistence adequate and dependable in these countries? Can they be sufficiently developed, so that a population increase need not entail grave dangers? These problems will form the subject of Part II of this study.

Population Densities in the Different Areas. Exclusive of the polar regions and a few uninhabited islands, the earth's surface comprises some 52.3 million square miles of dry land. This means that, on the basis of the 1960 figures, there was a world population density of about 68 persons per square mile. This figure for the world averages out very dissimilar figures for the different continents. Population density per square mile is 21 for Africa, 23 for North America, 26 for Latin America, 157 for Asia, 223 for Europe, and 5 for Oceania.

TABLE 10

Average Population Density of Continents
and Major Sub-Continents
(inhabitants per square mile)

	1920	*1960*
Africa	13	21
Northern America	13	23
Latin America	10	26
Asia	98	157
Europe	171	223
Oceania	3	5
U.S.S.R.	18	26

TABLES 11, 11A list the countries of extremely high and extremely low density, and also highlight the countries with a weak economic base burdened by dense population, as well as those countries with a strong economic base supporting a scant population.

The great number of African countries with low population densities is very striking, especially below the Sahara. The scantiness of population in North Africa and the Near East around Israel, Lebanon, and the U.A.R. is of course due largely to deserts and arid grasslands over large tracts. The U.A.R., excluding the desert, has nearly two thousand inhabitants per square mile.

TABLE 11

Countries with Very High Population Density, c. 1960*

Continent & Country	Inhabitants (per sq. mile)	Continent & Country	Inhabitants (per sq. mile)
Africa		*Europe*	
Rwanda	262	Belgium	780
		Czechoslovakia	280
Americas		Denmark	277
El Salvador	329	Germany (E.)	386
Haiti	396	Germany (W.)	562
Jamaica	370	Hungary	280
Puerto Rico	702	Italy	425
Trinidad & Tobago	440	Netherlands	896
		Portugal	251
Asia		Switzerland	344
Ceylon	401	United Kingdom	562
Taiwan	790		
India	357		
Israel	275		
Japan	658		
Korea (S.)	668		
Lebanon	409		
Pakistan	259		
Philippines	249		
Viet Nam (N.)	273		

TABLE 11A

Countries with Very Low Population Density, c. 1960*

Africa	Inhabitants per Sq. Mile	Asia	Inhabitants per Sq. Mile
Algeria	13	Eden & Protec.	4
Angola	10	Laos	21
Bechuanaland	10	Mongolia	3
Cameroun	23	Muscat & Oman	8
Central African Republic	5	Qatar	5
Chad	5	Saudi Arabia	10
Congo (Brazz.)	8	Trucial Oman	3
Congo (Leopold.)	15		
Fr. Somaliland	8	*Europe*	
Gabon	5	Iceland	5
Libya	3		

Madagascar	23	*Oceania*		
Mali	7	Australia		3
Mauritania	3	New Caledonia		10
Mozambique	21	New Guinea-Papua		10
Niger	5	New Hebrides		10
N. Rhodesia	8	New Zealand		23
Somalia	8	Solomon Is.		10
Sp. Equatorial Region	23			
Sp. Sahara	2	U.S.S.R.		26
Sudan	13			
Americas				
Argentina	21			
Bahamas	23			
Bolivia	8			
Brazil	23			
Brit. Guiana	8			
Brit. Honduras	10			
Canada	5			
Falkland Is.	0			
Fr. Guiana	2			
Paraguay	10			
Peru	21			
Surinam	5			

Key: "Very high" signifies countries of more than 5 thousand square miles with more than 250 inhabitants per square mile.

"Very low" signifies countries of more than 5 thousand square miles with less than 26 inhabitants per square mile.

Figures solidly underlined are for extremely agricultural countries in a weak trading position, in the previous table, and in the above table are for highly industrialized or strong trading countries.

Figures underlined (...) are for modestly industrialized countries.

The countries excluded because of their small area comprise the two Berlins, French Polynesia, Luxembourg, Malta, Ryukyu Islands, Western Samoa, and Zanzibar, as well as numerous minuscule territories.

* UN, *Demographic Yearbook 1962.*

To sum up, it can be said that world population is very ill-distributed over the earth's surface. Eleven out of every twelve persons inhabit the northern hemisphere, but settlement there is far from uniform. Elsewhere, identification of uninhabitable wastelands—to enable estimation of more realistic population densities based on habitable land alone—is such a complex problem that no hard and fast distinctions can be drawn among countries as to their relative carrying capacities. However, broad comparisons can clearly be made from the accompanying tables. For example, in Table 11, the countries with underlined high densities are at a severe economic disadvantage compared to the industrialized countries.

Among the countries which do not appear in either of these tables, because their densities lie between 25 and 250 inhabitants per square mile, are several predominately agricultural countries with densities of 100 to 250 which should be given special attention. An industrial country with 200 inhabitants per square mile is naturally far better off than an agricultural country with 100 per square mile. In Africa, Burundi (density 207) and Nigeria (101) are certainly hard pressed by their population. In Latin America, Cuba (158) and the Dominican Republic (166) are heavily populated for agricultural economies. So are Cyprus (161), Indonesia (139), North Korea (179), Nepal (174), Thailand (137), and South Vietnam (220). Albania, Greece, Portugal, and Spain, Europe's most agricultural countries, are rather densely settled.

On the other hand, there are several industrial or trading countries which have a remarkably low density considering their economic capacity. The U.S.S.R., the borderline case in the low density table, Uruguay, South Africa, Bulgaria, Finland, France, Norway, Poland, Rumania, and Sweden, have remarkably low population densities relative to their economies. This peculiarity rests even if the icy wastelands of U.S.S.R. and Scandinavia are excluded from our calculations.

The most densely inhabited countries of Asia are not India and the Chinese mainland, whose immense populations occupy great subcontinents, but the more compact countries like Ceylon, Japan, and Lebanon. Asia also has several very low density populations: the arid and desert lands of the Southwest, with high proportions of nomadic inhabitants, and jungle-clad Laos.

Europe is both the most densely populated continent and the

most uniformly settled, but there too, some wide variation in density is found. The Netherlands holds the world's record, 896 per square mile. Finland, Norway, and Sweden have the lowest densities in Europe, but are well above the lowest densities found in other continents.

In sum, there is no doubt that there is a great range of population densities relative to economic capacity, and that several agricultural countries are hard pressed by their population, regardless of their future population growth.

Urbanization has, of course, played a large role in human geography. By the end of the last decade, there were some 112 metropolitan areas with over one million inhabitants, where population densities came to the thousands per square mile. All told, these metropolitan cities account for more than 284 million persons, or 10 per cent of the world's population.

Cities and other communities with populations over 100 thousand held some 590 million people in 1960, representing 20 per cent of the world's population.

This process is obviously most advanced in countries of European civilization, that is, in Europe, U.S.S.R., America, Australia, and New Zealand.

Africa and Asia are the least urbanized continents. In Asia, the big countries, China, India and Pakistan, are plainly agricultural. Japan and Israel are the most urbanized countries in that continent; more than 50 per cent of all Japanese and nearly 80 per cent of the Israelis dwell in urban areas.

Africa's urbanization has gone further along the North Coast than below the Sahara, but the Union of South Africa is the most urban country on that continent. Oceania's urbanization pattern is most striking. In Australia over 80 per cent, and in New Zealand some 65 percent of the people reside in urban communities.

In Latin America, recent censuses show that two-thirds of the population are concentrated in the urban areas of Costa Rica, Ecuador, El Salvador, Paraguay, and the Dominican Republic. Argentina and Uruguay are also largely urbanized.

TABLE 12
Estimates of Urban and Metropolitan Population by Continents, c. 1960*

	% Urban	% Large Urban (100 thous. pop. and over)	% Metropolitan (1 million pop. and over)
Africa	15–20	5–10	1–5
Northern America	65–70	45–50	25–30
Latin America	45–50	25–30	10–15
Asia	15–20	10–15	5–10
Europe	50–55	30–35	10–15
Oceania	65–70	40–45	20–25
U.S.S.R.	50–55	20–25	5–10

* Homer Hoyt, "World Urbanization: Expanding Population in a Shrinking World," Urban Land Institute, *Technical Bulletin* #43 (Washington, D.C., 1962). Hoyt underestimated the extent of metropolization, but no more accurate up-to-date estimates have been made on a world-wide basis except his own less detailed calculations for 1962 which raise the number of million-plus metropolitan areas to 133, comprising 11 per cent of the world population (personal communications from Homer Hoyt and Jerome P. Pickard). See also Rand McNally's *Commercial Atlas,* 94th ed. (Chicago), p. 489.

Europe, North America, and the U.S.S.R. exhibit the thickest clustering of large, metropolitan and "megalopolitan" urban aggregations, and are only rivaled in this respect by Japan.

The Projection of Future World Trends. It is clear that attempts to work out future world population trends by simple extrapolation of the world population curve in the past have no scientific value. World population is not increasing at the geometric rate Malthus anticipated.

So many elements influence the demographic factors of mortality and natality, how they bear upon each other and upon economic and social conditions, and how they react to these conditions, that calculations have to be adjusted on some methodical basis. Actually, the world population is made up of a very large number of different nations and groups, all of whom are evolving under different biological, economic, and technological conditions, and all of whom are influenced by a particular range of moral and cultural convictions, and of religious traditions, peculiarly their own.

The aim of essays by Quetelet, Verhulst, and others was to state the laws of population growth mathematically (Verhulst's logistic law). These essays will be examined later.

Several authors have tried to work out a scheme of population models typifying past trends and situations, as a basis for estimating future ones. *Bilan du Monde* offers three main methods for arriving at such a theoretical scheme of population structure and growth.[10] The first is based on the number of births and utilizes data on marriages and the fertility of the population. In this way it has been possible to draw a distinction between old populations and young populations. The second method tries to characterize populations on the basis of their age structure. Here, too, use is made of indications regarding old populations and young populations. Thirdly, it is possible to work out a theoretical scheme by studying the relations between birth rate and death rate among various peoples. This last is the method generally accepted by the authors of this study, and the UN has worked it out extensively in a number of publications. Its *The Determinants and Consequences of Population Trends* has a discussion of population "types" and "stages" of development on page 44 of the English-language edition. Landry, in his *Traité de démographie,* distinguished three typical schemes which correspond to the three sets of demographic conditions, or situations:

1) The *primitive situation,* where population growth and volume are determined by the means of subsistence. Death rates and birth rates balance.

2) The *intermediate situation,* where a society's population level is still dictated by the means of subsistence, but in another sense than before. Now food supplies are viewed in terms of the standard of living, and have only an indirect effect upon marriage and fertility. In

other words, in coming under human control the latter are becoming independent of nature.

3) The *contemporary situation,* when fertility is generally declining. No longer influenced by economic developments, procreation tends to be limited voluntarily.

C. P. Blacker distinguishes five stages in population growth:[11] (1) the *high stationary,* marked by high natality and mortality; (2) the *early expanding,* with high natality and high but declining mortality; (3) the *late expanding,* with declining natality but with mortality declining more rapidly; (4) the *low stationary,* with low natality balanced by equally low mortality; and (5) the *declining,* with low mortality, lower natality, and an excess of deaths over births.

Other authors, such as Thompson in his *Plenty of People* and in *Population and Peace in the Pacific,* reduce Blacker's five stages to three, stressing man's degree of influence over the demographic factors. In the first, birth and death rates are high and not subject to any limitation. Growth is faint at this stage. In the second, birth and death rates are declining, the former at first less rapidly and then more rapidly than the latter. There is thus a population increase at the beginning of this stage, followed by a slow transition to the third stage, during which the birth rate falls even lower than the death rate.

In 1951 the UN published a report on world population growth.[12] World population was divided into three groups according to the correlation of birth rate to death rate. The first group comprises countries with low birth and death rates in Europe (northern, western, central, and southern), North America, and Oceania. The second comprises countries with a lower death rate, but a slightly higher birth rate. In this group we find eastern Europe (including the Asiatic portion of the U.S.S.R.), Latin America, and Japan. The third group includes the other parts of the world: countries with a high birth rate where the death rate, though beginning to decline here and there, remains generally high. For all three groups, the UN plotted estimated changes in birth and death rates to the year 1980.

Population projections have been drawn up by the UN in which a maximum death rate coincides with a minimum birth rate, and conversely. Again theoretically, a minimum of births and a maximum of deaths would lead to the lowest possible level of population. Besides this, a "medium" development has been projected, the curve of which falls between the "high" and the "low" assumptions. By the terms of the "medium" assumption, a rate of population change is projected that is least likely to soar wildly or to drop alarmingly. With the aid of this method, the UN published an interesting projection of world population development to the year 1980, broken down according to the three groups of countries (TABLE 13).

TABLE 13

UN Estimates of Population in 1950 and 1980, Prepared in 1951
for Three Groups of World Regions
(population in millions)

Regions	1950 (estimates)	Hypothetical Estimate for 1980		
		high	medium	low
GROUP I				
North America, Northern, Western & Southern Europe, Oceania	486	655	599	548
GROUP II				
Latin America, Japan, Eastern & Asiatic U.S.S.R.	533	938	809	718
GROUP III				
Africa, Near East, South & Central Asia, other Far Eastern territories	1,387	2,043	1,869	1,710
World	2,406	3,636	3,277	2,976

A further estimate of future world population growth was published by the UN in 1954, on the occasion of the World Population Conference in Rome. This particular projection was based upon a breakdown of the world population into 25 regions, and this time five different assumptions were employed. The estimated world totals for 1980 (in millions) were:[13]

High Assumption	Medium Assumption	Low Assumption
3,990	3,628	3,295

When we compare these figures with those the UN published in 1951, it is obvious that the estimates have gone up steeply. The 1954 figure on the low assumption is very close to the 1951 figure on the medium assumption, and the 1954 figure on the medium assumption goes nearly as high as the 1951 figure on the high assumption. The main reason for the general rise is that the methods of population projection have been improved. Not only do the most recent estimates seem much more trustworthy than the earlier ones, it has in the meantime been possible to correct by more exact data the figures for world population in 1950, the base period for all these estimates.

Thanks to still more improved methods, the UN published in 1958 a third set of estimates of world population growth. Again, these differ considerably from the two earlier sets of figures. These new projections are based upon a highly diversified analysis of the world population. There are four types or stages, some of them further broken down into sub-types, as follows:[14]

A. Constant high mortality, constant high fertility;
B. Declining mortality, constant high fertility;
  B-1. Mortality very high but declining, hitherto constant fertility;
  B-2. Mortality moderate and declining, hitherto constant fertility;
  B-3. Conditions intermediate between B-1 and B-2;
C. Low mortality, fertility now moderate;
  C-1. Low mortality, early decline in fertility, fertility now moderate;
  C-2. Low mortality, recent decline in fertility, fertility now moderate;
  C-3. Conditions intermediate between C-1 and C-2;

D. Low mortality, fertility now low;
   D-1. Low mortality, early decline in fertility, fertility now low;
   D-2. Low mortality, recent decline in fertility, fertility now low;
   D-3. Conditions intermediate between D-1 and D-2.

Classification by continents and regions is as follows: [15]

A. Middle Africa
B-1. Southwest Asia, Central South Asia, Southeast Asia, East Asia (without Japan)
B-2. Central America, the Antilles, Tropical South America
B-3. Northern Africa, Southern Africa
C-1. Northern America, Australia, New Zealand
C-2. U.S.S.R.
C-3. Temperate South America
D-1. Northern and Western Europe, Central Europe
D-2. Japan and Ryukyu Islands
D-3. Southern Europe.

On the above basis, two tables of future population estimates were drawn up, one for the years 1950–1975 on the high and low assumptions, another for the years 1975–2000 on the high, medium, and low assumptions. Figures obtained on the medium assumption in the second table are in most cases an extension of what had been obtained on the high assumption in the table of estimates for 1950–1975. In TABLES 14, 14A, population is broken down by continents only for the two periods. [16]

TABLE 14

Estimates of World Population, 1950–1975

(two assumptions)

YEAR:	1950	1955	1960	1965	1970	1975
Africa						
high	199	216	237	263	294	331
low	—	—	234	234	254	295

North America including Central America & Antilles						
high	219	240	262	286	311	339
low	—	—	261	282	303	324
South America						
high	112	125	140	158	179	204
low	—	—	139	154	172	190
Asia						
high	1,380	1,490	1,620	1,780	1,980	2,210
low	—	—	1,610	1,720	1,890	2,040
Europe						
high	393	409	424	440	457	476
low	—	—	423	435	447	458
Oceania						
high	13.2	14.7	16.3	17.8	19.4	21.0
low	—	—	16.3	17.7	19.2	20.5
Soviet Union						
high	181	197	215	234	254	275
low	—	—	214	232	249	266
Whole World						
high	2,500	2,690	2,920	3,180	3,500	3,860
low	—	—	2,900	3,120	3,350	3,590

TABLE 14A

Estimates of World Population, 1975–2000
(three assumptions)

YEAR:	1975	1980	1985	1990	1995	2000
Africa						
high	331	375	428	492	569	663
medium	303	333	368	410	459	517
low	295	318	341	366	393	420
North America including Central America & Antilles						
high	339	370	404	444	490	544
medium	339	369	400	434	471	510
low	324	344	364	384	403	421
South America						
high	204	234	271	314	368	432
medium	204	234	266	304	347	394
low	190	210	231	253	275	298

Asia
high	2,210	2,480	2,810	3,200	3,680	4,250
medium	2,210	2,470	2,760	3,090	3,460	3,870
low	2,040	2,200	2,370	2,540	2,720	2,890

Oceania
high	21.0	22.5	24.2	26.0	28.0	30.2
medium	21.0	22.5	24.1	25.7	27.5	29.3
low	20.5	21.7	23.0	24.2	25.5	26.8

Soviet Union
high	275	297	320	344	369	395
medium	275	297	318	339	359	399
low	266	282	297	311	323	333

World
high	3,860	4,280	4,770	5,360	6,060	6,900
medium	3,830	4,220	4,660	5,140	5,680	6,280
low	3,590	3,850	4,110	4,370	4,620	4,880

TABLE 15 shows the percentage increase of population for two decades, 1950–60 and 1960–70, based on the "high" projection made by the United Nations in 1957. The table also shows the estimated population increase for the period 1950–60.

TABLE 15

Increase of Population according to the "High" Projection,*
1950–60 and 1960–70; Estimated Actual Increase,
1950–1960, for the World by Regions†

Region	Estimated population increase (per cent) 1950–60	Increase according to the "high" projection (per cent) 1950–60	Increase according to the "high" projection (per cent) 1960–70
World total	19	17	20
Africa	23	19	24
America	23	22	22
Northern America	19	17	14
Middle America	29	29	31
South America	26	25	28

Asia	*21*	*17*	*22*
Southwest Asia	28	28	27
Southcentral Asia	18	16	22
Southeast Asia	22	19	23
East Asia	22	17	21
Europe	*8*	*8*	*8*
Northern and Western Europe	7	5	6
Central Europe	9	9	8
Southern Europe	9	9	10
Oceania	*27*	*23*	*19*
U.S.S.R.	*18*	*19*	*18*

* The "high" projection of the set prepared by the United Nations in 1957, *Future Growth of World Population* (New York, 1958), Table I-A.
† UN, *1963 World Social Situation,* Chap. II, Sect. IV.

These figures, it should be noted, result from correlating the two factors of natality and mortality. Therefore it becomes more than ever important to address ourselves to the changes anticipated in birth rates and death rates. The following table supplies us with estimates of change in these two factors between 1950 and 1975, together with the estimated natural increases. They have been obtained on the medium assumption—that is, of constant fertility and declining mortality, except in Middle Africa, where mortality is also assumed to remain constant:[17]

TABLE 16

Anticipated Changes in Birth Rates, Death Rates, and Rates of Natural Increase of Continents and the World, 1950–1975

| | 1950 | | | 1975 | | |
	Birth Rate	Death Rate	Natural Increase	Birth Rate	Death Rate	Natural Increase
World	39	25	14	37	17	20
Africa	47	33	14	46	29	17
North America	22	9	13	21	9	12
South America	40	19	21	40	12	28
Asia	46	33	13	43	20	23
Europe	20	9	11	18	10	8
Oceania	26	12	14	26	10	16
U.S.S.R.	25	7	18	22	7	15

In a later chapter, birth rates and death rates will be analyzed separately, along with the factors that influence them.

The question is, will these estimates in fact work out as expected? The UN's continuing refinement of its statistical methods permits us to believe so, though surprises cannot be excluded a priori.

The United Nations has not issued new population projections since 1958, but it is clear that the growth trends anticipated at that time were not exaggerated. Indeed, the latest estimate of world population for 1960 is 2,995 million, 75 million above the *high* projection foreseen in 1958, and 95 million above the low projection made but three years before. Most of the unanticipated 43 million persons enumerated at censuses in 1960 or 1961 were found in India and Pakistan. The difference between previously projected population and the actually enumerated or estimated population at the end of the last decade is partly due to faulty statistics from earlier periods. But certainly a considerable margin between expectation and reality was due to unforeseen growth as exemplified in Table 8. And faster growth still lies in store among the numerous underdeveloped countries which do not yet quite qualify for inclusion in this table.

Will the world be able to assimilate this enormous population increase? The particular potentialities of each country have to be studied, not just in terms of population density—which, as we have seen, is a relative notion—but also in terms of degree of economic development and, above all, degree of social and cultural development:

Experience has shown, even in Europe, that despite appearances to the contrary, the essential factor in human development is not capital, but men's skillfulness in bending nature to their will and making her yield up her riches.[18]

In the next chapter, a survey of the history of population theory will show that there is nothing new in current fears of overpopulation, but it will also show that populationist* doctrines have often enough in the past come to the fore.

NOTES

1. Julius Beloch, *Die Bevölkerung der griechisch-römischen Welt* (Leipzig: Duncker & Humblot, 1886), p. 507.

2. Eugène Cavaignac, for example, argues that Beloch's estimates for the population of the Roman Empire are too low. He urges a figure of 80 million at the beginning of the Christian era in his "Notes de démographie antique," *Journal de la Société de Statistique de Paris* (Jan. 1935), pp. 4–9. Nonetheless, the point we are making is correct.

3. John D. Durand, "Population Statistics of China, A.D. 2–1953," *Population Studies*, XIII, 3 (March, 1960), p. 249.

4. *The Determinants and Consequences of Population Trends* (New York: United Nations, 1953), p. 8.

5. Alfred Sauvy, *Fertility and Survival: Population Problems from Malthus to Mao Tse-Tung* (London: Chatto & Windus, 1961; New York: Criterion Books, 1961), p. 22.

6. Arthur McCormack, *People, Space, Food* (London & New York: Sheed & Ward, 1960), p. 1.

7. Marcel Reinhard, *Histoire de la population mondiale de 1700 à 1948* (Paris: Domat-Montchrestien, 1949), p. 143.

8. *Determinants and Consequences* (UN), p. 11 (Table 2).

9. Sauvy, *op. cit.*, p. 19.

10. *Bilan du Monde* (Paris-Tournai, Casterman), I (1958/59), 6–11.

11. Summarized in *Determinants and Consequences* (UN), p. 44.

12. "The Past and Future Growth of World Population—A Long-Range View" in *Population Bulletin No. 1* (UN), pp. 1–12.

13. *Proceedings of the World Population Conference, 1954* (New York: United Nations, 1955), III, 304.

14. *The Future Growth of World Population* (New York: United Nations, 1958), pp. 11–12.

15. *Ibid.*, p. 12.

16. *Ibid.*, pp. 69–71.

* This term, and "populationism" as well, are used in this book in a sense contrary to that given in Webster (2d and 3rd eds.) but which is sanctioned by the UN's *Multilingual Demographic Dictionary* (New York, 1958), paragraph 930. The French-language volume opposes the term to *malthusien*, and the English-language volume makes it a synonym of "expansionist." (*Translator's note.*)

17. *Ibid.*, p. 32.

18. Alfred Sauvy, "Evolution récente du Tiers-Monde" in *idem* (ed.), *Le "Tiers-Monde": sous-développement et développement* (Paris: Presses Universitaires, 1961), p. xxi. This is Cahier 39 in the INED series "Travaux et Documents."

Chapter 2

Historical Survey of Population Theory

OUR CONTEMPORARIES APPEAR to be split into two warring camps, where population doctrines are concerned. Thinking on the subject is dominated by the *Essay on the Principle of Population* by T. R. Malthus, first published in 1798 (2nd edition, 1803), and is either "Malthusian" or "anti-Malthusian."

Now, to attempt to get at the truth in matters of doctrinal dispute is rarely, if ever, easy. To the extent that we want to keep to the facts of the matter, it may seem imprudent as well as pointless to get embroiled in doctrinal controversy. And yet, how a matter of dispute arose in the first place is something that can be investigated scientifically. Indeed, the results of such an investigation can throw light on our understanding of the problem.

What we must ask ourselves, in the case of Malthus, is why the author took up the highly controversial position he did just when he did. Not only was he running counter to the views of the best minds among his contemporaries, he was running counter to the view he had himself expressed only two years before, in 1796, in "The Crisis." Then he had stated that "A growing population is the surest possible sign of a State's happiness and prosperity," and he had warmly supported Pitt's proposal of government loans to heads of households of more than three children.

At the close of the eighteenth century, it was the prevailing

37

opinion that continuing human progress would make possible the establishment of a just and happy society, and that world population posed no problem (Godwin, Condorcet, Rousseau). This opinion was reinforced by a widespread belief that the population had been growing smaller since classical times (Montesquieu), or at least since the beginning of the eighteenth century (Rousseau, Mirabeau). It was in explicit opposition to the views of Godwin and Condorcet, and a few others, that Malthus wrote the *Essay* in 1798.

Actually, in the eighteenth century France was already more densely populated than England, and was steadily growing. From about 21 million in 1700, France reached 24 million in 1770, 26 million in 1789, and 28 million in 1801.[1] The situation was such as to make us believe that a French Malthus (had he had such figures at his disposal) must have been as appalled as the Englishman was at the "population explosion," had he set out to "project" population trends for the next forty years in France, as had been done for the world population.* In 1801 a demographer would have been obliged to conclude that by 1820 the French population would reach 38 million, 48 million by 1830, 58 million around 1837, 68 million around 1841, and 78 million around 1844. Does this mean that Malthus was right? In point of fact, certainly not: his forecasts were not realized, nor would those of his French opposite number have been realized, either. (These would have been still wider of the mark. . . .) And yet, had these demographers been content to draw up their "projections," we must admit that they would have been more correct, as such, than the assumptions that had guided those whom Malthus set out to prove wrong.

How is it that these "projections" did not work out in reality? Why is it that partisans of an ill-founded optimism have time and again arrived at predictions less erroneous than the partisans of a pessimism more objective in character and founded upon more exact knowledge? The matter is one to inspire reflection. Not that

* It should be kept in mind that, to population specialists, "projections" are not thought of as "forecasts" or "predictions."

it would be fair to dispose of it with a witticism, like "Demography is the art of arriving at sound conclusions from faulty data." As Claude Bernard observed in his *Introduction to Experimental Medicine,* "Criticism does not consist in demonstrating where an eminent man went astray; such a discovery would not be very remarkable in itself, and could be of profit to science only if it showed how he went astray."

So it would seem pertinent to our inquiry to pass in review the various ways the population problem has been thought about over the ages, and to ask why and under what circumstances it has given rise to contradictory opinions. From our point of view, it matters little whether the opinions seem to have been well founded or not. Opinions are themselves matters of historical fact, and we shall now make a brief attempt to sketch the history of opinion on this topic.

BEFORE MALTHUS

Well before publication of Malthus' famous essay, political thinkers had addressed themselves to the problem of the relation between the numbers of human beings and the sum total of available means for sustaining life—especially food supplies.

Plato and Aristotle have frequently been cited, both by Malthusians and by supporters of an "optimum population level," as the ultimate ancestors, the real pioneers, of the view that the population of a civilized community should be kept within bounds. They would have been the first "eugenicists." And, indeed, they do seem to have provided for the intervention of the authorities in matters of human reproduction, from the point of view of quality as well as of quantity.

Of the two, Plato obviously goes farthest in this direction when he speaks of real city-states in the *Republic.* It is in his *Laws,* however, that he fixes at 5,040 the number of heads of households it is desirable to reach and not to exceed. The figure was arrived at, however, more out of considerations of administrative efficiency than with an eye to securing balance between the population and the available means of subsistence. The figure 5,040 is the product of $2^4 \cdot 3^2 \cdot 5 \cdot 7$ and has a great many divisors, including all the numbers under 9 and, above that, all the non-prime numbers up to 21, inclusive. Surely a great convenience for the functionaries who distribute food and collect taxes. . . .

Aristotle came closer to thinking about the problem as we know it today. In his view, the power of the city-state necessarily depends upon a harmonious relation between the people and the territory they inhabit, and he envisaged both these elements from a qualitative as well as a quantitative point of view. The city-state is made up of citizens, slaves, and aliens (metics). Like Plato, Aristotle is only concerned with the optimum number to be arrived at for the first class, the Eupatridae. The number of slaves and metics has little bearing upon the power of the city-state, for although they supply manpower and contribute to the wealth of the state, they do not help defend it in time of war and hence do not contribute to its security. Nevertheless, there should not be too many people in a city-state, as this makes its policing difficult. On this score, Aristotle's political concerns correspond to Plato's administrative ones.

Aristotle's opinion is that no particular control is needed to assure a minimum population. To him, rather, the danger lies in overpopulation, and the measures of control he specifies include abortion and infanticide. Such measures apply only to the citizen class; metics can always be expelled when they get too numerous, and where slaves are concerned, their masters have the right to control their numbers in every age group. Throughout classical antiquity, moreover, increase in the numbers of slaves and of barbarians "who are naturally slaves" (Thomas Aquinas, *Lessons on Aristotle's "Politics"*) represented a source of wealth to the citizen class, to be exploited as such like any other natural resource, animal or vegetable.

Long before modern demographic methods of measurement and research had been devised, then, man was thought of in two quite different ways: as consumer–manager–"producer," that is, as an appropriator of natural resources, but also as himself a natural resource to be exploited for the fruits of his "servile" labor. Aristotle expressed the distinction as that between *organon poietikon* and *organon praktikon.*

To an age when production techniques seemed essentially fixed once and for all, despite a few important discoveries, it scarcely occurred that the available means of subsistence might ever increase or be increased. The citizen's standard of living depended on how well the particular "living space" he owned could produce, and on the number of "instruments" at his disposal for exploiting it. According to Varro's classification, such "instruments" included farm implements and buildings ("mute" instruments), livestock ("semi-speaking" instruments), and slaves ("speaking" instruments).

Thus, population was not as yet thought of as a whole. As Alfred Sauvy puts it, there is a "dominating" population and a population "that is dominated." And while there have been many discussions as to the most desirable number a dominating population should attain, where the dominated are concerned the general view was expressed with conscious cynicism in the eighteenth century by a gentleman demographer, Turmeau de la Morandière: "Subjects and cattle must be multiplied."

Similarly, when Plato specifies a eugenic policy that forbids freedom of intercourse, though women and children (as well as property) are held in common, he does not intend it to apply solely to the class of citizens, but also to the two higher classes: that of the "magistrates" (or guardians of the law) and that of the "auxiliaries" (or lesser guardians), whom he compares to shepherds and to watchdogs, respectively. Ordinary workers—that is, the "flock" or "herd"—are subject merely to quantitative restrictions, not to qualitative ones. He relies more than Aristotle on propaganda as a means of keeping population up to the desired figure. Nonetheless, bachelors over thirty-five are to be heavily taxed, and children born of encounters not authorized by the regulations (of fathers older than the age limit for reproduction, for example) are not to be a burden upon the community and may even be put to death. The city-state under its "guardians," whose responsibility it is to apply the "Laws," is conceived of as analogous to the head of a family, with much the same responsibilities and worries. The Socratic philosophers find it natural to draw the analogy, and make a strict comparison of powers. And so, in as much as there was no respect for the individual human being—for the human person as such—the city-state could intervene in the life of its citizens no less than the master in the life of his slaves.

Now, for all that economic conditions bear upon everyone, upon the guardians no less than upon workers and slaves, still it was not from the point of view of "the means of subsistence" that problems of population were considered. What mattered was the "power" that numbers confer, over and above the degree of affluence, the station in life, or the available resources, as all these may be involved in administrative surveillance of "the herd."

To pose the population problem as one of arriving at an optimum figure can lead to quite unlike solutions. There are still cattle breeders who favor big herds (or flocks) of poorly nourished animals because, to them, the head count gives the measure of their own dominion. Others would like big herds, but are willing to limit number in favor of quality, and concentrate on raising well-nourished, carefully tended animals. Finally, there are those who regard their livestock solely as a source of wealth and merely try for maximum production at least expense. This third type of "stockbreeder" was still rare among the ruling classes of the ancient world, and not much more common in the Middle Ages, which may be considered as populationist in general tendency. In its manorial form, the feudal system did not quite treat the peasant as a slave, but he was his lord's serf, and each lord, in turn, was vassal to an overlord, his suzerain.

The big difference between classical antiquity and the medieval era was the fact of Christianity. Though it certainly did not bring with it a population doctrine, it did enforce new ways of looking at the problem. It emphasized man's eminent dignity as a creature of

God, under obligation to "increase and multiply and fill the earth and make it his," for he was "put in command of the fishes in the sea, and all that flies through the air, and the cattle, and all the creeping things that move on earth." He was *not*, however, put in command of his fellow man. Now that all men were equal in the eyes of God, there was no more master and slave. Of course, men would so interpret the Christian injunction as to make its observance as little painful or costly to themselves as they could, under the various conditions of time and place, and they would even go so far as to make its observance by others profitable to themselves. . . .

Though his name has sometimes been invoked by Malthusians, St. Paul was not at all an advocate of the limitation of births, and still less did he ever think of it as a solution, whether to an economic problem of subsistence or to a political problem of power. He was eloquent in praise of virginity as one of the divers ways by which the human person may attain fullest self-realization. As for marriage, he insisted both upon the husband's and the wife's mutual self-realization in love, and upon their joint role in the creation of new life. It was not long before deviations from this teaching made their appearance, rejecting one part of it on the pretext of carrying it farther. As early as the second century, St. Irenaeus found himself obliged to speak out against the discredit some were heaping upon marriage and procreation.

St. Thomas Aquinas is very clear on this score: the population is to be increased, and Aristotle's tendencies to favor its restriction are set aside. However, population increase is not to be envisaged as a means of supplying some particular degree of power to the prince or the state. For, although the end of marriage is to multiply the species, this is not everyone's duty. Celibacy is not to be prohibited (nor, for that matter, prescribed) for political or administrative reasons. Virginity, celibacy, continence are choices available to anyone who wishes to realize his or her spiritual destiny fully.

In the generally populationist climate of the Middle Ages, the Church's teaching was bound to stress respect for the individual and to defend the right to celibacy. In her struggles with the secular powers, the latter did not fail to reproach the Church for being destructive of humanity, in view of the numbers she called to a life of celibacy. No doubt the poets who were hired by the secular princes to take their part in struggles against the Church tried to see both sides of the question, but what seems most characteristic today is the way arguments based on the dignity of the Christian person fell into neglect, while the argument based on the power of the secular ruler was brought back into favor. At the same time, the topics of underpopulation and habitable territories were introduced.

When Johan de Meung composed his long conclusion to Guillaume de Lorris' *Roman de la rose* between 1265 and 1290—at the request of Philippe IV (Philip the Fair), then engaged in struggles against the Holy See and the Knights Templar—he made a notable attack on monks and other celibates for their failure to aid in the increase of the realm.

When Charles V (not the emperor, but the king of France dubbed "The Wise") had *Le Songe du vergier* written, probably by a group of legists, its aim was also opposition to the Holy See. In this work "that treats of matters in dispute between knight and cleric," the unique truth of the cleric is set off against the twofold truth of the knight, and the latter proclaims his allegiance to the two authorities against the supreme authority of the Church. What interests us here in the French text of 1377 is the knight's view that although religion forbids polygamy (which is a truth of faith), yet it would be "more profitable to the *res publica* if a man had several wives" (which is a truth of reason), for the best "conjunction" of man and woman is that which "most abundantly conduces to the procreation of children," and because "The natural law holds and teaches that the individual life which cannot perdure in and of itself—a thing impossible in nature—can perdure in its kind through generation." While the knight seems to have recognized that natural reason must bow before the lights of supernatural faith,[2] the argument had now been launched, and in the debate which follows over marriage and virginity, the cleric is so carried away by his victory over the knight on the score of monogamy *vs.* polygamy, that he allows the argument to continue on the "natural" plane and draws a conclusion which latterday Malthusians have seized upon in support of their own theses. This is the line that if the world or any part of it were insufficiently populated, then virginity would not be a great virtue but "great vice." If, on the other hand, there were ever "so great a multitude that the earth would not suffice for the subsistence of her inhabitants, then virginity and abstinence must be approved and accounted virtue." The argument has been put in the cleric's mouth by an adversary: it should go without saying that it does not reflect the doctrine of the Church at the close of the Middle Ages. The demographic views of the cleric merely represent one secular argument raised in opposition to another; the knight is much more power-conscious, and speaks for a populationist-minded sovereign.

Not before the end of the sixteenth century, in the works of Giovanni Botero, do we find the problems of population and subsistence approached from a modern point of view. He was secretary to St. Charles Borromeo, after whose death in 1584 he published two works: *Causes de la grandeur et de la magnificence de la Cité* (1588) and *De la raison d'Etat* (1589). The titles themselves suggest the plane on which the discussion is conducted, and in the first of these works is clearly formulated for the first time "the Malthusian antinomy" between population increase and the accumulation of wealth. Botero expressed it as "the generative power of mankind," on the one hand, and "the nourishing power of the States," on the other. Unlike those of his successor Malthus, his conclusions are optimistic, for he believed it possible to increase "the nourishing power of the States." While he does not rule out the possibility that a population maximum might be reached, which it would be dangerous to exceed, he considers that the colonizing of new lands should relieve any local overpopulation that might arise.

From this time forward, and right down to Malthus, we find two sorts of advocates of population increase: those who urge it for the greater glory and wealth of the secular ruler, and those whose conviction is founded upon belief in progress. The former are direct descendants of the ancient and the medieval populationists, in a tradition that has not altogether died out today—as we see in the instance of power-hungry totalitarian states. The human stud-farms of Hitler's Germany were the "eugenistic" side of a nationalist power politics which required a big population, both to justify its demand for *Lebensraum* and in order to obtain it by force. The domestic policies of Italian fascism were similar in spirit: emigration was stopped, and some Italians who had emigrated were repatriated, in order that Italy might be launched on a series of military adventures in search of "living space." This type of populationism applies only to the increase of a single people or nation, and is hostile to a similar increase in others. Based as it is on the principle of human inequality, it leads to the subjugation of alien peoples (*homines barbari qui sunt naturaliter servi*) and, indeed, with the policy of genocide, leads to their destruction.

There have been societies calling themselves Christian (the Antilles, for example, in the sevententh century) where slaveowners refused to let their slaves be baptized, for in certain cases this would have been to free them automatically. Here we can see how Aristotle's concept of barbarians (i.e., persons "who are naturally slaves") has been supplanted by that of "persons who have not been baptized." Moslems long took the same attitude to all whom they considered unbelievers.

Now, it was not against populationists of this type that Malthus took up the cudgels, but against the type whose convictions were founded on belief in progress—Godwin and Condorcet, most notably. In his day there were those who—like the marquis d'Argenson—went so far as to maintain that Europe in general, and France in particular, could support fifty times its actual population. Why, France alone might attain the figure of one billion, if only the waste lands were cleared and cultivated, and if only the country would rid itself of all its parasites, from its courtiers down to its beggars.

Like Condorcet, but even more strongly, Godwin believed that material progress would result, not just in more and better supplies of food, but also—and it was remarkably farsighted of them—in a checking of fertility. Once humanity has discovered how to keep the human body in a state of perpetual health and youthfulness, mankind will stop multiplying. No longer a race of children, perhaps become immortal, the race of men will readily gain mastery over the blind forces of the reproductive instinct. In the Eden of the future, as in the Eden of the past, man will no more be the slave of his senses. That this line of argument struck Malthus as puerile can hardly surprise us—we will come back to it. Ever since the late seventeenth century, discussion had been taking more and more an economic turn. Cantillon had argued that population tends to the maximum so long as multiplying the species entails no threatening economic consequences. That is, population reaches the level where increased mortality due to lessened well-being catches up with births. The notion was a primitive version of the concept of natural self-regulation. Once society is able, however, to maintain a certain level of well-being for itself and its descendants, then it will tend to bring births down to the level of mortality by fewer marriages.

What this comes down to is a translation of the ancients' point of view into economic terms. Concern for well-being now replaces concern for the power of the state, the city-state, or the secular ruler. In the most advanced households, restriction will be self-imposed. For working-class families it will now be necessary to obtain as many jobs as possible, in employment of as useful a character as possible, since not just the level of wealth but that of population as well now depends ultimately on the production required to support it—that is, on the working of the land, which in turn depends on the wishes, the habits, and the style of life of those who own it.

It must be remarked that proprietors were not always content to let things work themselves out in this "automatic" manner. They did not hesitate to take a hand in the reproductive process where, for example (as in America), they owned slaves, or when (as under certain tenant-farm systems) they were obligated to provide "their" peasants with a minimum subsistence. An eighteenth-century métayer contract in Umbria specified that the number of workers in each family was to remain stable, and to this end only eldest sons were permitted to marry, their younger brothers being authorized "to satisfy themselves with their eldest brother's wife."

Probably we should not be too quick to condemn this or that formula, this or that set of manners and customs. At the same time, however, we ought not to close our eyes to the facts of life in recent periods which we are too often accustomed to study solely in terms of political victories, works of art, and scientific discoveries.

The lot of the slave was better or worse as the price of slaves rose or fell, and the same has held true for all types of domination.

At a time when military conquests were flooding Rome with slaves, Cato the Censor had no compunction about writing in his book on agriculture: "When slaves fall ill, it is proper to give them less to eat." Either they will get back to work as soon as they are able, out of hunger, or they will do so immediately because they are malingering, or else they will die, which is no great loss. He also recommended that old and sickly slaves should be sold. To get the full force of such views, it is necessary to read the same Cato's advice on what to do when it is suspected that cattle may be ailing, what is to be done when, in fact, they are.

Two centuries earlier in Athens, at a time when slaves were scarce and prices high, Xenophon recommended that the slave whose labor is needed and whose farming is yielding a return, be well treated.

It was not long before things went the same way in Rome. Varro, who was born some thirty years after Cato died, recommended that slaves not be employed on insalubrious sites or at seasonal labor. They represent valuable capital, and you can get mercenaries to do such jobs more cheaply. Should the latter die, the owner is not out of pocket, and he does not have to pay their keep all year round merely to have them available for seasonal employment.

Much the same sort of thing went on in the eighteenth and nineteenth centuries as the labor market rose and fell. Linguet could write: "They will not forgive me for having demonstrated that a well-fed, well-groomed horse, protected from inclement weather and well cared for when sick, has a better life than the free laborer who hires out by the day." He thus showed how, under certain circumstances, "Domination may be less harsh for a slave class than for a class of free workingmen in an overpopulated territory" (Alfred Sauvy).

The marquis de Mirabeau, who was a disciple of Quesnay and father of the French Revolutionary leader, wavered back and forth (from edition to edition) between the two ideas which dominated thinking on the subject in the immediately pre-Malthus era. Wealth is the effect of population, and population is the effect of wealth. He was troubled by fears of depopulation, the cause of which he traced on the one hand to "the decay of agriculture," on the other hand to "the luxury and excessive consumption of a small number of inhabitants who dry up the seed of a new citizenry at the root":

In general and in principle, it is neither wars nor epidemics that depopulate the state. However, bring one horse more into the state and, all things else being equal, you are sure to kill off at least four men. Here I am only attacking the luxury animal liable to encourage every sort of abuse. Population and subsistence are to be measured on the same scale.

These are still the ideas of Cantillon, as Mirabeau himself acknowledges, but the language is that of the Physiocrats. There is a confidence in the natural order that neither Adam Smith nor Malthus will share, though the latter understood the Physiocrats better than the former, who was much too eager to refute their arguments to study them.

Dr. Quesnay contributed the article "Hommes" to the *Encyclopédie,* and in it he begins by taking the position that human beings constitute the power of a state:

As men multiply and consume what they produce, they are themselves
the first and constitutive cause of their own wealth. The rebirth and succession of the wealth of nations depend on how men are used and how
the population grows. What sustains the strength of kingdoms today is
their wealth, and what produces that wealth is the people in them.

Yet population growth must depend wholly upon increased wealth,
as the latter depends on how men and their wealth are used. It will
only be by growing progressively richer that a nation can arrive at
still greater wealth, population, and power. It would be idle, then,
for it to attempt to increase the numbers of its people, unless it has
first devoted itself to increasing its wealth:

People in a condition of poverty are of no account, neither for what
they produce nor for what they consume. Such persons, or rather such
families, have fallen into non-value, and should not under any circumstances be included within the population which is profitable to the
state. What stimulates people to work and makes them fear poverty is
the enjoyment of ease, the well-being work procures for them, the good
food, good clothing, and comforts it accustoms them to. This is why
hard-working men, profitable to the state, come out of the lowest
classes.

Quesnay fulminates against "The maxims of ferocious men who
claim that the lowest classes should be reduced to direst poverty,
so as to be forced to work." Vialatoux believes Quesnay has W.
Petty in mind, and possibly Colbert, but the criticism could apply
too to the theories of Adam Smith (as yet unpublished) regarding
the way in which the labor market is kept in balance. When the
Physiocrats spoke of "multiplying" wealth, what they had in mind
was an increase in the net agricultural output. To Adam Smith,
the market would serve as regulator of supply and demand by
bringing real prices ever closer to natural prices. It would have the
same effect upon labor, which is merely another commodity, the
price of which is called "wages." An inexorable economic law will
restrict the number of workers according to the needs of industry,
on the one hand, according to the available means of subsistence,

on the other. Wage earners can never hope for a return "beyond what is strictly necessary to keep them from dying of hunger and to permit them to reproduce" (P. Bureau).

FROM MALTHUS TO THE PRESENT

There had been many writers on the subject before Malthus, but none of them influenced him. Their influence (for some of them are very important) was rather upon Malthus' successors, the demographers proper. Of them the most important was probably Monthyon (though it may have been his secretary Moheau), author of *Recherches et Considérations sur la Population de la France* (1778). It seems to us more logical to discuss this work after having sketched the main outlines of Malthus' thought and character.

Thomas Robert Malthus (1766–1834) brought out anonymously at the age of thirty-two a small book which he called *An Essay on the Principle of Population as it affects The Future Improvement of Society, with remarks on the speculations of Mr. Godwin, M. Condorcet, and other writers.* The pamphlet met with such success that he set out on a vast search for information all over Europe, the result of which was a fat work, no longer anonymous, titled *An Essay on the Principle of Population; or, A View of its Past and Present Effects on Human Happiness.* Published in 1803, this is referred to as the second edition. A fifth edition appeared in 1817 which contains in an appendix Malthus' own summary of his ideas, with replies to the principal objections which had been raised.

Malthus was an Englishman. Influenced no doubt by their insularity, the English have always been much more aware of population growth than continental Europeans, and populationist doctrines have never caught on there to any comparable extent. An important special circumstance in England, also, is that when the convent establishments were closed in connection with the Reformation, private charity quickly found it impossible to keep pace with the mounting needs of the poor. Already under Elizabeth the state had to step in, and the consequences in the sphere of "poor relief" were both debatable and frequently debated. Workhouses were founded as an alternative to home relief, which was believed to encourage idleness and to swell the numbers of the poorer population. The workhouses themselves, however, led to a number of abuses, and in 1795 authority was given for aid to "the labouring poor" in their own places of domicile. Now the Poor Laws came in for criticism, from several sides. They were expensive to the state. Industry required a cheap labor force, and it was the view of economic liberals that the price of labor should be regulated by the market, without interference. Also, the population of England had grown from between 5 and 6 million in 1700 to 9 million in 1780, and the increase was ascribed to the effect of the Poor Laws.

Malthus set out to find an explanation for the twofold phenomenon of an expanding population and growing pauperism. He found it in a natural law, the working out of which he described mathematically: while the species multiplies in geometric progression, the means of subsistence increase in arithmetic progression. Did we belong to a lower species, limitation of our numbers would occur naturally as sources of food ran out; the excess population would be carried off by starvation, disease, warfare. To our species, however, which is possessed of intelligence and will, only two ways are open to us: the way of vice or the way of virtue. To resign ourselves to poverty is to fail to make use of our intelligence, but to make use of it is to choose one or the other way of limiting our numbers. "Physical restraint" is the way of vice, "moral restraint" the way of virtue. Obviously, in this connection, it is grossly unfair to Malthus to saddle him with responsibility for all that has been perpetrated since in his name. Not only did he raise his voice with the severity of a real moralist in opposition to measures of "physical restraint," he also foresaw that the way of vice, like that of poverty, could lead to serious depopulation, destructive alike of the species and of happiness. Vice can check human increase, but at the same time it slows down the production of foodstuffs. Thus, Malthus can be said to have foreseen Malthusianism—though it would be respecting his good faith to call it "Neo-Malthusianism"—and to have foreseen as well the danger of precipitating humanity along a course of self-limitation which must further aggravate the problem of how it is to feed itself. With fewer and fewer human beings sharing ever dwindling food supplies, the prospect for the future must narrow down to one of intolerable wretchedness. Vice "depopulates," vice "destroys," vice "exterminates."

We should then be able to understand how Malthus could write in the third volume of the 1817 edition of his *Essay:* "It is an utter misconception of my argument to infer that I am an enemy to population. I am only an enemy to vice and misery."

All the same, Malthus supplied the Neo-Malthusians with the "rational" basis of their argument, all the more telling for the fact that his pessimism was truly despairing. In his second edition he cut out the following passage from the first edition, but it is nonetheless characteristic:

Those who were born after the division of property, would come into a world already possessed. If their parents, from having too large a family, could not give them sufficient for their support, what are they to do in a world where every thing is appropriated? . . . It has appeared, that from the inevitable laws of our nature, some human beings must suffer from want. These are the unhappy persons who, in the great lottery of life, have drawn a blank. The number of these claimants would soon exceed the ability of the surplus produce to supply. . . . All who were in want of food would be urged by imperious necessity to offer their labour in exchange for this article so absolutely essential to existence. The fund appropriated to the maintenance of labour would be the aggregate quantity of food possessed by the owners of land beyond their own consumption. When the demands upon this fund were great and numerous, it would naturally be divided in very small shares. Labour would be ill paid. Men would offer to work for a bare subsistence, and the rearing of families would be checked by sickness and misery.[3]

Malthus had, moreover, few illusions regarding the efficacy of his "moral code":

I should be extremely sorry to say any thing, which could either directly or remotely be construed unfavorably to the cause of virtue; but I certainly cannot think that the vices which relate to the sex are the only vices which are to be considered in a moral question; or that they are even the greatest and most degrading to the human character. . . . I believe there will be found very few, who pass through the ordeal of squalid and hopeless poverty, or even of long embarrassed circumstances, without a great moral degradation of character.

. . . .

. . . Abject poverty, particularly when joined with idleness, is a state the most unfavourable to chastity that can well be conceived.

. . . .

. . . I have not the slightest hesitation in saying, that the prudential check to marriage is better than premature mortality.[4]

It is unnecessary to discuss the worth of a moralist's arguments when he is grappling with concrete situations. It is not at all to our purpose to observe that the moralist is so pessimistic, so overwhelmed in advance by the vice he wants to combat, that it is hardly astonishing if "disciples" of a more indulgent moral cast have twisted his words around to a "Neo-Malthusianism." Hope, too, is a virtue.

Immediately following Malthus, two opposing intellectual currents renewed the debate very much in the terms Botero had formulated long before: the antinomy between population growth and the means of subsistence.

Meanwhile, a specifically demographic school was shortly to see the light, whose bent would be rather toward analyzing facts and finding answers to specific problems than to elucidating normative principles. Their theories attempt to explain what has happened, as a means of throwing light on what remains to be done. Of course, the demographers were by no means wholly objective. The best example of this was supplied by the nineteenth-century positivists, who were very fecund in methodological elaborations but too often given to premature conclusions of a naiveté apparent even to the untrained. (All of which goes to show once again that fine scientists can be lamentable thinkers.)

It was the author of *Recherches et Considérations sur la Population de la France* (Monthyon or Moheau) who set demography on the path of statistical analysis of the facts. In this he had been anticipated by Vauban in France and by William Petty in England. Book II attempts to draw conclusions from the analyses in Book I as to "the causes of population progress and decadence." He distinguishes two sorts, of which the first consists of conditions in the physical environment, plus a few causes of a psychological nature, which he explains as follows:

Although character, mind, the affections do not belong to the physical order, climate, food, customs have a real influence over the soul, and as they modify it, it so acts upon the body, upon the health, and so affects the capacity for self-preservation, that we dare not overlook these influences. People of the lower orders are subject less than the other classes of Society to the terrible effects of the passions; their souls, like their hands, take on a sort of callus, and all their feelings are nearly always caught up in bodily movement and bodily discomfort.

The second sort of cause comprises moral, social, and political causes.

This author's views are populationist, but what interests us here is how he discerned the earliest beginnings of that crisis in the birth rate which was to take on such proportions later and which his successors were to call "the Demographic Revolution." (Direct control over births, rather than over marriages, is to be understood.) It had begun in the wealthy classes, but was already beginning to spread, according to what would later be termed "the law of capillarity." "Rich women," he writes, "for whom pleasure is the be-all and end-all of life, are not the only ones who regard propagation of the species as an old-fashioned attempt to take them in." Even in the author's own day:

Deadly secrets known to no other animal but man have spread to the countryside; nature is being circumvented even in the villages. Should these licentious practices go much farther, they will be no less deadly in their effects upon the State than were the plagues of former times; it is high time to arrest this terrible course upon which the population has embarked.

We shall have to come back to the matter of deadly secrets spreading to the villages. The author of the *Recherches et Considérations* had deep forebodings of the drop in the birth rate which was to occur in all the advanced countries during the nineteenth century and in the early years of the twentieth. It was this that Adolphe Landry called "the Demographic Revolution." He found the same cause for it, and so did his successors, most notably Arsène Dumont. The falling off in natality was due, not to any slackening of the "generative faculty," but to a slackening of the "generative will." The characteristic symptom was the practice of "voluntary restrictions" on birth in marriage, and not, as in the earlier phase, the large numbers of unmarried persons. The phenomenon spread from the wealthy classes, who were first to be infected, down to the very poorest, in a manner Arsène Dumont describes with his theory of "social capillarity."

The germ of this theory was present in Cantillon, when he recognized that the human population is not determined, as other living things are, by the level of the means of subsistence (a theory Townsend advanced in his *Dissertation on the Poor Laws* in 1786), but by the desire to keep up a standard of living no lower than that of our parents, who would not want to see their children worse off than they. The theory of "social capillarity" introduces a further element: desire to raise oneself in the social scale, one consequence of which is imitation of the behavior of the very rich by the very poor. We may note that all three theories lead to maximum levels of population, weaker and weaker with respect to the same level of the means of subsistence, and all three can be verified both before and after the "Demographic Revolution." Before, by the numbers of unmarried persons, as Cantillon expressed it in his theory:[5] "The most of men ask no better than to marry, could they only be put in a position to keep their families in the same manner they are content to live by themselves." And after, by voluntary restrictions on birth.

Arsène Dumont, who is nothing if not an anti-Malthusian, is sure that his "new population principle" will lead, not to over-population, but to depopulation. Landry remarked that the phenomenon had occurred before, in Greece from the fifth century on and then in Rome, after conquered Greece's civilization had overwhelmed its erstwhile conqueror.

The advantage of the "social capillarity" theory was that it accounted for the observed facts in the most advanced countries of capitalist civilization, where undefined aspirations toward progress and well-being had reached every stratum of the population. Though it may not provide a complete explanation, it nonetheless supplies an important psycho-sociological one.

As for the notion of a "Demographic Revolution," it is less sure that of itself it has quite the explanatory value ordinarily ascribed to it by demographers. The opposition between limitations on marriage and limitations on birth is probably not so clear-cut as claimed. In the modern world restrictions on marriage remain a factor in checking the birth rate. In France, within the 35–45 age group, 25 per cent of the male agricultural population is unmarried, as opposed to 12 per cent of the male population in all other categories.

At the same time, the proportion of bachelors among farm owners, big and small, and also among tenant farmers, drops to the level of the non-agricultural male population, or even lower. The difference is obviously accounted for by farmhands and agricultural workers not self-employed: 45 per cent of them are still unmarried between the ages of 35 and 39. What this means is that in the agricultural sector many men do not marry until they are in a position to have their own homes, and so marriage is delayed beyond the usual age. Many a tiller of the soil is in this way deprived of the right to found a family. For the age group 50–59, we find 11 per cent of the males still unmarried among independent farmers, and 30 per cent among farm laborers. Nor is this a case of voluntary bachelorhood; it has been established that 7 out of 8 desire, and between the ages of 18 and 20 still hope, to found a family.

Moreover, we can see that bachelorhood dictated by "economic" considerations is not enough to account for the low birth rate that prevailed prior to the so-called Demographic Revolution, at least not in certain regions and reaches of the population. At the same time, there were practices employed even then—perhaps consciously, perhaps not—to limit births in marriage.

Cantillon remarked that "females" in his day were "careful not to become mothers if they were not married," and that in country districts where "misconduct" on the part of young women was not at all unusual, the birth of a "little one" (a term used in certain parts of France to designate a natural child, to distinguish it from a child born in wedlock) was considered so shameful that a girl who found herself "surprised" (i.e., pregnant) might have recourse to abortion, or might destroy the child after giving birth to it secretly. Suicide was not exceptional as a last resort when these other means failed. So strong a disapproval of illegitimacy is hard to reconcile with well-documented facts concerning other parts of Europe, where the "Demographic Revolution" had not yet reached the countryside. Young women's chances of getting married in such regions were poor unless they *were* pregnant, and there were methods for regulating fertility, the secret of which doubtless need not have been sought farther afield than the traditional herb gardens of the peasant women.

Certain of these practices could very well be continued after marriage. It seems more than likely that nursing of the newborn, which delays re-establishment of the menstrual cycle, was sometimes prolonged for its limiting effect upon the fertility of a marriage. Sexual relations were prohibited during the nursing period and until the mother had been "purified." In some regions (in central Brittany, for example) the effect was further reinforced by a local custom decreeing that a nursing mother might not share her husband's bed, but must sleep with her own mother or with her older daughters.*

---

* It may be worth noting that, to some extent, the effect of such practices was automatically limited by infant mortality.

In the cities, most of these practices prove much less practicable. So far as unmarried females are concerned, only prostitutes have recourse to them; other unmarried women and girls are closely watched. In the case of births out of wedlock, abandonment of the baby takes the place of infanticide.

What seems most characteristic of the "Demographic Revolution" is not so much the substitution of restrictions upon fertility in marriage for restrictions on marriage, as the shift in the sex of the person now responsible for making decisions in matters of procreation. What had hitherto been decided according to tradition and more or less unconsciously, so long as the woman was responsible, must of necessity be consciously deliberate now that the man has become responsible. In any case, it is clear that from now on the father is reproached and held responsible for illegitimate births, and that the fertility of a marriage is henceforward up to him. Especially illuminating in this connection is a study made of the fertility of marriages in rural districts of Périgord, where a number of Breton families have been settled for several generations. The Breton families are much more prolific than the others, and it was established that the fertility of marriages between natives and newcomers depends on the husband's, not the wife's, origin.

The classical interpretation of the so-called Demographic Revolution, whether advanced by anti-Malthusians (who fear it) or by Malthusians (who welcome it), tends to attribute the lowered birth rate exclusively to the voluntary limitation of fertility in marriage and the deliberate procedures adopted to this end. And yet it should be asked whether there may not be other factors involved (biological ones, for example), and whether they may not also have played a part in the general weakening of "the generative will" which has come about as a result of capitalist civilization and a rising standard of living.

Before examining how and why certain doctrines are classed as Malthusian, certain others as anti-Malthusian, it might appear useful to mention certain demographic studies on the effects of known historical developments, first and foremost that of the aging of the population consequent upon the lowering of the birth rate and the prolongation of the average life span.

Studies of this kind, which are strictly scientific in character, can be used to justify doctrines of opposed or contradictory tendency over the whole range of Malthusian and populationist points of view.

It does not come within our purview, either to weigh the ethical arguments which may be invoked pro and con with respect to these opposed points of view, or to pass judgment on the various means by which they are implemented. Nor shall we, except insofar as they enter directly as factors into the relation between population growth and the means of subsistence, deal with those matters of prescriptive practice which are properly the sphere of the moralist and the theologian. Catholic positions on these matters, for example, seem cut and dried in the modern world, for they are very definitely opposed to Neo-Malthusianism. Does this mean that they have changed since the Middle Ages when, as we have seen, they were hostile to the populationist views of power-hungry secular princes? These positions, if they were indeed such as claimed, might appear oddly paradoxical. In a world inhabited by some 400 million, the Church would seem to have opposed population increase, while she is in favor of it in a world nearly ten times more highly populated. Actually, in both cases the Church has defended the freedom of the human person to choose the way best fitted for his or her self-realization, and her moral teaching has always urged the strait and narrow way. Whether in the city-state or the modern nation-state, whether in dealing with slaveowners or political leaders, the Church has always denied their right to impose either procreation or sterility upon any human being whatever, or to advise him to follow practices contrary to her moral principles, whatever the motive.

As for her own effort to gain enhanced respect and status for womanhood, an effort which Christianity launched once and for all nearly two thousand years ago, the Church may very well consider that it has led to restricted fertility in marriage. However, she does not conclude therefrom that enhanced respect and status for womanhood is a bad thing, so long as the means employed to realize it are not in themselves bad.

Catholic thought has most often had occasion to express public opposition to eugenicists who would interfere directly with natural processes. No authority, not even parental authority or that of human beings over their own bodies, can allow or sanction infanticide, abortion, or any other practice that mutilates or damages the human body. It is up to free, responsible individuals to resolve for themselves the difficult problems of conscience which arise, in the light of the moral teaching they have received or which is available to them. In this connection, it is as with any other sin: the question of whether to procreate or not to procreate does not fall into some special category distinct from the questions that arise in the other domains of life and death. Surely what is at stake is a certain conception of the value of human life, such as Emile Durkheim revealed in one of his observations on suicide in 1888: "They kill themselves most frequently in the professions that have the lowest birth rate."

Deliberately abstaining, then, from treating the moral problems which arise every day in the matter of population, we shall content ourselves in this chapter with examining two modern doctrinal tendencies: the theories of optimum population and the so-called "Marxist" theories.

A few economists have raised the issue of an optimum population level as a reply to Malthus in his own terms. Pierre Leroy-Beaulieu, for example, in 1881 presented a fable of "the three Malthuses." The first Malthus was a hunter, and he arrived at his pessimistic predictions regarding the overpopulation of his own group from a study of the quantity of available game. The other hunters didn't pay any attention to him, however, and instead invented the pastoral economy. Next came a second Malthus, this one a shepherd. When he arrived at the same dire prognostications with regard to pastoral society, the other shepherds went right ahead and invented agriculture. Then eventually appeared the third

Malthus, himself a member of agricultural society, but now the technical innovations of the industrial age came along to contradict him. In 1909, in an article entitled "From Malthus to Berthelot," A. de Foville expressed the same belief in progress, in the light of which there need be no fixed limit upon population growth.

Most often, however, theories of an optimum population have been advanced in justification of some more or less moderate Malthusianism. John Stuart Mill was first to point out the links between Malthus and those who had launched theories of an economically determined optimum population: Cannan, Wicksell, Wolfe, and their many successors. Mill gave a pessimistic twist to his own thesis, for although contrary to Malthus he believed that there is a constant tendency toward population growth, he also maintained that the means of subsistence are subject to "the law of diminishing return." To Mill, it was "not social injustice, but Nature's parsimoniousness" that is "responsible for the punitive effects of overpopulation." Although, as L. Buquet (1956) has written, "Belief in an economically determined optimum population strikes us as a myth, which several generations of economists have oddly supported," still the researches undertaken in this spirit are useful for the light they throw on the various notions of an "optimum" as yet arrived at, both in terms of economic levels and in terms of the point of view of different groups with respect to their own "optimum" and to that of other groups. Such researches led Alfred Sauvy to draw up four questions applicable to any population that includes a dominating class and a class that is dominated:

1) The optimum number of those to be dominated, from the point of view of the dominators. We have seen how, from classical antiquity to the nineteenth century, opinion was strongly in favor of a big number. What has happened since then (in Sauvy's words) is that,

The middle class has recapitulated on the national scale the same development that it went through earlier in the family circle. After having, in the nineteenth century, produced fewer and fewer descendants on the grounds that it could not afford more—while at the same time urging proliferation of offspring upon others—it finds today that 'other people's children' are far too costly, and is appalled at the rising numbers of them.

Today the tendency is to tender to all humanity the advice given by J. B. Say in the early nineteenth century: "People should be encouraged to save their money rather than to beget children."

2) The optimum number of those to be dominated, as they view the matter themselves.

3) The optimum number of dominators, from their own point of view.

4) The optimum number of dominators, from the point of view of those who are dominated.

Studies of this nature have brought out the fact that there is a population minimum, as well as a population maximum, under any set of given conditions. The statistical calculations on this point have given rise to endess discussion, which was taken account of by Sauvy when he noted that at the outbreak of the French Revolution, the optimum population in France was less than 24 million. Arthur Young, among others, suggested much the same when he published the account of his travels in France. According to J. J. Spengler, at mid-point of the twentieth century the optimum was still less than 42 million. However, according to Sauvy, such a quantum of increase could only suffice for a theoretical population which took no account of long-established conditions, "heritages" from the past. . . .

Sauvy's own optimum figure lay somewhere between 50 and 75 million, and J. F. Gravier felt that the latter figure was still too low. Sauvy has observed that "Inequality of income accommodates itself to overpopulation, and vice versa."

When we now turn to the conclusions demographers have come to, not just for a single country, but for the world, we find still wider divergences of opinion. Differences are more freely expressed when the investigators are not bound by class considerations

founded upon qualitative theories regarding the population of their
own country. Racists in rich countries are not just alarmed to see
the beginnings of human solidarity threatening to make "other
people's children" cost more than they can afford; they openly
refuse to give the same status to groups with a mounting birth rate
as they give groups which are reducing theirs. Such racists are
appalled at the mounting numbers of "colored people," especially
now that these "barbarians" are no longer willing to admit that
they are "naturally slaves." Until 1960, William Vogt was probably
the most openly cynical theoretician of such a view, but at the
Vevey conference that year, the rector of the University of Lausanne, R. Matthey, went farther. He actually stated that Hitler's
worst crime against humanity was to have rendered odious for a
long time to come the concepts of racism and eugenics.

Without going quite so far as this—more or less moderately
populationistic with respect to their own class or their own people,
considered as an "elite" or "the Lord's appointed," more or less
genocidal with respect to other classes, other peoples—most demographers who are trying to arrive at an ideal figure for the world's
population treat, each in his own fashion, the problem to which our
own researches are directed. We shall thus have occasion to come
back to this matter.

One original voice that is still to be heard amid all these arguments, is that of Karl Marx (1818–83). It has been echoed until
recent years by all Communists, whether they be Leninists, Stalin-
ists or Titoists. Vogelnick, the Yugoslav member of the UN Population Commission, declared in February 1947: "You capitalists
refuse to have a planned economy, but you are quite willing to have
a planned population—scaled down to the anemic requirements
of your economy. We are trying to do just the opposite: to adapt
our economy to our population." When he said that, he was faith-
fully echoing Marx's own views.*

* Titoists are no longer so positively orthodox, but other Communists
have not changed their tone. Yet even the most orthodox have spoken up
less frequently on this subject over the last few years.

At the same session, however, the Ukrainian representative, Rabichko, took a somewhat different line: "I should consider it barbaric were this Commission to envisage limitations on marriage, or on births in marriage, in any country whatever at any epoch whatever. With adequate social organization, it is possible to deal with any population increase, no matter how great." The member may perhaps have been imprudent to generalize so widely. At the moment the Soviet Union may well be still deploring, as Catherine II deplored in 1769, "the insufficiency of the population of the Empire," and may well be hoping that the demographic expansion of certain peoples will upset the capitalists' applecart. But there is nothing to justify our supposing that this is more than a momentary tactical position. Such would seem to be what Alfred Sauvy was conveying when he wrote: "The Marxist doctrine on population is a fighting one, a necessary attitude which will evolve once the only enemy left to vanquish is the natural environment."

Well before Marx, certain thinkers had noted that society was so structured by the tastes and decisions of the dominating class that the effect was to waste wealth which ought to have been expended on "the humbler classes," to satisfy their elementary needs. From the earliest centuries, the Fathers of the Church thundered forth against rich men who failed in their duty "to administer the goods of the poor." Later, St. Bernard inveighed against luxury, even against the luxury prevailing in religious establishments. At the start of the great Enclosure battle in England, St. Thomas More referred to sheep as "eaters of men." After Marx, Effertz, the theoretician of "ponophysiocracy," wrote:

When we consume goods which have been wrenched from the earth, we are excluding our fellow men from enjoyment of the earth. Old people of charitable disposition who build hospitals for aging dogs are no better than abortionists, people who maintain stables no better than murderers.

Marx, however, went beyond the conception of justice through redistribution of the wealth and directed his attack at the system of production itself, and precisely as to how it creates a "relative overpopulation" by self-imposed limitations on capacity. "Whereas the means of production should be at the service of the worker, the worker is at the service of the means of production."

This "relative overpopulation" appears long before the population has reached its maximum, with reference to the subsistence the system is capable of producing, or has actually produced already. This is why "relative overpopulation" and "seeming overproduction" may appear simultaneously. In 1827 Sismondi had already remarked:

Never has the population attained limits beyond which subsistence cannot increase, nor is it likely it ever will. What occurs is, that not all persons desirous of obtaining subsistence possess the legal right or the technical capacity to go about getting it for themselves directly from the land, while, on the other hand, those who have legal monopoly of lands find it far from their own interest to make the lands produce as much as they can produce.

In all countries landowners have been firm in their opposition to methods of cultivation designed solely to increase subsistence, and not to increase revenue. Long before the growth of population might be checked by any country's inability to produce greater subsistence, it is checked by the population's incapacity to purchase it or to devote its labor directly to its production.[6]

Karl Marx took up these observations and developed them with the aid of two theories of his own, "surplus value" and "the organic composition of capital." Drawing on what Darwin had claimed to be indebted to Malthus for—namely, for his theory of the struggle of the fittest, based on the biological law according to which the excess of vital power thrives on the means allotted to it—Marx went on to observe that Darwin

. . . does not see how he ruins Malthus' theory when he discovers geometric progression in the animal and vegetable kingdoms, for Malthus' theory consists in opposing to the geometric rate of progression at which mankind multiplies, a chimerical arithmetic rate of progression in the reproduction of plants and animals.[7]

Now, none of these different approaches to the population problem can be set aside until we have, first of all, analyzed more fully what we believe we know of the realities in this domain. More important to go into, deeply and at length, than the venturesome projections of optimists and pessimists, are the theories that claim to account for the coexistence (which we must all recognize as such) of a "seeming overproduction of food" within "a world of waste" and "relative overpopulation." How is it that two-thirds of humanity today goes hungry?

NOTES

1. Cf. Joseph Vialatoux, *Le Peuplement humain* (Paris: Les Editions Ouvrières, 1959), 2 vols.

2. *Ibid.*, II, 67–73.

3. Thomas Robert Malthus, *First Essay on Population, 1798*, with notes by James Bonar (London: Macmillan, 1926), pp. 203–204; *Population: The First Essay* (Ann Arbor: Ann Arbor Paperbacks, 1959), pp. 71–72.

4. T. R. Malthus, *An Essay on the Principle of Population; or, A View of Its Past and Present Effects on Human Happiness*, etc. 5th ed., 3 vols. (London: John Murray, 1817), III, 118–19, 119, 124, 364.

5. Richard Cantillon, *Essai sur la nature du commerce en général* (1755), was reprinted in 1952 by the Institut National d'Etudes Démographiques (INED), Paris.

6. J. C. L. Simonde de Sismondi, *Nouveaux Principes d'Économie Politique*, etc., 2d ed., 2 vols. (Paris: Delaunay, 1827), II, 269–70.

7. Karl Marx, *Histoire des doctrines économiques*, 8 vols. (Paris: Alfred Costes, 1925–50), 16–17. Transl. by J. Molitor of the *Theorien über den Mehrwert* (Kautsky ed.).

Chapter 3

The Biological Laws of Population

THE HUMAN POPULATION is subject to biological laws, some of which are common to all living things. Malthus' law, for example, does not apply solely to human beings.

Malthus' law may be stated as follows: When a living thing is so situated that there are no limits upon its reproductive powers, it multiplies very rapidly, in geometrical progression. In other words, it increases at the rate of compound interest, a snowballing process whereby deceptively small increments, such as the one to three per cent per annum typically found in human populations, double the population size within a generation and even within twenty-five years.

What happens when we apply this law to creatures whose coefficient of reproductive capacity is much higher than that of the human species? Calculations to this effect have been made, with truly dismaying results.

Barber observed that *Bacillus coli* divides in two every twenty minutes. At this rate, enough of the bacteria would be produced in thirty-six hours to cover the surface of the earth several times over with an unbroken film. Cohn worked out another bacterial reproductive sequence, such that if the same rate of multiplication were assured, in four and a half days a population of 10^{36} would be reached, that is, a volume equal to that of all the oceans combined. Lane Clayton, working with other bacteria, and Slater and Richards, working with yeasts, have arrived at similar results.

Protozoa and Protophyta in theory have the same sort of capacities. Ehrenberg has established that a single Paramecium could in a few days produce a volume of protoplasm equal to ten thousand times the volume of the earth. Stylonychia, one of the Infusoria, reproduces itself five times per day by segmentation. Could it keep up this pace for one month, a single individual would produce a total of 2^{150} or about 10^{44}, which is one million times the volume of the sun.

Among the metaphytes and the Metazoa, capacity for cellular reproduction is not quite as great as in one-celled life. Carrel and Ebehling, however, observed a culture of fibrous chicken tissues capable of doubling in volume in two days. Transplanted at suitable intervals, the development went on at the same rate for ten years. Were each of the new tissues to have been kept under the same laboratory conditions, the initial culture would have multiplied to 2^{180} or 10^{53} times its initial volume. Thus, had the initial culture been no larger than one cubic millimeter, it would have grown to the volume of 10^{41} cubic meters.

Sexual reproduction does not proceed at such a pace, but nonetheless insect reproduction is very fast. One pair of houseflies, if we follow Malthus' law, would in six months produce 6,000 billion flies. Cousin has observed that one pair of *Lucilia sericata,* a meat fly, could theoretically produce in nine months (that is, if it escaped the winter cold which kills it) no fewer than 100^{18} or 10^{56} of its number, or approximately 10 million times the earth's mass.[1]

When we pass on to the animal world, the reproductive pace does of course slow down, but it is still fast enough to scare any Malthus that might appear among these species. A field-mouse Malthus, for example, would calculate that a pair of his own kind could produce 22 descendants in two months, and 252 in one year. Nor would these calculations be purely theoretical, for when field-mice have been bred under the most favorable conditions, we find (Kostitzin): 20 after six months, and 200 within one year. All that keeps these figures from being spun out indefinitely is that limiting factors enter in.

Limiting Factors. Under natural conditions, living matter is prevented from expanding in this manner, first of all, because of the multiplicity of organisms: the latter get in each other's way. Even among unicellular organisms, crowding has the effect of limiting their proliferation.

Suppose we put a single microbe in a suitable culture and observe how population increase proceeds. At first, growth follows Malthus' curve of geometric increase until it reaches a maximum point; from this point it drops off and finally disappears. (See TABLE 17.)

TABLE 17

Microbe Population in Closed Environment (non-sporuliferous species). P = maximum population; P_0 = initial population; t = time

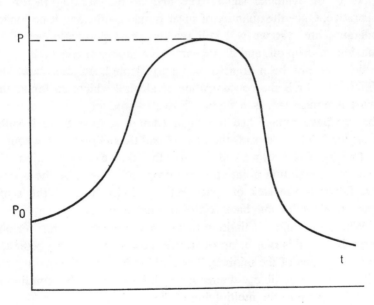

Three phenomena can have occurred:
  1) Lack of food. As we say, the environment may be exhausted, used up.

2) Lack of space.

3) The environment may have been poisoned by metabolic waste-products.

In this particular instance, it seems to be the third factor that plays the biggest part. This factor best explains how it is that, well before the nutrients in the culture have all been consumed, and before the population has grown to any very important degree, we see mortality on the increase and, still more marked, a falling-off in the multiplying of the species. Now, it would surely be absurd to suppose that, faced with the threat of excessive population, the microbes had initiated a system of birth control!

Let us take, for example, a sweet mash in which there is an alcohol-producing yeast. If the sugar content is not strong enough, the yeast population will be limited in numbers by the insufficient quantity of available sugar. The first of the limiting factors is operative. Once the quantity of sugar is made sufficient, it no longer operates, and yet we will still see the yeast population attain a maximum, drop off, and disappear—even though there is still sugar which has not been transformed into alcohol. In this case, the limiting factor is the concentration of alcohol which, so far as the yeast is concerned, is a metabolic waste-product, a poison. Now that we have replenished the sugar content so that there is sufficient food, let us pour off the alcohol and thus eliminate the source of toxicity. Even so, we will discover that the yeast population still reaches a maximum point and then drops off. This time the operative factor is the lack of space between individuals of the same species. We will come back to this phenomenon shortly.

Where the different limiting factors are concerned, what we observe is now this one being operative, now that one, in obedience to nature's law of the minima. The limiting factor is the one which, within the observable circumstances, brings about the conditions least favorable to the multiplying of the species.

However, certain species produce a reaction-phenomenon by developing "resistant strains." Just at the moment when population increase seems about to be checked by unfavorable environmental

conditions, strains appear which are capable of sustaining themselves for a very long time without reproducing.

For example, a sporuliferous microbe produces many more
spores when conditions begin to become unfavorable and when
asporulate reproduction begins to be checked. When proliferation
of the species has ceased and the nonresistant strains have disappeared, the culture will still contain spores that are far from dead.

When we take some of these spores and put them in a "new"
environment, we see that they begin all over again to produce
strains capable of multiplying. The population will grow rapidly, at
first according to Malthus' law, then, as their growth is checked,
more slowly. After a maximum is reached, population will drop off.
(See TABLE 18.)

TABLE 18

Microbe Population in Closed Culture (sporuliferous species).
P = total population; P_M = maximum population; P_0 = initial
population; V = Verhulst's logistic maximum

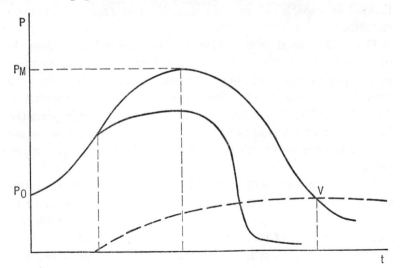

In the initial period of population growth, there are few or no resistant strains. This is why, when you try to destroy sporulating microbes by heat, it is necessary to repeat the operation at the moments when all the spores have germinated and no new ones have had a chance to form. This is the principle of Tyndallization.

The limiting factors we have been calling attention to turn up in every branch of biology.

Resistant strains are a fairly widespread phenomenon. Most often, they are tied in with modifications of the environment not solely due to population increase. Resistant strains may develop in reaction to unfavorable changes of temperature, for example. In this instance they insure survival of the species over long periods when normal members are killed off.

Resistant strains are found, not only among the spores of algae and the fungi, but also among the cysts and eggs of certain animals, the seeds of plants, etc. Among the seeds, some are much more resistant than others: these are the so-called "hardy" plants. Not only are they highly resistant to unfavorable factors, they keep for a very long time their capacity for giving birth to new members, themselves capable of reproduction. This is their "germinative strength."

Plants that need highly special environmental conditions in order to multiply often develop "hardy" strains. Thanks to these strains, plant species hold their own and remain capable, when the right moment comes, of reconstituting an abundant population. These "hardy" strains account for the fact that in certain years the fields run riot with wild mustard or with poppies; such years are known, in rural communities, as "wild mustard years" or "poppy years."

Every living species to be found in a climate with marked seasonal differences has had to develop a resistant strain in order to survive there. In the case of plants, this is a carefully protected seed or some sort of underground root or tubercle. In the case of animals, it is a cyst, egg, or nymph, or even an adult capable of digging in and living off the fat it has stored up during the warm months (hibernating animals, for example).

From all this evidence, we are now in a position to conclude that if we want to produce resistant strains in a species, we should not put the individual members in too favorable circumstances, for such strains appear in any great number only when the circumstances worsen.

On the other hand, were it our purpose to obtain a maximum yield of nonresistant strains, we would make sure that they had the most favorable conditions, and by assuring this we could prevent the development of resistant strains and thereby compromise the future of the species.

To go back to our curve of population growth, we can now understand that a species capable of producing resistant strains— whether in reaction to seasonal changes of temperature or the toxicity of metabolic wastes, or in compensation for a periodic scarcity of essential food—will eventually have a new population increase. This time the maximum attained will be determined by the new environmental conditions, or—more precisely—by their least favorable circumstances. Here we come up against another case of nature's law of the minima.

Let us go back to the example of fermenting mash and suppose that the environment is under the strict control of other living things, who see to it that the sugar (or subsistence) level remains adequate and that the quantity of alcohol being produced never reaches the point where it interferes with the multiplying of the yeast cells (to whom it is a toxin of metabolic origin). The limiting factor which would remain and now make itself felt, would be lack of space to grow in. The population curve would still reach a peak beyond which it could not continue upwards. However, in this case there would be no steep dropping off from the maximum point, once it had been reached. The graph of this development is Verhulst's S-shaped logistic curve, which spells out the consequences of a certain rate of growth under specified limiting conditions. When the effect of the limiting factor is slight in relation to the coefficient of reproduction, and if the initial population is small, then this process is the same as in Malthus' law. In other words, Malthus' law is a special case of Verhulst's logistic law, valid when the effects of limiting factors are negligible in comparison to reproductive capacity. However, if the original population of the limiting factor were large, they would have to be given greater weight in the calculation. In this case, the population tends toward a limit which depends entirely on the coefficients of reproduction, regardless of the initial population. If the environmental conditions never changed, the population of a particular species would tend to remain stable. This is a convenient abstraction, but we must next incorporate in our line of reasoning allowance for the environmental changes which, in fact, do occur.

Now, among the conditions that constitute an environment, some vary much more often than others. Climate, for example, varies continuously, and without reference to changes in population. In our own climate, for example, the so-called annual species disappear or—more precisely—are reduced to resistant strains and appear again in the spring. In tropical climates, the dry season produces the same phenomenon in many species.

On the other hand, all the living elements within a given environment are interrelated. When some external event occurs—a climatic change, for example—the variations it produces among the population of one species has repercussions upon the populations of other species sharing the same environment.

Of all the close ties between different living things, parasitism in the broadest sense is the easiest to observe. It includes the parasites proper and the predators, in relation both to their prey and to their own parasites. Moreover, it is a phenomenon so widespread in nature that ecology, the science of environment, has sometimes been reduced to the simple question: "What eats what?"

Two characteristics of the parasite are especially important in their influence upon the environment: specificity (with respect to the host species) and mobility. The laws of parasitism, as Vito Volterra stated them, were drawn up from study of simplified situations in which specificity of adaptation was never in question, and where a closed environment restricted natural mobility: one species unfailingly playing the role of parasite or predator, another species that of host or prey.

A classic observation of the type was reported by Joseph Townsend in 1786 in the course of his *A Dissertation on the Poor Laws by a Well-Wisher to Mankind*. The last sentence of the quotation which follows indicates the significance the data had for him:

In this sequestered spot [the island of Juan Fernandez], John Fernando placed a colony of goats, consisting of one male, attended by his female. This happy couple finding pasture in abundance, could readily obey the first commandment, to increase and multiply, till in process of time they had replenished their little island. In advancing to this period they were strangers to misery and want, and seemed to glory in their numbers: but from this unhappy moment they began to suffer hunger; yet continuing for a time to increase their numbers, had they been endowed with reason, they must have apprehended the extremity of famine. In this situation the weakest first gave way, and plenty was again restored. Thus they fluctuated between happiness and misery, and either suffered want or rejoiced in abundance, according as their numbers were diminished or increased; never at a stay, yet nearly balancing at all times their quantity of food. . . .

When the Spaniards found that the English privateers resorted to this island for provisions, they resolved on the total extirpation of the goats, and for this purpose they put on shore a greyhound dog and bitch. These in their turn increased and multiplied, in proportion to the quantity of food they met with; but in consequence . . . the breed of goats diminished. Had they been totally destroyed, the dogs likewise must have perished. But as many of the goats retired to the craggy rocks, where the dogs could never follow them . . . few of these, besides the careless and the rash, became a prey; and none but the most watchful, strong, and active of the dogs could get a sufficiency of food. Thus a new kind of balance was established. The weakest of both species were among the first to pay the debt of nature; the most active and vigorous preserved their lives. It is the quantity of food which regulates the numbers of the human species. . . .[2]

Under such conditions, the fate of the parasite population is very closely linked with that of the population being preyed upon. Just as soon as the former grows to the point where it endangers the latter, its growth is checked for lack of food. And vice versa:

as soon as the parasite population stops growing, for whatever reason, then the numbers of its prey increase. Now, food supplies being better and other conditions not having worsened, the parasite population begins to grow again, and its growth continues until once more the species being preyed upon decreases in number. So long as neither development goes beyond certain limits, there can be said to be a strict built-in check upon the population growth of each species by the other, such variations as occur falling between a minimum and a maximum number with respect to an average. The variations will be regular and recurrent for each of the two populations. This is the phenomenon upon which Vito Volterra based the first of his three biological laws, namely, the so-called "law of periodic recurrence." His second law is termed the "preservation of averages," and his third, "the disturbance of averages." The last was formulated as follows: "As deaths among the prey population increase, the average goes down for the predator population, and as deaths among the predators increase, the average goes up for the prey population."

The third law makes clear what happens when one or the other species is subjected to a noteworthy increase in mortality. We can only conclude from it that the limiting factors work to the advantage of the prey or host species, and to the disadvantage of the predatory or parasite species, under these circumstances.

Such formulations, however, assume conditions of strictly constant host-specificity, and a type of parasite unable to move to another environment. These are conditions rarely realized except in laboratory-controlled situations.

With less rigidly specialized adaptation and/or with mobility possible, the situation alters. For example, a parasite species may make a massive attack, and succeed in destroying every individual among the host population in a particular area before its own multiplication has been sufficiently checked for balance to be established. In such a case, the disappearance of the host species in the given area may have as its consequence the disappearance of the parasite species. Most often, however, the latter will turn to other species as its source of food. Similarly, even when all sources of food have been destroyed in a given area, if only a small number of the parasite (or predator) population can move to another area, then it can manage to survive and flourish in the new environment. Host-specificity is not absolute among parasites, even though this may seem at times to be the case. Thus, when the mongoose was introduced in Jamaica to check the number of rats and snakes, it did not stop when it had carried out this useful role, but went on to multiply at the expense of all the other small animals, including the chickens the natives raise for table and for market. So, in its turn, it became a real pest.

It is rare to find a really exclusive specificity of this type among parasites and predators. When it does occur, it seems to be the result of degeneration in the species, brought about by long and unchallenged dependence on a particular host. The insects which have managed to keep the same forms for really impressive lengths of time—grasshoppers, termites, black beetles—are all omnivorous. As Stuart Chase put it, it is a matter of indifference to them what they eat: mustard plasters, Egyptian mummies, Jefferson's draft of the Constitution, are all the same to them.

On the other hand, parasites or predators which have for a very long time found abundant food supplies at their disposal, become overadapted and lose those characteristics of their species which a parasitic existence does not require. Only those organs necessary for the capture of their prey, or for installation within the host body, are elaborately developed. Nothing is more instructive in this connection than to compare the Copepoda of shore regions with Copepoda which have become parasites. The latter have lost their swimming organs, indeed, all organs which would relate them to existence outside the host body.

An example from among the predators is Machairodus, a mammal of the cat family, whose razor-sharp canines enabled it to attack the enormous pachyderms which lived at the end of the Tertiary and the beginning of the Quaternary. When the latter became extinct, the predators disappeared themselves.

However, though the character of host-specificity is not always so strong as to rule out adaptation to a new host, the character of mobility presents a still more remarkable phenomenon. This occurs when some very sudden alteration in the environment transforms a seemingly sedentary species into a migratory species—or rather, when a migratory strain appears within a seemingly sedentary species. This mutation seems to be related to population density.

From what we know today of the biology of locusts, it appears that in regions where these insects have long been settled, they are solitary and sedentary, anything but capable of joining a migratory swarm. Various influences, however, among which population density seems to predominate, bring about a mutation and a gregarious, migratory generation of locusts suddenly appears. In certain species of locust, the gregarious generation is produced as soon as there are more than four hundred individuals per acre. Of course, specialists have distinguished intermediate forms. There is the case of the great swarming of locusts under Charlemagne, when locusts from the Crimea came as far west as the south of France. There they subsided into a sedentary life until the Second World War. Then, when the forests of Landes were destroyed by fire, conditions favored the multiplying of the species, and concentrations of the insect were found in which the mutation to gregariousness and migratory flight had taken place. This case increased our knowledge, but it also showed how complicated even the simplest phenomena can be, where the self-regulation of natural populations is concerned.

Grasshoppers, like men, are endowed with mobility and are not overadapted to special environments. At the same time, however, they multiply as only insects can. As many as 100,000 eggs have been found within an area of one square meter. This fertility is essential to the survival of the species.

Consider now the situation of the host, rather than that of the parasite. Resistance to the inroads of the latter may vary widely and take seemingly contradictory forms. On the one hand, it seems that no plant or animal in good health is ever attacked by a parasite which, nonetheless, is perfectly capable of destroying a whole population of the former once it is not in good health. Thus, in the Wichita National Forest a simple wire fence is enough to keep grasshoppers away from grasslands being protected from grazing animals. Obviously, they are perfectly capable of jumping through the fence; what restrains them is the fact that they have an easier time of it on the other side, feeding on a plant weakened also by the grazing cattle. Specialists in the study of Cryptogamia and entomologists will long be arguing over whether a given insect attacks a given plant because it has been weakened by a fungus, or whether the fungus has attacked the plant because it was damaged by an insect.

Among animal species, it is no less hard to tell whether a predator like the fox or the hawk is really a destroyer of certain types of small game, or whether by attacking the weak and sickly members of the species he does not actually protect the species as a whole from infection. In the latter view, he would be insuring the survival of the fittest, a true agent of "natural selection."

In another connection, although host-specificity in parasites seems to be a secondary characteristic of degeneration—an over-specialization with respect to a host in abundant supply—the action of the parasite upon the host species may bring about transformations in the latter that tend to assist the survival of individuals possessing these secondary characteristics. The details of such transformations are often grouped under the heading "acquired immunity." Unlike the resistance of healthy individuals to all such inroads upon their integrity, acquired immunity is most often a narrowly specific adaptation. It corresponds, in most cases, to a hypersensitivity with regard to a particular parasite. Moreover, there are natural immunities that also correspond to hypersensitivity and that present many of the same features in detail. Most American species of grape used in viniculture (V. Riparia, V. Rupestris, V. Berlandieri, etc.) are supposed to be resistant to Phylloxera, but this does not mean that they are not attacked by the insect, nor that the latter does not manage to live on them. What happens when this plant louse attacks the root of an American vine is that the plant forms a sort of scar tissue around the wound (a process known as suberization), a protective shield that keeps the parasite from burrowing any more deeply into the plant. When the same thing happens to a European vine (V. Vinifera), there is no such self-protective reaction. It does not appear harmed at first contact, and there is no suberization of tissue. The Phylloxera is able to take over the whole plant, which is speedily cankered and dies, before it has had time (or so it would seem) to suffer from the parasite's attack.

There are a number of septicemias that appear to involve an analogous process. In a sufficiently sensitive individual, Streptococcus produces immediate local reactions: a boil, an abscess, or whatever. In a less sensitive individual, however, the microbe will be enabled to multiply more or less throughout the whole organism, and such defense reaction as occurs will not occur (if ever) until the whole bloodstream is poisoned.

The bearing of sensitivity on immunity also appears in cases where individuals can withstand limited attacks by a parasite, but not massive ones. In the face of massive attack, sensitivity proves unavailing and the supposedly immune individual turns out to be more susceptible than individuals who have not been immunized. Chickens vaccinated against tuberculosis (Koch's bacillus) do not normally suffer its attack. Compared with control chickens, they may be considered immune. However, when vaccinated chickens are injected experimentally with massive numbers of Koch bacilli, they are quickly killed off. Subjected to the same massive injections, non-vaccinated chickens will merely display violent local reactions—sufficient, in many cases, to throw off their attackers.

It would seem that the nature and results of the reactions on the part of living things may vary enormously, with the quantity and intensity of the events to which they are exposed.

Now, there are two main reasons why the problem of parasitism cannot be treated quite so simply as we have been presenting it so far:

a) The same species of parasites (or predators) attacks several host species (or prey species), and the same host species (or prey species) is attacked by more than one species of parasite (or predator). Thus the problem is complicated by other problems: rivalry among species which feed on the same host (or prey), rivalry among the latter with respect to their abilities to resist their various parasites (or predators). We have seen how parasitism (or predation) may serve a species by eliminating its weaker members and preserving the most fit. Similarly, substitutions may occur as between host (and prey) species.

b) Parasites and predators are in turn host bodies (and prey) to other living species. Within the balance of nature there are long chains of symbiotic relationship in which each link in the chain serves as parasite (or predator) to another, host body (or prey) to yet another.

Very often, parasitism is one of the major elements that check population growth in the parasitic species. We have noted cases of parasites which, transported from their natural habitat where they had been preyed upon by their own parasites (known as hyperparasites), have so increased in numbers as to destroy their normal source of food supply. The new environment would become a wasteland to them, if new limiting factors did not come into play to re-establish the balance of nature.

Icerya Purchasi, for example, an Australian scale insect which had been introduced in the south of France, was causing serious damage there until Novius cardinalis, its most deadly predator, was also introduced. In all countries today specialists in plant diseases are recognizing the invaluable role of hyperparasites in their efforts at control.

When we study population variations among a given set of symbiotic relationships, it is always tempting to make them appear simpler than they really are, or to reduce them to a few complex terms. In his study of the island of Comodo (in the Malay archipelago), Kostitzin examined three population groups: the big carnivorous reptiles, which he studied from the point of view of their numbers, the herbivorous mammals that serve as food for the reptiles, and the plant life. He studied the last two groups from the point of view of their "biotic mass."

Some, perhaps, will wonder what possible bearing such studies can have upon problems of human population. We must never forget, however, that man is a predator with respect to the whole of nature. He has little specificity of adaptation, for he tends to utilize anything and everything—and in the greatest possible number—to satisfy needs which are sometimes of his own creation. He is not content just to feed himself, but also dresses and ornaments himself, and he forges tools which in their turn produce more things to be consumed, new desires to fulfill. Although, as with every other living thing, his alimentary needs have limits relative to the volume of the human population, his desires are limitless. The record of his behavior supports the view that he kills for the sake of killing, destroys for the sake of destroying, and that he only hurls himself at nature for the forever unassuaged pleasure of enslaving it. And finally, in aid of his predations, modern man (at least) possesses tools infinitely more powerful than those of any other animal.

Moreover, and in this respect modern man is also much better endowed than the other animals, he is extremely mobile. When one environment proves unfavorable, or when he has used it up, he can transfer his destructive passions to another.

Like all parasites, man is obliged to obtain from certain living things products he himself is not capable of synthesizing. Plant life, especially, has properties only it can supply him with. Certain amino acids and certain vitamins, for example, are indispensable to human life and beyond human powers to synthesize. Like the adult guinea pig, man cannot retain vitamin C, but must constantly replenish his supply (L. Randoin and P. Le Gallic). Possibly he did possess this faculty once and has since lost it, for it still exists in the embryo and occasionally among very young children, at least to some extent. Very exceptionally would it be found among adults (Giroud, Le Blond, etc.).

Furthermore, man is a social animal, a source of wealth to other men. As a result, the practice of murder (whether or not with cannibalistic undertones) is rather promptly superseded by that of taking slaves, a more rewarding form of conquest. First it is young women, then adult males, who are taken in bondage. Later, the practice of taking care of the old and the sick appears—even the old and the sick who are not related to him by blood—for man learns to recognize in his fellow man something besides physical strength.

No animal cares for the aged of its species in the way man does. Kostitzin observed this in the following passage:

As far as the growth curves of animals are concerned, they present one remarkable peculiarity. Save for man, they never go beyond a maximum point. This means that the only portion of animal life which comes under observation is the ascending portion—it is as though there were no such thing as aged animals.

Man constitutes a value to his own species, and among civilized peoples this value is accorded, not just to the human being who is physically strong or has potentialities for becoming so, and not just to human beings who formerly possessed such strength, but also to individuals who appear incapable of ever being or becoming strong.

Adam Smith made this point in the introduction to his famous work:

Among the savage nations of hunters and fishers, every individual who is able to work, is more or less employed in useful labour, and endeavours to provide, as well as he can, the necessaries and conveniencies of life, for himself, or such of his family or tribe as are either too old, or too young, or too infirm to go a hunting and fishing. Such nations, however, are so miserably poor, that from mere want, they are frequently reduced, to the necessity sometimes of directly destroying, and sometimes of abandoning their infants, their old people, and those afflicted with lingering diseases, to perish with hunger, or to be devoured by wild beasts. Among civilized and thriving nations, on the contrary, though a great number of people do not labour at all, many of whom consume the produce of ten times, frequently of a hundred times more labour than the greater part of those who work; yet the produce of the whole labour of the society is so great, that all are often abundantly supplied, and a workman, even of the lowest and poorest order, if he is frugal and industrious, may enjoy a greater share of the necessaries and conveniencies of life than it is possible for any savage to acquire.[3]

Still, even primitive man most often protects his young, or at least those who are well constituted, but in some such societies, the old people die off when they have lost their powers for resisting the more hostile factors of the environment. At a slightly higher stage, the old man is looked after and honored for his past services to the tribe. Only with civilization does man look after the infirm and the abnormal, or in the instance of children, permit them to live. The struggle against infant mortality, the care of the "hopelessly" ill, these are marks of human civilization, despite the protests raised from time to time by those who view man solely as an economic animal. Such people, who stress the material returns which the species can produce, rather than the eminent dignity of the human person, are becoming alarmed at the medical progress realized in countries where infant mortality formerly operated as a check on excess population—most notably in those countries of Asia which Paul Claudel so aptly called "quivering shoals of human spawn, more numerous than the dead." To what new catastrophes do they look forward to "take up the slack," now that hecatombs of infants no longer "preserve" the species?

Besides worrying about overpopulation, they often complain that the blessings of natural selection are being circumvented; the humanitarian views of civilized man, it would seem, doom the species. For instance, Earnest Hooton and Alexis Carrel have warned that the human race is rapidly deteriorating through the humanitarian efforts made to assure the survival of the weak. Sir

Charles Darwin, no less than the Rector of the University of Lausanne, R. Matthey, also echoes such fears of humanity's qualitative worsening. At the Vevey Conference in April, 1960, Darwin declared, "It is not too much to say that a very severe struggle for life is one of the basic conditions which has led to all the wonders of biological evolution." We have already noted above how far Matthey went on the same occasion. René Sand pointed out long before, however, that

. . . The partisans of natural selection forget two things. First, it operates at the expense of the strong—in microbic diseases, for instance. Second, for every weak individual eliminated, several are created who stay alive. Poverty and disease rarely kill off at one fell swoop. More often, they cripple their victims or otherwise leave them with impaired powers. A selection that operates so carelessly, so unknowingly, is scarcely natural selection.

And we might add that the human species owes some of its most highly valued contributions to individuals whom an unrestrained natural selection would in all likelihood have eliminated, were it not for humanity's tendency to look after its "weak" and "helpless."

It seems, indeed, that as mankind has protected them more and more in the course of time, the "weak" have themselves made ever more signal contributions to progress. Countless great men have had syphilis or tuberculosis. Charles Darwin, the author of the *Origin of Species,* was afflicted with a congenital infirmity; one of his five sons became a scientist no less remarkable than his father, and three other sons made very honorable contributions to various sciences. As for Sir Charles, he has earned the right to put the following letters after his name: K.B.E., M.O., M.A., Sc.D., and F.R.S. (Cambridge). His own example proves what the world might have lost, had his grandfather's congenital infirmity been allowed to end the distinguished family line which his great-great-grandfather, Erasmus Darwin, the poet and physiologist, was first to make widely known and honored.

It is true that Sauvy considers the oversimplified thesis (that of Hooton and Carrel) to have been refuted from various quarters with arguments "more generous than rational." We permit ourselves the observation that it matters little whether facts are generous or not; it is quite enough that they exist, to upset any would-be rational argument.

Be that as it may, man appears in nature as a parasite, one especially dangerous to his immediate environment and consequently to the future of his own species. That this animal has nonetheless established himself, and even developed to the point of pre-eminence among the species, must seem a profoundly mysterious matter. What has happened is that man has not been content to remain a parasite on nature, but has learned to dominate it. After countless trials and errors, he has succeeded in transforming it to his own profit: in this achievement the labors of successive civilizations find their meaning.

And yet, however special—and specially privileged—he may be, man also remains an animal and as such subject to biological laws which he can only control so long as he respects them. In connection with "resistant strains," we remarked above that such forms appear when the environment becomes hostile to the individual, or to the population, and threatens to check its growth. That holds true for the Protista, both plant and animal, and for all plants whose seeds, rhizomes, or underground tubercles appear as resistant strains with respect to the adult plant. It can be verified that the sexual reproduction which produces the most frequently found seed-form of resistant strain, only takes place when the one or two parents are checked in their future development. A healthy tree, capable of getting through winters and dry seasons, does not put out blossoms, nor does it bear fruit. Only when old age threatens, or when some accident ages it prematurely, does sexual reproduction come to the aid of the species. We may note that the same tree may be too weakened to reproduce at all, but most often an elaborate blossoming marks the approaching end of the individual plant. Like extreme weakness, superabundance prevents sexual reproduction.

Can such observations be usefully extended to all living things, in particular to the higher animals and to man himself? Let us look at how an isolated individual is constituted, that is, let us examine it ontogenetically. We have to distinguish between the phenomena of growth (increase in mass, volume, numbers of cells) and the phenomena of development (profound changes in structure or in function).

What we find is that in animals as in plant species, the individual begins to put out sexual cells capable of reproducing similar individuals, only at the end of youth or the beginning of adulthood. Then there is a phase of decline, when the reproductive faculties diminish in power along with other activities and there is even, in some cases, a physical shrinking. If no accident supervenes to accelerate the process, the individual dies, as we say, of old age.

According to Weismann's schemata, this development is produced by aging, which

in principle only involves the soma, i.e., the cells destined to disappear with the individual. The reproductive cells are not subject to it, or not immediately, since when conjugated with a gamete of the opposite sex, or even when activated without conjugation (parthenogenesis) they are capable of reproducing a new individual. Thus their survival is potentially unlimited. Here we must note a fact that always astonishes those who are not biologists, though it is irrefutable: whenever one of our body cells dies (as happens thousands of times a minute, with the ordinary desquamation of our skin and mucous membranes), it is the first time such an accident has befallen it since the beginning of life on earth. Until this moment there has been no protoplasmic discontinuity between cell and cell, from one set of reproductive organs to another, in all the billions of living creatures which have succeeded one another. Looking back into the past, every cell thus represents the end point of an uninterrupted line of living matter. On the other hand, looking forward, nearly all of the billions of cells that make up our body will die with us. Only such of our germinative cells as shall have played their full role—produced viable eggs, then embryos, then the bodies of our children—will live on after we die. If our offspring, in turn, have descendants, these cells will live on indefinitely. So far as they are concerned, the chain of life will be broken only when our line dies out completely.[4]

It follows that in animals, too, sexual reproduction is a means of producing strains resistant to the senescence which inexorably overtakes the cells of the soma. It is brought into play as soon as senescence begins to put the individual life in peril.

To conclude from the above, in the spirit of Godwin and Condorcet, that a humanity which had found the secret of eternal youth would no longer tend to multiply, is but a step which any rational mind might be tempted to take. On the basis of facts we shall go into later, Doubleday a century ago, and Josué de Castro more recently, presented a hypothesis to the effect that the lowering of the birth rate among the wealthiest classes may well be one instance of a much more general biological law at work.

In as much as evolutionists have generally conceded that phylogeny (the development of the species) so closely parallels ontogeny (the development of the individual) that, in their eyes, it is legitimate to reason by analogy from one to the other, then ought we to concede that the senescence which overtakes every individual must also, sooner or later, overtake every species, the human species as well? There is no harm in the proposition that species age as well as individuals, if we take it as a working hypothesis and remember that there are species alive today as for long geological eras which are still in the prime of youth. Also, we should try to define what is meant by the aging of a species.

We have stated that the forms of life which have survived most nearly intact since their earliest appearance on earth, are those capable of putting up with all sorts of conditions and of feeding on almost anything. Among the most primitive insects, the black beetles, the grasshoppers, and the dragon flies go back through four geological eras. What, then, of the so-called higher insect species, those which are so wondrously and specially adapted? How far back do they go, and what is their future?

Despite the fearsome rate at which they multiply, so few individuals survive that it is almost a miracle when, every year, the species is reborn out of the annual carnage. Parasites and predators alike have disappeared entirely, along with the host and prey species to which they were specifically adapted. In the course of their parasitism, all sorts of "useless" functions had been dispensed with. Might not so high a degree of specialization be less the carrying of useful faculties to their most efficient pitch, than the abandoning of faculties seemingly—and as of a given moment actually—useless? Natural selection notwithstanding, might it not be that certain properties are chosen for special development due to an impoverishing of genetic capacity for several possible developments, an impoverishing which might itself be the main phenomenon of a species' senescence?

If we seem to be asking questions, rather than answering them, it is to emphasize that here we are in the sphere of doctrinal hypothesis and nothing we say is to be understood as affirming, still less denying, the contrary hypothesis. And yet, as of any given moment, is not scientific truth the simplest working hypothesis available to account for the known facts?

In adopting, though but provisionally, this notion of specialized adaptation as a selection among faculties consequent upon an impoverishment of the capacity for possible developments, we are led to turn again to certain passages of Fr. Teilhard de Chardin's *The Phenomenon of Man:*

Among the higher insects a cephalic concentration of nerve ganglia goes together with extraordinary wealth and precision of behavior. We cannot but wonder when we see all the living things in the world about us, so marvelously adjusted and still so terribly remote. Are they our rivals? Or successors perhaps? Must we not rather say a multitude pathetically involved and struggling in a blind alley?[5]

Might not the cause of this impasse lie in the way specialized adaptation involves a choice among possible solutions? Does the blocked future of the higher insect species have any meaning for any or all of the other species, and for the human species in particular? Let us turn again to Fr. Teilhard de Chardin:

In the course of the Tertiary era, the ungulates radically transformed the adjustment of their feet; the carnivores reduced and sharpened their teeth; the Cetacea streamlined themselves like fish; the Proboscidea greatly complicated their incisors and and their molars. Meanwhile the primates on their side had kept their ulna intact and also their fibula; they jealously hung on to their five fingers; they remained typically tri-tubercular. Are we to consider them therefore the conservatives among mammals, the most conservative of all?

No; but they have shown themselves to be the most wary.

In itself, at its best, the differentiation of an organ is an immediate factor of superiority. But, because it is irreversible, it thus imprisons the animal that undergoes it in a restricted path at the end of which, under the pressure of orthogenesis, it runs the risk of ending up either in monstrosity or fragility. Specialization paralyzes, ultra-specialization kills. Palaeontology is littered with such catastrophes. Because, right up to the Pliocene period, the primates remained the most "primitive" of the mammals as regards their limbs, they remained also the most free.[6]

When we combine these views of Fr. Teilhard's with Vito Volterra's laws, we arrive at a more rational basis for optimism regarding man's future.

When we study an expanding curve, such as that for the world population (Table 19, I) and try to foresee how it will develop, two possible solutions are available. One is catastrophic (Table 19, II) in obedience to Malthus' Law, with the species disappearing abruptly after a maximum point of growth has been reached. The other is a logistic solution (Table 19, III), where, as the limit is approached, the curve gradually smooths out and remains stationary at the level of greatest magnitude compatible with the environment. This is the solution envisaged by Verhulst's logistic law.

TABLE 19

World Population Growth: The Two Alternatives

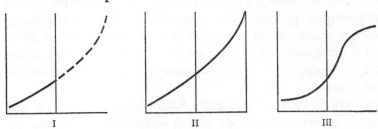

I II III

Two further characteristics of the human race are important in this connection. On the one hand (as Townsend argued), the maximum human population compatible with a given environment is not solely fixed at the level of available subsistence. Man attains a certain level of well-being, and one of the ways he keeps it secure for his descendants is by limiting their number (as Cantillon pointed out). Moreover, he aspires to move upward in the social scale and still more to assure that his descendants will continue to do so. When society includes a more leisured class whose standard of living is envied, and whose way of life is imitated, then there is a further lowering of the maximum population level desired. This comes about through the law of "social capillarity," as Arsène Dumont described it. In this case, the desired level of maximum population may drop so low as to bring about depopulation; it can also lead to the disappearance of the species, if the population falls below a minimum.

To illustrate this point of view, which may seem abstract, take the well-known phenomenon of population flight from the country to the city, which has occurred in lands where agriculture has attained a high degree of productivity. What economists think of as the optimum population may be exceeded in an exclusively agricultural community, in the sense that there are more hands available than are necessary, strictly speaking, for full exploitation of the community's resources. At the same time, however, its population may already have fallen below a "demographic" minimum necessary to maintain its present numbers. And indeed, it does seem that there is a population level below which the number of unmarried persons (of marriageable age) rises shockingly. Possible choices as to a marital partner have narrowed down, and if there were only more people everyone could "find a shoe that fits," with a consequent decrease in the numbers of unmarried persons.

To assure such a population's subsistence in the face of progressive agricultural methods, one of two conditions must be met. Either the community must cease to be exclusively agricultural, or else the dimensions of the community must be expanded by putting it into frequent social contact with inhabitants of some wider area. But this is another problem.

Another consideration is the fact that man is capable, not only of adapting to his environment, but of modifying it. Like the other parasites, he can destroy the environment he lives in, and like the monster of legend, bring about his own undoing. There is no lack of cases in point. He can also, with the aid of his technical knowledge, make the earth "his" and administer it to his own purposes. P. Leroy-Beaulieu's fable of the three Malthuses still has a message for our generation, and we should measure it against the facts.

So far as we can make them out, the laws of biology do not provide sufficient grounds either for optimism or for pessimism. They apply to man the animal, man the living thing. What we have to study now, is this special animal, this specially privileged population, so as to learn whether he can choose wisely for his species, between a course that leads to senescence and death and one that leads to renewal of youthful vigor.

NOTES

1. Marcel Prenant, *Adaptation, écologie et biocoenotique* (Paris, 1934).
2. James R. McCulloch (ed.), *A Select Collection of Scarce and Valuable Economical Tracts* (London: Harrison & Sons, 1859), pp. 417–18.

3. *An Inquiry into the Nature and Causes of the Wealth of Nations*, ed. by Edwin Cannan (New York: Modern Library, 1937), p. lviii.

4. Cf. Henri Prat, *Métamorphose explosive de l'humanité* (Paris, 1960).

5. *The Phenomenon of Man* (New York: Harper, 1959), p. 153.

6. *Ibid.*, p. 158.

Chapter 4

How Actual Populations Have Grown

WORLD POPULATION

THE HUMAN RACE, though it constitutes one of the animal populations, goes far beyond the other species in respect to the faculties at its disposal. It has more and other possibilities open to it, and the checks and limits upon its development are vastly different ones. It is true that mankind is subjected to the laws of nature, but it is also capable of mastering them through its own creative powers of intelligence and desire, with the help of techniques and tools the latter have inspired. The farther human development carries us from our primitive origins, and the greater our mastery over the earth's natural forces and our own bodies, then the freer we become of those limiting factors which rule the individual and collective lives of the irrational animals.

While as a general rule mankind has always sought out the most fertile regions and most favorable climates, yet we are by no means slaves to climate. Excessive humidity, as in tropical Asia, has not prevented one quarter of the human race from making its home there. Moreover, mankind's choice of settlement has often been conditioned by what lies under the surface of the earth in the way of mineral riches. As nature's lord and master, man seeks his fortune in dangerous and forbidding places as well as in readily accessible ones. He is not doomed to perish. He can not only adapt to cold climates, he can create artificial climates. The Russians, the North Americans, the Scandinavians have all made enormous strides toward conquering the vast frigid regions at the two poles. Nor has excessive aridity proved too much for mankind: the search for sources of water has been carried very far, and techniques of irrigation also testify to the persistence of the human genius.

To be sure, as we saw in the preceding chapter, there can never be total independence from biological law. However, a host of mysteries which mankind had failed to solve throughout many long centuries have at last been analyzed, explained, and mastered by *homo sapiens.*

Human settlement over the planet has become less and less a matter of biological factors, more and more a matter of social and cultural factors. How else explain the fact that men have flocked to lands by no means ideal in respect to soil or climate, and left sparsely-peopled vast areas both more fertile and less rude? Or the fact that populous nations have not exterminated the peoples they conquered, but instead have reduced them to slavery? What made the Germans attack the Poles, a nation with far greater population pressure than their own? Human population density does not come about through the automatic operation of biological determinants such as Malthusian laws and Verhulst's logistic curve imply. Rather, both in the way it comes about in the first place and in the way it approaches its limits, it is the result of diverse economic, social, cultural, and religious circumstances, all of which have varied widely from country to country and from age to age. It has been a simple matter of fact, not the expression of some law. The expanding curve of world population, far from having been produced in a closed culture under laboratory conditions, is the sum total of thousands and thousands of population curves extending back into time as well as over the entire surface of the globe. The individual populations have reacted, each in its own fashion, to historical events and to local influences.

Why do the indigenous people of the Malaysian Federation lag far behind the rapid growth of the Chinese settlers? Why are certain coastal tribes in Tanganyika—and, indeed, in other parts of tropical Africa—shrinking while neighboring tribes expand into their territory? Why have the Polynesians of Hawaii, the Melanesians of Fiji, and the Africans of the Guianas, Surinam, Trinidad, Mauritius, and Natal increased more slowly than the Orientals and East Indians settled beside them? Why would the population of large parts of northern Italy and France have fallen were it not for a ready supply of immigrants from the more prolific shores of the Mediterranean?

Questions like this compel us to recognize that the demographic developments in each of the human population groups are highly local and specific.

Studies of plant and animal populations began to be made only after demographic theories such as those of Malthus and Verhulst had been elaborated. What they have shown is that flora and fauna, even better than the human race, can be made to fit the formula. Human behavior has not lived up to the forecasts of the demographers, because it is not just the result of the operation of biological laws. Godefroy gives us an example of population increase within a limited area.[1] In Czarist Russia, the *mir* was a form of the collective ownership of property—in this case, of the land. In certain *mirs,* population was increasing so rapidly as to create considerable overcrowding. From time to time there would be a new redistribution of the available land, and what determined the size of each lot was how many sons each peasant had. As the people were very prolific, the size of the family lots got smaller and smaller. At the same time, in order to be sure of getting the biggest possible lot when time for the next redistribution should come around, every family tried to outdo every other family in number of births.

A diet poor in animal protein may probably lessen the capacity of the liver to neutralize the *liquor folliculi,* and may thereby increase female fertility. However, in itself, this biological law is not enough to account for a particular pattern of human behavior; there are other important factors that influence fertility, or rather, that influence the sexual appetite of a poor man whose diet is low in animal protein. There are a great many non-biological factors that influence fertility, to be discussed in a later chapter in greater detail. Here we mention only a few:

Religious Factors. The great religions differ enormously in their traditions, dogmas, and moral doctrines relative to human sexual behavior, marriage and the purposes of marriage—the procreation and rearing of children—abstinence, contraception, divorce, monogamy, etc.

Religious attitudes and philosophic systems have long been influential with respect to population growth in certain countries. Of course they have varied from country to country and from age to age, even within the same confession. In the demographic sphere, the Catholic religion has had a particular influence upon the population growth of the French Canadians, the Irish, and the Dutch Catholics. However, as a general rule, Catholics may be said to have taken part in their own fashion in all the typical demographic developments of their respective countries: the lowering of birth rates and death rates, changes in respect to nuptiality and fertility. Nor is Catholic behavior in these respects necessarily uniform within any one country. The Italians, for example, are nearly all Catholics, but while the Italians of the south are very prolific, those of the north have a birth rate among the lowest in the Western world. The French, although Catholic, were among the first in Europe to be drawn to Malthusian ideas and practices, and it was only on the eve of the Second World War that their birth rate reversed its long downtrend. In Belgium, and even more in Luxembourg, the Catholic population is Malthusian in attitude. Only Sweden has a lower birth rate than Luxembourg.

In general, Protestants are less prolific than Catholics, though there are some notable exceptions: the Mormons in the United States, for example, and some Calvinist groups in the Netherlands. Religious affiliation alone can scarcely account for such variations in patterns of behavior.

Political Factors. Like ancient and medieval history, modern history affords a number of instances of populationist policies on the part of governments. Sometimes the end in view has been economic, sometimes imperialist. Or, as was the case in France on the eve of the Second World War, there has been fear of depopulation and policies to encourage larger families have been instituted.

When we compare the measures governments have taken with the results obtained, it is clear in this connection too that men and women do not respond automatically and obediently to the calculations of cabinet ministers regarding how social economic, and military problems should be met. The effect of family legislation in France has been debatable. It seems that some part, at least, of the German people did as the Führer told them to do, but only for a few years. The case of Japan is noteworthy. Just at the moment when their "living space" was extending over the Asiatic mainland and every sort of employment opportunity was opening up in the conquered territories—and when the government was launching a populationist policy—at just that moment the Japanese birth rate began to check its rate of increase.

Psychological Factors. Among certain peoples, fertility is highly valued, whether for religious reasons, as a sign of social prestige and well-being, or because it represents an increase in the economic power of the family or the clan. Elsewhere, matters pertaining to sexuality are thought of very differently. What a contrast between the liberal sexual habits of many primitive peoples and the prudishness and frigidity of certain social classes in a society that is taboo-ridden.

There is the same sort of variability in how various other factors relating to population are regarded—surely a psychological matter. Primitive peoples look at infant mortality very differently than civilized peoples do. Often it is considered solely—along with other demographic factors—from a statistical point of view, without regard for ontological considerations. The native tribesman lives and dies without ever making a single calculation, whereas we draw up statistical tables so as to gain control of our own numbers. We may even go so far as to take pride in the fact that the death rate in our country is lower than it is in a neighboring country.

The sexual behavior of intellectuals is much more influenced than is that of other groups by world problems and fear of war. They get much more preoccupied with such questions as hunger and overpopulation than do persons of less reflective disposition. They pay much less exclusive attention to the purely sexual aspects of married life, for their broader cultural interests and their appreciation of the arts, which they enjoy with their families, reinforce their spiritual love and provide a substitute sublimation for their sexual urges.

Factors Attributable to Modern Civilization. Western civilization introduced the phenomenon known as the Demographic Revolution to all the so-called advanced countries in the course of the nineteenth century. When the most striking feature it brought with it is studied in detail—namely, the decline in fertility among the most "advanced" groups of the population—it will be seen to come down, at least in part, to a substitution of limitations on birth for a limitation on marriages.

Doubtless the post-war "baby boom," which has recently occured in most Western countries, represents further proof of the fact that population does not develop automatically along predetermined lines. Nonetheless, we may confidently affirm that the demographic revolution is closely tied in with the phenomena of industrialization and urbanization, phenomena which in the course of time were not without influence upon agriculture and rural communities.

The low birth rate of the city-dweller is explained by a whole series of causes, some socio-psychological, some external, but none of them much related to the availability of living space or food.

Natality in agricultural sectors has maintained a higher level than in the urban and industrial sectors, and is explained by other factors. Family ties have remained strong. Children are looked upon as new members of a kin group broader than the immediate family circle. They cost no more than it takes to feed them, and their care may be the responsibility of a wide kin group. They can begin to make economic contributions at an early age. Moreover, in agricultural communities needs and aspirations scarcely extend beyond immediate concern for the enhancement of family power and prestige. The sense of community is based more upon the network of family relationships than upon conjugal union— the latter constitutes, rather, a sexual institution.

These same factors account no less for the differences in fertility to be remarked among different professions. Especially prolific groups like miners, fishermen, sailors, and in general all who must do hard physical work for a living, display sociological traits very like those of the peasants (narrow social outlook, marriage treated as a sexual relationship), and it is these which explain, at least in part, their relatively high fertility rates.

On the other hand, in urban cultures the immediate family tends to be cut off from its kindred. The child's birth and rearing is an expensive proposition. City-dwellers have an enormously wide and growing set of claims upon their interest and attention. Social mobility is especially marked. Women are emancipated at a number of levels and are themselves drawn to engage in occupations.

For the remainder of this chapter, we shall analyze a number of specific populations and show how the above-mentioned factors play their part. In this way we may be aided to appreciate mankind's very considerable independence of the biological laws and limiting factors to which animal populations are subjected.

SOME EXAMPLES OF DEMOGRAPHIC TRENDS

In the sections which follow, some examples of demographic trends have been analyzed both for highly industrialized or "developed" countries and for countries not as yet industrialized or "underdeveloped." When allowance is made for the different levels and conditions to be found, it will be seen that the same tendencies apply as applied for the world population in the preceding section.

Rural and Urban Populations in Western Europe and North America. In the modern sense of the term, urbanization has gone hand in hand with Western industrialization. Both phenomena originated in northwestern Europe and North America. Today urbanization is to be found on every continent, and with the spread of Western civilization economic and social development will bring urbanization to countries which may yet for some time to come cling to a predominately agricultural pattern of social and occupational organization.[2]

Taking only cities and aggregations of more than 100,000 inhabitants (the number of which went over the 1,000 mark between 1950 and 1960, according to the United Nations *Demographic Yearbook*), we find them occupied by some 413 million people, or 15.1 per cent of the world population. Western Europe and the English-speaking world have been especially affected.

Obviously, urbanization is not restricted to the biggest cities. Cities of fewer than 100,000 inhabitants have most of the same characteristics, though there are some urban aggregations, both larger and smaller than this figure with predominantly rural populations, which may even include farm workers. The criteria vary from country to country and from region to region within a country, and are determined by the different countries' cultural, political and economic histories, the type of habitat, population density of the surrounding countryside, etc. Moreover, big cities differ in character from continent to continent. The metropolitan areas of America all resemble each other by their skylines, but as you move outward from the centers of these cities you see that a great part of the population lives in one-family houses set on individual plots of land with grass and trees. Only quite recently have big apartment houses, of the type long familiar in European urban agglomerations, begun to be built. This fact explains why American cities cover so much ground, while European cities have a higher population density.

The high population density of European cities in general corresponds to the high density of population in the countries as a whole. The Netherlands, Belgium, the United Kingdom, West Germany, Switzerland, and Luxembourg, together with the north of France, make up the most highly industrialized sector of northwest Europe. The proportion of the population active in non-agricultural occupations varies from 95 per cent in England and Wales to 74 per cent in Luxembourg. Only Switzerland among them is not highly urbanized. The Netherlands has the lowest percentage of non-agricultural population in relation to the total population (55 per cent), and Scotland has the highest (83 per cent).*

What is most striking about Western Europe, then, is that quite apart from population density, all the countries are highly industrialized and a majority of the population lives in the cities. This pattern becomes even clearer if the frozen wastes of Scandinavia and the mountain heights of Switzerland and Austria are discounted.

TABLE 20 clearly proves that a country's density of population influences its degree of urbanization only through the working out of a number of different factors, themselves sometimes independent of culture and the human will, such as in the case of Norway, Switzerland, and to a certain extent Scotland. Climate and terrain in these countries oblige people to live in a few relatively restricted areas. Sometimes, however, "human" factors play a decisive role. Although a good part of Austria and Switzerland is uninhabitable, population densities are much higher than in the Scandinavian countries, yet their degree of urbanization is the lowest of all the countries of Western Europe. The Netherlands, similarly, whose population density is three times that of Denmark, although its area is considerably smaller, is much less urbanized than Denmark. Among the human factors that apply are the length of time a region has been settled, its traditions of

---

* These data refer to circa 1950 because they have not been brought up to date for all Western European countries. However, the picture has remained much the same.

TABLE 20

Urbanization and Occupational Structure, and Population Density
in Western Europe, c. 1950*

Country	Urban Population (% of total pop.)	% of Working Pop. in Non-Agric. Occupations	Population Density (per sq. mi.)
Scotland	83	93	171
England & Wales	81	95	769
Denmark	67	75	272
Belgium	61	88	769
Luxembourg	58	74	321
Western Germany	57	77	544
Sweden	56	80	41
Netherlands	55	81	894
France	53	73	210
Norway	51	74	28
Austria	45	68	215
Switzerland	38	84	326

* W. Kusters, "Problèmes économiques et démographiques de l'Europe occidentale," *Social Compass*, V, 57–58.

land distribution, democratic regimes and forms of civilization, wars, threats of invasion, and modern industrialization—this last, especially, which, though connected with natural resources and geographical situation, is nonetheless realized by human genius.

The fact that population density does not play an immediately decisive role in the matter that concerns us here, is strikingly confirmed in the case of North America. Both Canada and the United States are countries of considerable area. Even when you subtract in Canada the Yukon and the Northwest Territory, as well as the northernmost portions of several other provinces—all as being more or less uninhabitable—the two countries still cover an enormous area, though their populations are small in relation to it. There are only 18 million Canadians, 5 per square mile, and 180 million inhabitants of the United States, 52 per square mile. The two countries thus compare with Norway, Sweden, and Finland in Europe with respect to population density, though they are much more heavily industrialized and urbanized. The North Americans are, so to speak, concentrated in a few spots scattered about the subcontinent, most notably in the northeast and on the Pacific coast.

The United States, now one of the most urbanized countries in the world, did not enter wholeheartedly into the industrial revolution until the mid-nineteenth century. The process of accelerating urbanization, accompanying industrialization, did not prevail over the contrary tendency for the population to spread into the new agricultural lands behind the expanding frontiers until the turn of the century. The urban population did not exceed the rural until the First World War. By 1960, 70 per cent of Americans lived in urban areas, a proportion equaled in Europe only by such countries as northwestern Belgium, Denmark, Sweden, and the United Kingdom.

Now, though there is much more living space in North America than there is in Europe (a circumstance which has favored the emigration of several tens of millions of Europeans to the United States and Canada), the process of urbanization and the flight of the rural population to the cities developed about as quickly there as in Western Europe. And this despite the fact that there are also demographic differences between these two parts of the world. Though there has been everywhere since the beginnings of modern Western civilization a decline in natality, in the United States the birth rate has stayed between 23 and 20 per 1,000 population since 1946, and in Canada over the same years it has stayed between 26 and 29 per 1,000, thanks especially to the French Canadians in the province of Quebec. The North American subcontinent is thus steadily growing, and its population has been constantly rejuvenated by thousands of immigrants. Western Europe, meanwhile, though in general heavily populated, seems to have been aging, to have grown tired, even exhausted, as a result of two terrible wars. Malthusianism first, and then Neo-Malthusianism, both pessimistic in their outlook, originated in the English-speaking world and were given their earliest practical application in England, France and Sweden. In Western Europe, only the Netherlands, Ireland, Portugal, and Spain have an average birth rate over 20 per 1,000, and over the period 1952–61, only Portugal fluctuated as high as 25 per 1,000. At the same time, in consequence of the aging of their populations, death rates (save in the Netherlands and the Scandinavian countries) are relatively high: between 11 and 13 per 1,000 population.

Despite these not insignificant demographic differences, and the fact that available space for expansion is much greater in North America than in Western Europe, the phenomenon of urbanization has had parallel consequences in the two parts of the world: namely, a considerable decline in natality in the cities, compared with the rural population. Obviously, there are variations in the degree to which this observation applies. Some cities fairly devour their inhabitants; in them the rate of reproduction has so declined that only a steady influx of excess rural population keeps their total figures high. One result of this flight of the rural population is that the latter risks losing its traditional vitality, not only through a lowering of the birth rate, but by the loss of people in the age groups when reproductive capacity is at its peak. There is a whole literature on this development in France, where extensive regions of the countryside have become depopulated. Vienna and Brussels are also cities of a "man-eating" type. Elsewhere there is better demographic balance between city and country. When this occurs, the influx from the latter to the former does not exceed the demographic surplus produced by rural regions, that is, does not eat into the numbers that can comfortably be supported by the rural economy.

Whether the cities drain off the population of the countryside or merely provide jobs and a livelihood to those who need them, the urban populations have a steadily falling birth rate, in any case, a lower one (when fertility rates are adjusted), than the rural population of the same country, notably the population in the rural hinterlands of the city in question. For example, there is in each of the United States a negative correlation between degree of urbanization and birth rates, with the possible exception of the North Central states. Obviously, other factors besides urbanization are at work in determining the birth rates of the various states. The high figure for New Mexico is accounted for by the numbers of Mexicans who live there, and the high figures for the southern states of Louisiana, Alabama, and Mississippi by the numbers of Negroes there. The high rates for Idaho and Utah seem accountable, to a considerable extent, by the Mormon influence in that part of the country. The low rates in such states as New York, Pennsylvania, California, Illinois, and Michigan are due to the fact that they all have cities of more than a million inhabitants: New York, Philadelphia, Los Angeles, Chicago, and Detroit. Metropolization, of course, has a much more intense ef-

TABLE 21

Birth Rates in the United States by Statistical Region, 1960
(per 1,000)

New England	23
Middle Atlantic	22
East No. Central	24
West No. Central	24
South Atlantic	24
East So. Central	24
West So. Central	25
Mountain	27
Pacific	24

fect on fertility than urbanization in small towns. For a number of reasons, the New England states come closest to the European picture demographically as also in other respects.

Canada presents much the same picture as the United States in its general outlines, although this young country's population is more subject to emigration as well as immigration. The table brings out clearly the difference between English-speaking and French-speaking Canada. In the provinces of Quebec (82 per cent French in 1961) and New Brunswick (38 per cent French

TABLE 22

Recent Birth Rates and Urbanization* in Canada
(by Province)

Province (descending order)	Urbanized Population 1960 (%)	Birth Rate 1960	Birth Rate Average 1946–50
Ontario	62	26	25
Quebec	57	27	30
British Columbia	53	25	24
Manitoba	51	26	22
Alberta	48	30	28
Nova Scotia	37	27	29
New Brunswick	23	27	34
Saskatchewan	26	27	26
Newfoundland	18	33	36
Prince Edward Island	—*	27	31

* Urban population: population in centers of 30,000 or more inhabitants. Prince Edward Island had no center with population above this limit, but 17 per cent of its population dwelt in centers of 10,000 or more inhabitants.

in 1961), urbanization is a factor of relatively little importance because of the French Canadian's notable fondness for big families. We might call attention to the differences in natality between the urban and the rural districts of Quebec. The figure for British Columbia can be explained by the number of English-speaking Canadians who move to the Pacific Coast when they reach retirement age. Even though Ontario is more highly urbanized, the figure for British Columbia is the lowest for Canada.

All in all, North America presents a different demographic picture than northern and western Europe. For the years 1955–59, births in northwestern Europe* averaged 18 per 1,000. Every country of non-Communist Europe, outside the Iberian Peninsula, has a birth rate under 22 per 1,000 (only Ireland and the Netherlands top 20 per 1,000), and for some countries it is much lower: 14 in Sweden and 16 in Luxembourg, most notably.

* The countries bounded by Finland, France and Ireland, excluding the Germanies and Switzerland.

However, Europe cannot be treated as an entity, and it is important to distinguish between country and urban areas. Further, though the degree of urbanization remains everywhere a significant influence upon natality, still each country has its own history, its own cultural and religious pattern, and its own demographic tendencies. Thus, although Switzerland and Austria are much less urbanized than the Netherlands, they are also much less prolific. Luxembourg, a Catholic country, has a much lower birth rate than Protestant Norway. What holds true within each country, is the demographic difference between urban and country areas. More prolific, the countryside serves as a reservoir of manpower for the cities. In those countries, or in those areas within countries where agriculture has developed harmoniously—that is, where it has adapted to modern scientific methods and its productivity has increased in consequence—the flight of population to the cities has been kept within bounds. Relations between the urban areas and the neighboring countryside have remained balanced. In other regions, the flight to the city has taken on alarming proportions, and with the loss of inhabitants within the age groups best fit for marriage and family life, the countryside has been literally depopulated.

The plight of certain rural areas in France is well known. Thibault's studies of particular districts in Picardy tell how the total population dropped from 5,969 in 1931 to 1,414 in 1946. Between the same dates the birth rate dropped from 25 to 15 per 1,000, while throughout the 110 years from 1836 to 1946, the number of deaths always exceeded the number of births.[3] Among more recent studies might be cited those of Mendras, Mallet, Jollivet, and Durousay on two districts in the department of Puy-de-Dôme.[4]

There is yet another phenomenon that has a bearing upon demographic developments in rural areas closely associated with urban areas. Neundörfer has noted that in several countries of Western Europe there is a tendency for the birth rate in rural regions adjoining big cities to come down to the birth rate in those cities. In England since the war, there has been a rapid standardizing of the crude reproduction rates throughout the country, to which development only metropolitan London is an exception.[5] There the rate falls below the average for the country. The reason for this seems to be that increasing numbers of city dwellers prefer to live in far-flung suburbs, and that when they retire they prefer to spend their old age in the country. It will be necessary to draw up more careful distinctions than in the past between merely "rural" (or non-urban) regions and regions actually engaged in agricultural pursuits, for example, adding an in-between category, such as the "rural non-farm" category used in American censuses.

However, in certain other countries, though the same tendency can be seen at work in the countryside immediately adjacent to the urban centers, still the differences between the latter and the "country" proper remain clear. An example of this is shown in TABLE 23.

TABLE 23

Birth Rates, Urban and Rural Switzerland, 1937–1959

| | Births per 1,000 Population | |
	1937	1959
Urban Cantons		
Zurich	12.6	16.7
Basel (city)	11.4	14.7
Geneva	9.2	13.4
Rural Cantons		
Nidwald	22.5	23.6
Uri	22.0	23.9
Valais	21.6	22.3
Schwyz	19.6	22.2
Grisons	18.7	19.2
Obwald	18.5	21.1
Appenzell Inner Rhoden	18.4	17.6

In this connection, it must also be observed that the factor of religion comes into play. The rural cantons of Switzerland are for the most part Catholic, whereas the urban cantons are not.

Jacqueline Beaujeu-Garnier cites figures from L. Henry's *Fécondité urbaine et rurale,* showing gross reproduction rates in France for 1946:

Big cities (more than 50,000) 1.23
Small cities (10,000 to 50,000) 1.43
Small towns (2,000 to 10,000) 1.56
Rural communes 1.66

In his study of demographic trends in the various regions of Europe,[6] Kusters observes that of the 30 regions with the highest birth rates in Europe, only 8 are industrialized to any important extent. These are the Oporto district in Portugal, the cantons of Nidwald and Uri in Switzerland, the province of Limburg in Belgium, the provinces of Northern Brabant and Limburg in the Netherlands, the Naples region in Italy, and the Pas-de-Calais in France.* It is worth noting that without exception these are predominantly Catholic regions. All the other regions of Europe with the highest birth rates are agricultural in character.

POPULATION OF JAPAN

Japan is another well-documented case in point.[7] According to more or less reliable estimates, Japan did not have any very notable demographic expansion after the sixteenth century. The total population gradually increased from about 18 million at the end of the sixteenth century to perhaps 26 million at the end of the seventeenth century, and remained more or less stable down to 1850. There are sources which give a figure of 26.5 million for the year 1726, and a figure of 27.2 million for the year 1852, representing less than a 10 per cent growth over more than a century. This stability is to be accounted for, first, by the longstanding practice of infanticide in Japan by a good part of the population, a practice to which neither Buddhism nor Shintoism

* In all of which regions, miners or fishermen make up an important part of the population.

ever made violent opposition. Then, too, the country was periodically racked by severe famines and epidemics. Until 1853, moreover, Japan was closed off from the outside world. Only after Commodore Perry and the treaty of March 31, 1854, between the United States and Japan, was it possible to import wheat and other foodstuffs in times of famine. With this development, infanticide began to be less widely practiced, and humanitarian considerations made themselves felt. Nonetheless, the long practice of infanticide by the Japanese seems to have some bearing on their present-day willingness to permit abortion—a matter we shall have occasion to discuss shortly.

When the Emperor Meiji came to power in 1857, the feudal system was abolished. The Empire made itself over on the European model, and the Japanese economy took such strides that by the eve of the First World War Japan was a great world power. Of interest from a demographic standpoint, is the fact that the vicious circle of famine and population pressure on the means of subsistence was broken once and for all. The Malthusian era had ended, and although the population doubled within the next sixty years (it was around 30 million in 1870), the standard of living appreciably improved.

At the same time, Japan had now to face very serious problems. On the one hand, there was her ever-increasing population, and on the other hand, there were all the difficulties of making over the economic and social structure. Peasants fled the countryside in very great numbers, seeking jobs in the cities, and created a grave problem of underemployment which the country has not altogether solved today. Another indication of Japan's economic plight was the high and constantly growing number of Japanese who left for other countries.

Emigration. From the time it started at the end of the nineteenth century, Japanese emigration has looked toward many countries and continents.[8] The first movements headed in the direction of the American continent: mainly to the United States, Canada, Hawaii, Peru, and Brazil. Despite difficulties (increased by American annexation of the island and a law forbidding the immigration of foreign workers without a contract), the number of Japanese in Hawaii steadily increased from 1885 to 1900, and had another spurt forward a few years later, coming to a total of 80,000 in 1910, 109,000 in 1920, 140,000 in 1930, 158,000 in 1940. Emigration to the U.S., especially to California, also increased steadily although a considerable number of emigrants returned to Japan, especially between 1908 and 1924. There were 72,000 Japanese in the United States in 1910; 111,000 in 1920; 139,000 in 1930, and 127,000 in 1940. Emigration to Canada has always been much slighter: the figure for 1941 was 23,000.

Japanese emigration to Latin America (Peru and Brazil) began on a small scale and did not become sizable until after restrictions were placed on emigration to North America. In 1936 there were 20,000 Japanese in Peru, but that same year legislation was introduced to prohibit any more. Between 1924 and 1937, about 151,000 Japanese emigrated to Brazil. In 1940, there were 290,000 Japanese residents in Brazil.

Thus, by the Second World War, the total population of Japanese origin in the two Americas came to more than 600,000.

Now, when we compare the above movements to those which were directed toward countries bordering Japan, we find some important differences:

(1) The movement toward Asia took on much importance only after 1900.

(2) It was political in character, being the logical extension of Japanese victories against the Chinese and the Russians (Korea, Formosa, Manchuria).

(3) The emigrants were no longer for the most part agricultural workers. More than 90 per cent of them consisted of urban white-collar workers who occupied positions in industry and in the civil and military administration of the new Japanese empire.

(4) From 1910 on, the number of Japanese emigrants to the Asian countries was much higher than the num-

ber who left for the Americas. In 1940, there were
nearly 3 million emigrants to Asian countries, exclusive of military personnel.

Before World War II. Japan's emigration policy was merely
one aspect of its over-all policy, calculated to utilize population
pressure as an instrument of political expansionism, a weapon in
conquering needed "living space." This policy led the government to adopt a populationist attitude and to stamp out infanticide and abortion. In 1941 the Japanese government went
so far as to publish a demographic program, setting the figure of
100 million as "the minimum goal" to be reached by 1955.[9]

In this connection we must once again observe that, where
demographic developments are concerned, people do not act or
react automatically as do other forms of life. The Japanese people
had for centuries lived under a more or less "Malthusian" regime,
and population growth had been slow. When, after the nation was
launched into modern times, its population continuously increased
decade after decade, it was transformed into a young people with
a high rate of increase. Yet, just at the moment when its "living
space" on the Asian continent had been appreciably enlarged,
and all sorts of employment opportunities were opened up in the
new areas of the Japanese Empire—and when its government
was urging an expanded birth rate—at just that moment the Japanese birth rate began to decline.

TABLE 24

Population of Japan and Rates of Increase over Five-Year Periods,
1920–1940

Year	Total Population (millions)	Period	Rate of Increase
1920	55.4		
1925	59.2	1920–25	6.8
1930	63.9	1925–30	7.9
1935	68.7	1930–35	7.5
1940	72.5	1935–40	5.6

The Japanese social and family system is such as to put up no opposition to the demographic effects of industrialization and urbanization, most notably declining birth rates in urban areas, occupational-group reproductive behavior, low fertility among the middle classes, etc.[10]

Already by 1900, urbanization had taken strong hold in Japan. Sumya estimates that some 400,000 peasants have emigrated to the cities every year since the beginning of the century.[49] By 1960, 64 per cent of the Japanese lived in urban municipalities of at least 30,000 inhabitants.[11]

It can hardly be claimed that the extensive emigration of the Japanese prior to World War II had much to do with speeding up the demographic decline. The study published in the *UN Population Bulletin* says on this score:

As a result of the emigration of Japanese civilians from Japan between 1920 and 1940, partly balanced by Japanese migrants returning to Japan, it has been estimated that the number of Japanese of the homeland aged 10 years or over in 1940 was some 1.7 million smaller than it would have been had this migration not occurred.[12]

The reduction of the Japanese population in metropolitan areas due to migrations between 1920 and 1940 was more or less compensated for by Korean emigration to Japan, so that the total population of the country was scarcely affected by migratory movements.

After the Second World War. In 1945, Japan had 72.2 million inhabitants. This number has since grown appreciably. According to the 1960 census, the total had gone up to 93.4 million. This means for the last decade a population increase of 12 per cent, which compares with an increase of 15 per cent for 1920–30 and 14 per cent for 1930–40. Between the Second World War and 1950, the population rose by 10.7 million. To account for the great increase between 1945 and 1950 there was, first of all, the return to Japan of some 6.3 million soldiers and civilians between October 1945 and May 1950 from the countries where they had been living before the war or where they were engaged in wartime activities. If we subtract from this figure the 1.2 million Chinese and Koreans who left Japan at the end of the war, the increase from this cause comes to 5 million. Subtracting this next migration balance, we arrive at a natural increase of 5.7 million in the first post-quinquennium equivalent to a 16 per cent growth in ten years, higher than the interwar figures. The second reason for the appreciable increase is the postwar "baby boom," which occurred in Japan as in so many other countries.

In TABLE 25 we can see Okasaki's figures of birth rates, death rates and rates of population increases for the period 1933–56[13] (figures for 1957–61, and for post-war population growth added by authors).

TABLE 25

Population of Japan—Birth Rate, Death Rate, and Rate of Natural Increase, 1933–1961
(per 1,000)

Year	Birth Rate	Death Rate	Rate of Natural Increase
1933–37	30.8	17.4	13.4
1945	24.2	27.0	−2.8
1946	22.4	19.9	2.5
1947	34.3	14.6	19.7
1948	33.5	11.9	21.6
1949	33.0	11.6	21.4
1950	28.1	10.9	17.2
1951	25.5	9.9	15.6
1952	23.3	8.9	14.4
1953	21.5	8.8	12.7
1954	20.0	8.2	11.8
1955	19.3	7.8	11.5
1956	18.5	7.8	10.7
1957	17.3	8.3	9.0
1958	18.1	7.5	10.6
1959	17.6	7.5	10.1
1960	17.2	7.6	9.6
1961	16.9	7.4	9.5

Immediate Post-War Population Growth in Japan

Date of Enumeration	Per Cent Increase per Annum
11/1/45	—0.4
4/26/46	3.1
10/1/47	4.8
8/1/48	3.3
10/1/50	1.7

What is particularly striking about this table is, first of all, the steady decline in mortality through the immediate post-war years. It indicates clearly the degree of progress attained by the country's public health services. Still more striking, however, is the way the birth rate dropped after the "baby boom" years, from 34 per 1,000 in 1947–49 to 17 per 1,000 in 1961. The downward trend has been steady since 1949, but evidently is flattening out. Since the birth rate declined much more rapidly than the death rate, the rate of natural increase thereby has dropped below the pre-war level. Thus, Japan's rate of population growth is now below 1 per cent per annum, in striking contrast to the rates of 2 and 5 per cent found in the rest of Asia. The present Japanese rate of growth is also in striking contrast to its own rapid rates of growth before and shortly after the Second World War.

It is interesting to compare UN projections of the Japanese population with those published by the Institute of Population Problems in Japan, which is headed by Dr. Okasaki. The Institute's projections, issued in 1957, when the United Nations was preparing its *Future Growth of World Population,* and most recently in 1960, show the shift in forecasting required by the persistent ebb in Japanese fertility, as well as the progressive refinements in projection techniques.

TABLE 26

Projected Japanese Population Growth, 1955–1975
(in millions) : Three Projections

Year	United Nations (*millions*)	Institute of Population Problems 1957 (*millions*)	Institute of Population Problems 1960 (*millions*)
1955	89.1	89.1	89.3
1960	95.1	93.8	93.9
1965	102.0	97.3	98.2
1970	109.0	100.7	102.2
1975	116.0	103.9	106.3

For the years approaching 2000, the divergence is still more marked, though it should be mentioned that the UN projections include the Ryukyu Islands with Japan (TABLE 27).

TABLE 27

Estimated Japanese Population Growth, 1975–2000
(in millions)

Year	United Nations[a]			Institute of Population Problems	
	High	Medium	Low	1957[b]	1960[c]
1975	117	117	110	104	106
1980	124	124	114	107	110
1985	133	132	118	108	112
1990	141	139	121	109	113
1995	150	146	123	108	113
2000	159	153	125	107	113

[a] U.N., *Future Growth of World Population* (New York, 1957).
[b] Issued in 1957.
[c] Issued in 1960.

The causes of the falling birth rate in Japan are abortion, contraception, and sterilization. Periodic abstinence plays a very minor role. All three methods are encouraged under the Revised Eugenics Protection Law adopted by the Japanese Diet in July 1948.

The number of sterilizations performed by authorized physicians and reported to the authorities totaled 300,000 for the period 1949–58, and of these 9,000 were operations on men. However, the real number of female sterilizations over the same period may have been closer to 1.25 million.

There is no way of estimating how many couples practice contraception. When the government became alarmed at the mounting number of abortions, it sponsored and publicized education in contraception, among other ways by bringing to Japan Mrs. Margaret Sanger. There seems to have been greater use of contraceptive measures after this. Okasaki, however, is of the opinion that the open, unrestricted sale of contraceptive devices has had a disastrous effect upon the sexual morals of Japanese young people. He believes that birth-control propaganda has increased the number of abortions. Moreover, other writers share his opinion.[14] On this subject Riallin says:

To conclude, the normal procedure is to have recourse to contraception after an abortion, because the operation is so unpleasant that the patient does not want to have to go through it again. And the opposite holds true: few women give up contraceptive methods with a view to having an abortion later. And yet contraceptives may be so imperfect, technically, or those who use them so inexperienced, that all too often women must submit again to abortion to terminate an unwanted pregnancy.

Koya attempts to disprove the contrary, but it seems that he has misinterpreted the statistics in his article on an experiment in "Family Planning" in the village of Joban.[15]

Granted the scope of the Revised Eugenics Protection Law, we can see the relationship between births and abortions in TABLE 28. Since the statistics report only officially recognized operations, the actual number of abortions must be much higher. Basing his calculations on Muramatau and Ogino, Riallin got a figure

TABLE 28

Births and Legal Abortions in Japan, 1949–1961
(in thousands)

Year	Births	Abortions
1949	2,696	246
1950	2,338	489
1951	2,138	638
1952	2,005	806
1953	1,868	1,068
1954	1,770	1,143
1955	1,731	1,170
1956	1,665	1,159
1957	1,567	1,122
1958	1,653	1,128
1959	1,626	1,099
1960	1,606	1,063
1961	1,586	1,035

of 2 million abortions for the year 1956, higher than the birth figure for the same year. W. D. Borrie, a Neo-Malthusian, is probably quite correct when he writes that Japan is the only Asian country that seems really to be on the way to a rational control of the population problem. About a century ago, Japan had its own "Malthusian" regime. Today, it practices Neo-Malthusianism.

The Consequences of Neo-Malthusianism. Okasaki has called attention to some of the demographic consequences of Japan's present policy. Though unemployment statistics are anything but alarming—as of 1956 there were only half a million persons out of work, from a labor force of 43 million—the figures do not quite banish concern over Japan's underemployment and "invisible unemployment."

It is estimated that there are some 5 million Japanese who are underemployed and/or unemployed in agriculture and commerce. The mining and other industries face a serious problem of underproduction due to primitive technology and lack of specialized skills, such that modernization can only put more men out of work. As the economic and technological progress continues, the government has to face a new and serious problem: how to make more jobs.

The declining birth rate is not going to make things easier, but harder. For some decades to come, there are going to be more and more young people of employable age. In crude figures, the age group 15–59 came to 62 million in 1960. It will have reached 71.5 million in 1985, and is expected to drop to 68 million in the year 2000. What is still graver, there is going to be a serious alteration in the over-all age distribution over the next half century. (See TABLE 29.)

TABLE 29

Age Composition of Japanese Population, 1960 and 2000
(in percentages)

Age	1960[a]	2000[b]
0–14	30	17
15–29	28	18
30–44	20	21
45–59	14	19
60 and over	9	26

[a] UN, *Demographic Yearbook 1962.*
[b] Ayanori Okasaki, *Histoire du Japon: l'Economie et la Population*, p. 163, Table 70.

This redistribution of the demographic structure will have serious repercussions on the country's occupational structure. Though there will be about as many people of working age (between 15 and 59) as ever, both in crude figures and percentage-wise, still the group as a whole will have aged to a marked degree as the century comes to a close. This cannot but have an effect on production. Moreover, there will be the grave problem of a high percentage of old people. While in 1950, before the impact of "Eugenic Protection," for every person 60 years of age and over there were six persons active in productive employment, by the year 2000 there will only be two of the latter for every older person.

POPULATION OF THE MAGHRIB

The Maghrib is often thought of as one of the world regions where population expansion has been greatest and gives most cause for concern.

And yet, mention should be made of the fact that none of the three countries of the Maghrib (Morocco, Tunisia, and Algeria) keeps a careful register of births and deaths such as the European countries, for example, do. Available figures are all based on estimates which have become gradually more thorough, so that some part of the increase in the native population must be attributed simply to improved statistics. At the same time, however, present population increase in this area is very considerable.

One element to be kept in mind in study of this area is the existence of a population of European origin: 3.4 per cent in Tunisia, 3.5 per cent in Morocco, and as of 1960, 10 per cent in Algeria. Independence disturbed Algeria more than Morocco and Tunisia, and it is still too soon to discern the new trends. Yet it is instructive to examine the Maghrib as a case of striking demographic differentials in a common environment.

Population distribution is far from uniform. Morocco has 70 inhabitants per square mile, Tunisia has 88 per square mile, and Algeria 13 per square mile. The Saharan districts of southern Algeria have only 588,000 inhabitants over a total area of nearly 770,000 square miles, or 1 person per square mile. So the settled area of Algeria has a population density of more than 100 per square mile.

It has been said that "Algeria is overpopulated, because it is so unevenly populated." However, we should note that the highest population densities in northeastern Algeria—Babor, over 250 people per square mile, Djurdjura, over 500 per square mile, and Tizi-Ouzou, about 250 per square mile—are significant mainly because of the poverty of the region. Both Europe and Asia have whole countries as densely populated. (See Table 11.) These figures should restrain charges of "pockets of overpopulation" in portions of Algeria.[16]

Both the Muslim and the non-Muslim populations were differently distributed in the Northern Territory of Algeria before independence. Non-Muslims accounted for 23 per cent of the population in the department of Oran, 13 per cent in the department of Algiers, and 6 per cent in the department of Constantine.

A further phenomenon to be noted is the intensity of urbanization. In 1886, 11 per cent of the Algerian population lived in towns of 2,000 or more inhabitants, whereas by 1948, the figure had gone up to 24 per cent. A study of thirty cities and towns in 1953 showed 70 per cent of the non-Muslim population living there, and only 13 per cent of the Muslim population, although the total population of those cities and towns included more Muslims (1 million) than non-Muslims (700,000). The thirty communities consisted of 8 communes in the department of Algiers, 4 in the department of Oran, the city of Constantine, and the 17 towns of subprefecture rank.[17]

The five biggest cities of Algeria have all grown very rapidly since the beginning of this century (TABLE 30).

TABLE 30

Growth of Five Algerian Cities, 1900–1959

(in thousands)

City	1900		1930		1959	
	Muslim	Non-Muslim	Muslim	Non-Muslim	Muslim	Non-Muslim
Algiers	135	120	100	210	460	350
Oran	16	80	32	130	180	190
Constantine	27	25	50	47	190	41
Sidi-Bel-Abbès	7	18	15	27	75	40
Bône	10	29	26	37	83	47
Total	195	272	223	451	988	668

Among the economically active non-Muslim population, some 50,000 are engaged in agriculture and fishing. Muslims in the same occupations totaled 2.8 million. In Morocco, too, the majority of Europeans are engaged in urban trades and businesses, while some 85 per cent of the Muslim population devote themselves to agriculture.

In view of such variations in population density, ways of life, and cultural traditions, over-all conclusions are risky to draw. Since the data we possess for Algeria are the fullest and most reliable, our analysis will be centered on that country.

There had been no marked increase in the non-Muslim population before independence, their annual rate of increase being about 1 per cent per year. The Muslim population has been increasing two and a half times faster.

Using once again the results of the 1953 survey of thirty Algerian cities and towns, cited above, we find the breakdown for that year listed in TABLE 31.

TABLE 31

Population of Algeria, 1953

(crude figures rounded to nearest thousand)

	Non-Muslim Crude Figure	Rate	Muslim Crude Figure	Rate	Total
Population January 1, 1953	1,019		8,263		9,282
Births	19	18.7	336	40	355
Deaths	9	8.7	109	13	118
Excess of births	10	10.0	227	27.0	237
Emigrations 1/1/53			300		300
Departures, 1953			134		134
Returns, 1953			122		122
Excess of departures			12		12
Population as of 12/31/53					
(excluding emigrants)	1,029		8,478		9,507
(including emigrants)	1,029		8,778		9,807

With reference to the non-Muslim population, it will be noted that the crude birth rate was close to that for metropolitan France in 1953—19 per thousand—but the crude death rate was much lower, at 9 per thousand, than that for urban France, which was 13 per thousand.

This last figure, it will be noted, was the same as that for the Muslim death rate, a remarkable fact which ought to warn us not to draw conclusions too hastily on the basis of crude rates, whether of natality or mortality.

The age breakdown of the Algerian population is significant.

TABLE 32
Comparative Age Structures, France and Algeria
(in percentages of total population)

Age Group	Metropolitan France (1954)	Algeria (1953) Non-Muslim	Muslim	Total
0–14	24	26	42	40
15–19	7	9	12	11
20–60	53	54	41	43
60 and over	16	11	5	6
Total	100	100	100	100

One conclusion to be drawn from TABLE 32 is that although the crude death rate appears to have been much lower for the non-Muslim population of Algeria than for that of metropolitan France, this is due to the comparative youthfulness of the Muslim population. Actually, male life expectancy at birth was a trifle lower for the non-Muslim in Algeria than in the mother country. It follows then that the crude death rate of the Muslim population, equal to that for the population of metropolitan France, is also accounted for by the extreme youth of the population.

The study of thirty Algerian cities and towns shows that this same characteristic youthfulness appears also in the urban areas, where it has been magnified by the flight of population from the rural areas during the period of rebellion.

When we compare the crude birth and death rates, as between the group of thirty cities and towns and for the rest of Algeria (predominately rural, the so-called *bled*), we are led to some conclusions that at first glance may surprise.

Natality is higher in the thirty cities than it is in the bled, and

TABLE 33

Comparative Demographic Structure, Metropolitan France
and Algeria, 1953
(per 1,000)

	Metropolitan France	30 Sample Algerian Towns Non-Muslim Population	Muslim Population
Marriage rate	14.5	16.6	24.2
Birth rate	18.8	20.4	46.1
Death rate	13.0	8.6	19.5
Rate of increase	5.8	11.8	26.6
Rate of infant mortality	38.0	46.0	181.0

this was so for the non-Muslim population (20 compared with 15) as well as for the Muslim population (46 compared with 40).

Mortality figures were practically the same in the bled for the non-Muslim population (9.4 compared with 8.6), but higher in the cities (20 compared with 12) for the Muslims.

With respect to natality, the Muslim rate is undoubtedly influenced by the youthfulness of the population. As for the non-Muslim rate, it is probable that the few Europeans who lived in the bled enjoy a higher economic and social status than the average non-Muslim in the towns and cities.

As for the non-Muslim mortality rate, the age of the population played an important part, and at the same time the non-Muslim rural population had not been emigrating to the cities to the same extent as the Muslim rural population.

Possibly we should here take account of the matter of vital statistics being recorded more carefully in the cities than in the country, but if this were held to explain the higher Muslim death rate, then it should also explain the higher European birth rate. P. Gasc's studies of this matter in France have called attention to the fact that, in the cities, births are the more important event, while deaths are more important in the country.

With regard to Muslim mortality, the youthfulness of the urban population ought to have brought about a lower death rate than in the bled, but it has not, and so we must assume that the urban population has been, not just urbanized, but proletarianized—indeed, in G. Tillon's expression *clochardisée* (pauperized).

Undoubtedly, far from the cities, the fellahin's standard of living may be appallingly low and may justify the proverbial saying: "We are like the chickens. If we don't keep scratching the ground, we get nothing to eat." Those of them, however, who flee to the cities, may find themselves in a no less precarious situation. Without employment, the worker cannot escape dire poverty. In the study of the thirty urban aggregations, the infant mortality figure for the Muslim population was 181 per thousand births—higher than the total urban *and* rural infant mortality of many underdeveloped countries in the 1950's. It has never been as high in metropolitan France since 1861, the year when accurate statistics began to be kept.

It is sometimes claimed that polygamy, as authorized by the Koran, is a factor in the Muslim population structure in North Africa. This is another occasion to beware of hasty conclusions. Just how much of a factor is it? In 1948, nearly 97 per cent of the male Muslim population was monogamous, 3 per cent had two wives, and less than 0.2 per cent was polygamous. At the same time, note must be taken of what is called "progressive polygamy" —that is, the repudiation of wives and often children as well, so that out of the 7 per cent of widowed and divorced persons, there are four women to every man in Algeria. In any case, the average Muslim family has three children, which is one more than the non-Muslim families.

And yet, as of 1953, only a tenth of the Muslim families benefited from family allowances, compared to a fourth of the European families. So it is hard to blame the "population explosion" among Algerian Muslims on these family allowances. The more so, since it appears that birth control is beginning to be practiced by the better-educated Muslims. This trend was brought out in a round-table conference on Algerian social welfare problems, headed by Professor Mesnard in 1953:

Among Muslim craftsmen, tradesmen, and intellectuals, an effort is being made to limit births. The theologians have noted it as a growing trend; it is already being practiced in the upland plains of the interior.

It seems that family allocations are actually encouraging the movement:

In the department of Oran, families receiving the allowances, especially in the "skilled labor" category, with a low standard of living, have a falling birth rate. This would confirm a fact which has been noted widely elsewhere, that a rise in the standard of living is matched by a decline in natality.

What might be argued is that the birth rate is as high as it is among Muslims only because the family structure is such that the man can persuade his wife to make it so. The man, or more precisely the family—the man as head of the family—wants many pairs of hands around him as insurance against going hungry. The wife, in general, would prefer to limit the number of children. Over 35 per cent of Muslim women work, although only about 25 per cent of them are aged 15 to 60. Thus we see that a good many of them are working who are younger than 15 or older than 60.

With the development of urbanization, with changes in the standard of living and in the status of Muslim women, it seems as though Algeria's demographic future—and that of the entire Maghrib—is being influenced by factors likely to invalidate the general tenor of population predictions so far drawn up for this complex situation.

POPULATION OF FRENCH CANADA

The growth of Canada's population since 1921 is shown in TABLE 34, by provinces:

TABLE 34

Population of Canada and of Canadian Provinces, 1921–1957
(in thousands)

	1921	1931	1941	1951	1957
Canada	8,788	10,376	11,507	14,009	16,589
Newfoundland				361	426
Prince Edw. Is.	89	88	95	98	99
Nova Scotia	524	513	578	643	702
New Brunswick	388	408	457	516	565
Quebec	2,861	2,874	3,332	4,056	4,758
Ontario	2,934	3,432	3,788	4,598	5,622
Manitoba	610	700	730	776	860
Saskatchewan	757	922	896	832	879
Alberta	588	732	796	939	1,160
Brit. Columbia	525	694	818	1,165	1,487
Yukon	4	4	52	9	12
Northwest Terr.	8	9	12	16	19

As can be seen from this table, Ontario and Quebec are the most populous provinces; they are also the heartland of Canada's dual national life, and they give a good opportunity for drawing comparisons between French- and English-speaking Canadians.

Canada was born along the banks of the St. Lawrence and the shores of Lake Ontario, Lake Erie and Lake Huron. Canada's history is above all the history of Quebec and Ontario. It is worth running over a few facts of that history, the better to understand two populations different in their religions, their cultures, and their traditions, and whose demographic trends still present different patterns.

After the first French colonists landed in Nova Scotia (Acadia) in 1605, a small population gradually built up which, at the beginning of the eighteenth century, numbered some 2,300. Another French colony was established in New Brunswick. In 1755, the English, to whom Acadia had been ceded in 1713, deported the bulk of the population to New England. The few who escaped resettlement provided the nucleus of the French minority which still lives in the maritime provinces, especially in New Brunswick.

Those French who moved on down the St. Lawrence at the time Acadia was being settled, were never disturbed to any such degree, although troubles with the English did not really end until Canada obtained dominion status in 1867. The city of Quebec was founded in 1608, Trois Rivières in 1634, and Montreal (the former Ville Marie) in 1642. Going through all the hardships of colonists in the period—disease, the hostility of the Indians, threatened encroachment by the British—the French colony in the province of Quebec began to thrive in the last quarter of the seventeenth century. A population of 10,000 in 1681 grew to 42,000 in 1739 and to 70,000 in 1760.

From the start, French Canadian growth was characterized by a high birth rate. The France of the Ancien Régime did little to encourage emigration to this poor, faraway land. In Paul Veyret's words, "The sugar cane of the West Indies weighed more heavily in the scales than the furs of the St. Lawrence valley."[18] It is estimated that there were no more than 10,000 immigrants from the mother country over the whole period from 1608 to 1760.

The French Canadians, for the most part, were quick to make the land their own and to learn to live by their own resources. Mainly an agricultural population, they were united also by their religion, for French Canada was never a refuge for religious minorities like the colonies which the English established in the New World and which drew dissidents from England, Holland, and other countries. The Huguenots found a haven in Germany, in Switzerland, and in the Netherlands, but not in French America.*

And so the inhabitants of Lower Canada clung to their Catholic family traditions and defended them against the English Protestants who, as immigration mounted, came to surpass them in numbers. However, they also became cut off from a mother country which gave little thought to her far-flung sons. The conquest of French Canada by the English in 1763 was not an issue of international politics, and the French Canadians felt little desire to lay

* Such French Protestants as did eventually come, only did so after spending some time in other European countries, most notably in Holland.

down their lives for a king in Paris. Of course, after 1763 such slight emigration as there had been from France to Canada stopped entirely. Surrounded by the English, and cut off from France as well as from the rest of the country around them, the French Canadians also lost their ruling class in 1763, when it sold its vast properties to the English and went back to France. The 70,000 inhabitants of the St. Lawrence valley had only their natural vitality to sustain them in the struggle to survive as the only Latin population in the English-speaking world of North America. Their isolation was complete when, during the American War of Independence, British loyalists left the United States and settled north of the Great Lakes. The presence of these 15,000 loyalists between the St. Lawrence and the prairies of what was to become the province of Ontario, cut off the French from the vast territories of central and western Canada. As they were settled, the future provinces of Manitoba, Saskatchewan, Alberta, and British Columbia all became predominately English-speaking. These, but most of all Ontario and Manitoba, were to become, from the end of the eighteenth century on, the magnet of the great Canadian immigration.

Two Canadas: English Canada, Built Up by Immigraton, and French Canada, Built Up by Its Own Birth Rate. Population increase in the English-speaking provinces of Canada is largely due to the immigrants from Europe who began to arrive in important numbers from 1870 on. The number of such immigrants between 1866 and 1951 has been estimated at about 7 million. As there are no data on nationality prior to 1900, it is not known what percentage of these immigrants came from the British Isles, but it must have been considerable. The figures after 1900 show that of the 5 million who arrived between 1900 and 1951, almost 60 per cent of the total—3 million—were English, Scottish, and Irish. There were 437,000 from the countries of northwest Europe (Scandinavia, Germany, Holland) and Austria, plus an unknown number who reached Canada via the United States. These were all rapidly anglicized and have reinforced the Anglo-Saxon element. Sizable numbers of immigrants came also from the countries of central,

eastern, and southern Europe. The great bulk of all these immigrants settled in the English-speaking provinces. For the years
1901 to 1951, the breakdown is noted in TABLE 35.

TABLE 35

Immigration to Canada, 1901–1951

Area	Distribution of Immigrants (% of total)
Maritime Provinces (Prince Edward Island, Nova Scotia, New Brunswick)	4
Alberta, Saskatchewan, Manitoba	39
British Columbia	12
Ontario	29
Quebec	15

Although these figures are subject to a considerable margin of
error,[19] they do show unequivocally that the predominately English
provinces attracted 85 per cent of all the immigrants over the
half-century. The province of Quebec, with 30 per cent of Canada's
population, received only 15 per cent of them, and these settled
mostly in the region of Montreal, Canada's biggest city.

It is thanks to these immigrants, who for the most part have
been young, that the population of English-speaking Canada has
kept abreast of the French Canadians. In this connection, it must
be noted that only to a small extent is the increase accountable
for as a mere quantitative expansion of the total population by the
newcomers. Rather, it is a question of their effects on Canadian
nuptiality and fertility. It is little known, but indisputably a fact,
that there has always been a sizable number of English-speaking
Canadians who leave Canada. Although, between 1851 and 1951,
over 6 million immigrants settled here, during the same period,
probably over 6 million persons left, the great majority for the
United States. The total gain in numbers, then, comes only to
about 400,000. This process of countervailing streams of migration
is one of the basic demographic facts about Canada.

Immigration, thus, has kept Canada from being emptied of her population, drawn by the magnet of life south of the border. As a general rule, the new arrivals were younger than the emigrants whose places they took (statistically speaking). So immigrants have helped sustain Canada's birth rate, while accelerating the decline of the death rate. English-speaking Canada's gross and net reproduction rates are rather low, but the population has been constantly renewed and rejuvenated in this manner, and so its total has significantly increased.

TABLE 36
Growth of Ontario's Population, 1871–1951

Years	Per Cent
1871–1881	19
1881–1891	9
1891–1901	3 (opening of the West)
1901–1911	15
1911–1921	16
1921–1931	17
1931–1941	10 (the Depression)
1941–1951	21

The continuing influence of the newcomers on the potentially declining birth rate of the English-speaking population has been felt most clearly in Ontario and further west. Obviously, increase through immigration did not always contribute to natural increase in direct and simple fashion. During the early years, and especially at the beginning of this century, men outnumbered women and the preponderance of unmarried males influenced nuptiality rates and birth rates alike. The ratio of males to 100 females stood as high as 558 in the Yukon in 1901, and 179 and 149 in British Columbia and Alberta in 1911. Only in Quebec were there ever more women than men. Newfoundland and the Yukon are the only parts of Canada with a persistently large excess of males. All the other provinces have moved toward a sex ratio of 100 males to 120 females in recent decades.

For the country as a whole, masculinity was especially high between 1901 and 1921, years of especially heavy immigration

(3,400,000 immigrants reported between 1906 and 1915). After the Second World War, immigration lost much of its "pioneer" character and newcomers to Canada were better balanced with respect to sex distribution. The figures for Manitoba from 1881 to 1911, for Saskatchewan and Alberta from 1901 to 1931, and for British Columbia right down to the Second World War, show clearly the extent to which immigrants headed for these last un- settled lands of the great American West. Colonizing in the Yukon Territory and in the Northwest Territories still has a pioneering character, but the extreme disproportion between the sexes is no longer what it was earlier in the century in the Yukon. The province of Quebec, throughout the period, has remained outside the mainstream of the great migratory movements. This circum- stance has favored the French Canadian birth rate and may be considered one of its causes.

TABLE 37 summarizes the expansion of the Canadian popula- tion, in relation both to population growth through immigration and to population growth through births. The data are supplied for five- year periods from 1911 to 1940 and require no comment.

TABLE 37
How Canada's Population Grew, 1911–1940
(in thousands)

Period	Total Increase	Increase by Births (%)	Increase by Immigration (%)	Number of Immigrants per 1,000 Births
1911–15	2,374	45	55	120
1916–20	1,575	74	27	36
1921–25	1,736	71	29	40
1926–30	1,915	62	38	62
1931–35	1,228	93	7	8
1936–40	1,216	94	6	6

Although the province of Quebec received only 15 per cent of the immigrants to Canada between 1901 and 1951, its birth rate has always been the highest in the country. This is all the more striking when it is realized that more than 40 per cent of Quebec's population lives in the urban aggregations of Montreal and Quebec.

The country regions and the small towns and villages of Canada have been most successful in clinging to a populationist way of life. Gilles Boileau, of the Research Bureau of the Société Canadienne d'Etablissement Rural in Montreal, has made demographic studies of a number of dioceses and parishes in rural Canada. What his researches show is that alongside certain regions which seem to be changing, on the whole the rural districts of French Canada have preserved birth rates and fertility rates that are so remarkably high—and the proportion of old people in the population remains so remarkably low—that this part of Canada may truly be considered altogether exceptional within Western civilization.[20]

Between 1945 and 1956, sixty parishes had an average birth rate of 35 per 1,000—the figure for all of Canada in 1956 was 28 per 1,000. In the same parishes, the death rate was relatively high: 11 per 1,000 compared with 8 for the country as a whole. The fertility rate, which indicates the relation between numbers of births and numbers of women between 15 and 49, is higher in Canada than in any other country with a European population. For 1956, it was 119 for the country as a whole, 145 for the sixty Quebec parishes. Lastly, the aging index, which for Canada as a whole is lower than in most Western countries—.28 in 1956— was .20 in the sixty parishes, where the population is still younger.

Obviously, the average figures cited above are based on figures that vary from parish to parish. The actual birth rates varied from 27 per 1,000 to 41, and the fertility rates from 138 to 178. As for the aging index, some parishes have fewer than 10 persons of 60 and over for every 100 young persons under twenty (a ratio of 10 to 100 gives an index of .1). In no parish did the index run higher than .25.

To explain this extraordinary demographic pattern in the country districts of Quebec, the influence of the Catholic religion is not enough. There are countries wholly Catholic in religion which give a very different picture—even a diametrically opposed one. Take Austria, for example, a Catholic country with birth rates below 20 per 1,000, since the 1920's; it plunged to 13 in the 1930's. In northern Italy, the provincial birth rates vary from 10 to 13 per 1,000 at most. Nor is the French Canadian pattern explained solely by the fact that these are predominately rural regions. There are many rural regions elsewhere—in France, for example—where the birth rates are extremely low.

In fact, a whole series of factors has to be taken into consideration, each of which is in turn cause and effect. There is not just religion, but religious observance, there are education and the cultural tradition, governmental controls, social taboos, national feeling, historical and socio-psychological factors—in short, all those human factors which prevent us from ever reducing human behavior to a set of clear-cut scientific laws, such as serve to account for animal behavior.

What seems fairly clear is that birth-control practices have never spread to the Quebec countryside. Such practices have, however, become widespread among Catholics in other countries. Jacqueline Beaujeu-Garnier supplies some figures on the relation of births to marriages in 1947, from which we quote the following:[21]

	Marriage Rate	Birth Rate
	(per 1,000 population)	
British Columbia	9.9	17.8
Ontario	9.3	20.0
Quebec	9.0	31.1

She adds: "Early marriages and multiple marriages are most characteristic of those who practice birth control." She goes on to quote the paradoxical remark first used about France: "It is in the times and places where the most marrying goes on, that the fewest children are born."

How strong and enduring these factors are, is clearly demonstrated among those French Canadians who live in little colonies within predominately English-speaking regions of Canada. Boileau illustrates this in a study he made of demographic patterns within seven French Canadian parishes in Saskatchewan. The average birth rate from 1947 to 1956 was 37 per 1,000. So high a rate is no doubt explained by the predominately agricultural character of the seven parishes. For Saskatchewan as a whole, among Canadians of non-French origin, the birth rate was 23. The difference cannot be attributed to a different marriage rate either, for in the seven parishes the marriage rate of 8.4 was at the same level as that of the rest of the province. On the other hand, infant mortality was considerably higher among French Canadians in Saskatchewan (43 per 1,000) than among other ethnic groups in the province. Among Canadians of German origin it was 29, of British origin 30, and of Polish origin 36. Thus, the French Canadians of Saskatchewan repeat another feature of the Quebec pattern. Infant mortality in Quebec is also higher than for the country as a whole: nearly 40 per 1,000, as opposed to about 30. In the seven Saskatchewan parishes, the fertility rate is extremely high, 119, as is the case in the sixty rural parishes of Quebec cited above, where the rate was 145.

Taken together, the above facts show clearly a population pattern among French Canadians different from the other ethnic groups within the country—by whom they are greatly outnumbered. The physical environment, which constitutes a major factor in the life of animal populations, is also an important factor in the life of human populations, but it is never the decisive, sole determining factor.

THE "BABY BOOM" AFTER 1945 IN THE WESTERN COUNTRIES

"Baby boom" is a typically American expression, but as a post-World War II phenomenon it is not to be understood as something distinct and apart from the other population trends and patterns of Western populations since the end of the nineteenth century. The baby boom would be incomprehensible unless we recognized that for half a century (in France for a century) the population of the Western countries has no longer been dominated by mortality. More and more, death had been successfully brought under control. Now population became subject to natality—a natality no longer simply reflecting the peoples' biological fecundity, but a highly calculated matter involving ever more refined technical procedures. Of course, the various countries do not all present the same picture, and within each of them there are profound differences of behavior. Thus, for example, the Catholic portion of a country's population is everywhere more fertile than the non-Catholic portion, the countryside in general is more prolific than the cities, and the demographic patterns of Ireland, the Netherlands, and Iceland are all appreciably different from those of France, England, and Austria. Nonetheless, general trends are observable everywhere, although they may make themselves felt in different degrees and with a varying "time lag"—with a considerable "time lag" in the southern countries, for example. It is necessary to repeat once more: mankind does not behave in automatic, predictable fashion. England (with Wales), Austria, and Sweden had the lowest birth rates in Europe prior to World War II and a baby boom after it—but not all in the same proportions —and in the fifties they all slumped back again to the bottom of the list. Yet they are all very different countries:

. . . Each of these countries belongs to a different region in Europe, each has a different historical and political background and in both World Wars one had been victorious, the second defeated and the third neutral.[22]

The baby boom should also be looked at from the typically human point of view of population development. Asking herself what had brought on such a reversal of trends in the United States, Jacqueline Beaujeu-Garnier says: "One is lost in conjecture. The only fact beyond dispute is that nobody expected it."[23] Alfred Sauvy, speaking of the demographic situation in Europe right before the war, stated that everyone had been fearing—and with reason—a sharp rise in sterility as a result of the war, but that events did not confirm this well-grounded fear.[24]

The baby boom after 1945 should not be thought of solely as a "making up for" population losses caused by the war. There had been some sign of an upturn in the birth rate immediately before the war. Although the outbreak of hostilities in 1940–41 temporarily obscured the course of events, this upturn assumed definite dimensions while the war was still going on.

Before the 1914–18 War. The population outburst of the nineteenth century increased the population of Western Europe more in a hundred years than the previous thousand years had accomplished. And that despite heavy overseas emigration. This extraordinary increase had begun to slow down by the beginning of the present century. In the last half of the nineteenth century, in fact, birth rates were declining in every country of Western Europe. France was at the head of the movement for the voluntary limitation of numbers of children. Extraordinarily rapid increase was thus followed by an appreciable slowing down. These figures show the percentage growth in population for a few countries:[25]

	1890–1900	1930–1940
Great Britain	12	5
Sweden	7	3
Switzerland	13	4
France	2	1
Germany	14	9
Belgium	10	4

Around the turn of the century, birth rates were falling in a number of countries, as TABLE 38 shows.

It should be stated that the steady drop in the birth rate after World War I followed from a whole series of phenomena which the development of modern civilization brought with it: urbanization, industrialization, female emancipation, weakening of religious feeling, and—most important of all—medical progress in lowering

TABLE 38

Birth Rates in Several European Countries before 1914

Country	1900–04	1910–14
Germany	34.3	28.2
Belgium	27.9	22.5
Denmark	29.0	26.4
Finland	31.3	28.2
France	21.2	19.0
England & Wales	28.2	24.3
Ireland	23.1	22.7
Italy	32.6	31.8
Norway	28.5	25.3
Netherlands	31.5	28.2
Scotland	29.4	25.9
Spain	35.1	31.1
Sweden	26.4	23.7
Switzerland	28.2	23.8

mortality. It is tempting to say that there is an almost necessary correlation between the drop in the death rate and the drop in the birth rate. Sauvy has calculated that if the fertility of French women had remained at the seventeenth-century level down to our day, then the falling off in infant mortality and in the death rate generally would have produced by now a French population of more than 450 million. At the same time it is true that the Neo-Malthusian reaction was pushed to such panicky, self-seeking extremes that the very survival of several European peoples was endangered.

The First Baby Boom. The 1914–18 war brought about an abrupt decline in births in many European countries, especially those most immediately touched by the war. In Belgium, France, Germany, Great Britain and Italy the birth rate dropped far below pre-war figures. In countries like Australia, New Zealand, the Netherlands, Scandinavia, Switzerland, and the United States, there was also a considerable decline.

After the war the birth rates in all these countries took a brief surge forward, though in only a few was the pre-war level regained. For all of Western Europe, however, this baby boom truly had the character of "making up for" the wartime drop in births. It lasted only about two years, and it had no effect on the general trend toward lower fertility levels which had characterized Europe since the late nineteenth century.

TABLE 39

Birth Rates in Some European Countries, before, during, and after World War I

Country	1905–09	1915–19	1920	1921	1922
Belgium	25.1	13.6	21.8	22.1	20.6
Denmark	28.4	23.8	25.4	24.0	22.3
France	20.1	11.4	21.5	20.8	19.4
Italy	32.6	22.7	32.2	32.1	30.8
England & Wales	26.7	20.9	25.5	22.4	20.4
Scotland	28.1	21.5	28.1	25.2	23.5
Netherlands	30.0	25.7	28.6	27.6	26.1
Switzerland	26.4	18.9	20.9	20.9	19.7
Sweden	25.6	20.8	23.6	21.5	19.6
Norway	26.7	24.0	26.1	24.2	23.3
Finland	31.0	23.3	27.1	25.9	25.0
Ireland	22.7	20.6	22.2	20.2	19.5

In all these countries, the birth rates for 1922 were lower—in most cases appreciably lower—than they had been before the war. In most of them the birth rate of 1922 was about the same as in the quinquennium disturbed by the First World War. The general trend to smaller families had reasserted itself.

The Interwar Years. The years from 1920 to 1940 were characterized by two major developments.

First, the world-wide economic depression brought with it so severe a drop in the birth rate that some Western countries, at least, were no longer replacing their existing populations. Sauvy has published net replacement rates for the countries of Europe as of 1938, and concludes from them that in a very large part of northern and western Europe the population was declining:[26]

Iceland	1.23	Germany	0.93
Ireland	1.21	France	0.91
Portugal	1.17	Belgium	0.86
Netherlands	1.16	United Kingdom	0.83
Italy	1.13	Norway	0.83
Greece	1.12	Sweden	0.80
Finland	1.04	Switzerland	0.78
Spain (1940)	1.01	Austria	0.72
Denmark	0.94		

As our next tabulation will show, birth rates were at their very lowest in the years 1935–38.

Second, just at its lowest point in the late thirties, the level of natality began to rise again, or at least ceased falling. The downward trend was halted and reversed. In several Western countries, including the United States, Australia, and New Zealand, birth rates briefly took an upward turn just before World War II. In some countries the outbreak of hostilities necessarily halted this reversal of trend, and in other Western countries the war may have prevented its development, but higher birth rates were resumed late in the war. In other countries, especially in Scandinavia and in the Western countries outside Europe, there was no such interruption. So in some of the war years, the birth rates in Western countries were considerably higher than they had been when they were at their lowest ebb before the war. There were remarkably few exceptions to this picture despite the disturbance of intense hostilities. Thus, the First and the Second World Wars did not have the same effect on Western European, North American, and Australasian birth rates.

The Baby Boom after 1945. Just as after World War I, all the countries of Western civilization, with the exception of Germany, had a considerable rise in the number of births after World War II. Like its predecessor, this baby boom undoubtedly involved a desire to "make up for" births not wanted during the war, and was a result of men coming back home from the services, from POW camps, and from forced labor camps. But there was more to it than that. After 1946–47, the birth rates did not drop again as

TABLE 40

Lowest Pre-War Birth Rates Compared with Wartime Birth Rates

	Lowest in 1930's	Highest 1940–43*	Lowest 1940–43*
Austria	12.8 (1937)	21.8	17.1
Belgium	15.4 (1937)	15.0	12.2
Denmark	17.7 (1935)	21.4	18.3
Finland	19.1 (1936)	24.2	16.6
France	14.8 (1939)	15.9	13.4
Germany	14.7 (1933)	20.1	14.9
Ireland	19.1 (1932)	22.3	19.0
Italy	22.4 (1936)	23.5	19.9
Netherlands	19.8 (1937)	23.0	20.3
Norway	14.3 (1935)	18.9	15.3
Portugal	26.2 (1939)	25.1	23.8
Spain	16.6 (1939)	24.5	19.7
Sweden	13.7 (1935)	19.3	15.1
Switzerland	15.0 (1937)	19.2	15.2
England & Wales	14.4 (1933)	16.2	13.9
Scotland	17.4 (1939)	18.2	17.1
United States	18.4 (1933)	22.7	19.4
Canada	20.0 (1937)	24.1	21.5
New Zealand	16.2 (1935)	22.8	19.7
Australia	16.4 (1934)	20.6	18.0

* The figures underlined are those exceptional cases where the wartime birth rate was below the pre-war trough.

they had after 1920–21, to below the pre-war level. They have stayed just a bit higher than the pre-war level. According to Sauvy, who is rarely inclined to optimism, what has happened ". . . is not the effect of a true reversal of trend, but a slackening of the downward trend of the past hundred years."[27] It does seem to be the case that, though the birth rates—truest sign of a people's vitality —have risen, they have not risen to such an extent that every European country can be confident that its present population is being replaced.

Whatever the future may hold, it remains true that the baby boom of 1946–47 falls within a totally different framework of existing population trends than did the earlier one, though both did share in a post-war desire to compensate for the war years. The baby boom after 1918 occurred at a time when birth rates had been going down in every European country since the beginning of the century—and that trend persisted when the baby boom was over. After World War II, however, the baby boom had the effect of reinforcing a reversal of trend which had made itself felt before the war. (See Table 44.) Once the second baby boom was over, the birth rates persistently kept above the pre-war levels in most Western countries for a long time. Outstanding exceptions were on the Mediterranean and Scandinavian margins of Western Europe, such as Italy, Portugal, and Denmark, where the level eventually sank under the lowest average 1930–39 levels. In all Western countries the birth rates have been lower since 1949 than in the immediate postwar "baby boom" years. Some students of the matter have spoken of a "stabilizing" of the birth rate, but if such a thing exists at all, there is a better case for it in the Western countries outside Europe than in Europe itself. TABLE 41 shows the changes over the past fifty years.

Careful study of this table will impress one with the fact that the same general trends show up in all these countries, despite their very great differences of cultural, political, and military history, of religion, climate, traditions, and demographic patterns.

Excluding three southern European countries, no correlation appears between the height of the pre-war level and the magnitude of the increase up to 1946–1947; examples of large increases in the birth rate are found both for countries with rather low pre-war rates and for those with somewhat high pre-war rates.[28]

At the same time, there is no clear correlation between the different traditions spoken of above and population patterns in the same countries over the past few decades. This is unmistakable when we compare, for example, birth rates in a Catholic country like Portugal (26 per 1,000 in 1939; 25 in 1961) with those of New Zealand (16 per 1,000 in 1935; 27 in 1961), or those of

TABLE 41

Birth Rates in the Western Countries in Various Periods between 1910 and 1961

Country	1910–14	Lowest Quinquennium 1930–34/35–39	1945–49*	1950–54*	Highest in 1955–61*	Lowest in 1955–61*
New Zealand	26.2	17.4	25.1	24.5	27.1	26.0
United States		18.8	24.1	24.9	24.9	23.3
Portugal	33.8	27.1	25.4*	24.0*	24.5*	23.4*
Australia	28.1	17.3	23.1	23.0	22.9	22.4
Netherlands	28.2	20.3	25.9	22.1	21.3	20.8
Ireland	23.0	19.5	22.5	21.4	21.3	20.9
Finland	30.2	20.0	27.0	22.8	21.2	18.4
Italy	32.0	23.2	21.2*	18.3*	18.8*	17.9*
France	18.8	15.1	20.1	19.3	18.6	18.0
Norway	25.4	15.0	20.8	18.7	18.5	17.3
Switzerland	23.8	15.4	19.4	17.3	18.1	17.1
Belgium	22.4	15.6	17.3	16.7	17.4	16.8
England & Wales	24.3	14.9	18.0	15.5	17.6	15.0
Scotland	25.9	17.7	19.3	17.8	19.5	18.1
Denmark	26.4	17.9	21.6	17.9*	17.3*	16.0*
Sweden	23.7	14.4	19.0	15.5	14.8	13.7*

* The figures emphasized denote post-war birth rates below lowest quinquennium of 1930–39 period.

France (15 in 1939; 18 in 1961) with those of Germany (15 in 1933, 18 in 1961). The same conclusion is reached when we compare scantily populated countries with countries of high population density.

NOTES

1. J. Godefroy, *Sociale Prognose* (Tilburg, 1960), p. 13.

2. The distinction between urban and rural populations varies from country to country. In English-speaking and Scandinavian countries, administrative and juridical definitions obtain. In a number of countries, the size of the population in the principal town serves to divide the two categories: 1,500 in Ireland, 2,000 in Germany, Austria, and France, 5,000 in Belgium, the Netherlands, and Greece. The Swiss employ occupational structure as a criterion, and distinguish three categories according to the percentage of inhabitants solely engaged in agriculture: from 10 per cent to 40 per cent, from 40 per cent to 60 per cent, and more than 60 per cent. In this connection, see Jacqueline Beaujeu-Garnier, *Géographie de la population,* 2 vols. (Paris: M. T. Génin, 1956–58), I, 160.

3. M. Thibault, *Essai démographique sur l'évolution de quelques communes picardes depuis 1820.*

4. *Crises d'une société agricole traditionnelle et pratique religieuse* (unpublished MS).

5. Beaujeu-Garnier, *op. cit.,* I, 144.

6. W. Kusters, "Problèmes économiques et démographiques de l'Europe occidentale," *Social Compass* (The Hague), V, 2, 57–83.

7. The main sources used here were Ayanori Okasaki, *Histoire du Japon: l'Economie et la Population,* INED Cahier No. 32 (Paris, 1958), and Irene Taeuber, *Population of Japan* (Princeton: Princeton U. Press, 1958).

8. "International Migrations in the Far East during Recent Times—The Countries of Migration" in *Population Bulletin No. 1* (UN), pp. 13–30.

9. Jean-Louis Riallin, "La Prévention des naissances au Japon: politique, intentions, moyens et résultats," *Population,* 15, 2 (April/May, 1960), pp. 333–351.

10. Wilfred D. Borrie, "The Population Explosion and the Far East," *Pacific Affairs,* XXXIII, 2 (June, 1960), 181–91.

11. "Urban-Rural Development in Japan," R.E.M.P. (*Research for European Migrations Problems*) *Bulletin,* VIII, 3 (July/Sept. 1960), pp. 63–67.

12. *Population Bulletin No. 1* (UN), p. 26.

13. Okasaki, *op. cit.,* p. 108.

14. See, for example, the report of "The Fifth (1959) Public Opinion Survey on Birth Control in Japan," (Tokyo, 1959).

15. Yoshio Koya, "Five Year Experiment in Family Planning among Coal Miners in Joban, Japan," *Population Studies*, XIII, 2 (Nov. 1958).

16. A good introduction in English to the population of Algeria up to independence is Dorothy Good, "Notes on the Demography of Algeria," *Population Index*, 27, 1 (Jan. 1961), pp. 3–32.

17. J. Serra, *La lutte des Algériens contre la faim* (Algiers, 1954).

18. Paul Veyret, *La Population du Canada* (Paris: Presses Universitaires, 1933), p. 10.

19. Cf. D. M. McDougall, "Immigration into Canada 1851–1920," *Canadian Journal of Economics and Political Science*, X, 2 (May, 1961), pp. 162–175.

20. *Evolution démographique de la population rurale dans 60 paroisses de la province de Québec depuis le début du siècle* (Montreal, 1956). Unpublished MS.

21. Beaujeu-Garnier, *op. cit.*, I, 295.

22. *Recent Trends in Fertility in Industrialized Countries* (New York: United Nations, 1958), p. 14.

23. Beaujeu-Garnier, *op. cit.*, I, 234.

24. Alfred Sauvy, *L'Europe et sa population* (Paris: Les Editions Internationales, 1953), p. 58.

25. Tabulation from *ibid.*, p. 31.

26. *Ibid.*, p. 32.

27. *Ibid.*, p. 61.

28. *Recent Trends in Fertility* (UN), p. 11.

Chapter 5

The Population Factors: Mortality and Natality

CHANGES IN LIFE EXPECTANCY

COMPREHENSIVE POPULATION DATA are still lacking for large parts of the world, and information about the past is even more scanty. By the end of 1962, about one-tenth of the world had never been covered by census, and some of the censuses conducted in recent years in underdeveloped countries with no statistical expertise are highly inaccurate.[1] Mortality data of any very comprehensive character are available for only about 36 per cent of the world's population, although acceptable estimates are available for another 18 per cent, leaving some 46 per cent of the human race in *terra incognita*.[2] Thus it is extremely difficult to arrive at any simple picture of the problem.

Only recently has there been careful investigation on this score, and at the present time only a few countries are in a position to draw up tabulations by age group, profession, social class, standard of living, etc. Nonetheless, such as they are, the data are the foundation of all we know about present and future population trends even in the most highly developed countries.

There are two methods we can bring to bear upon the topic of mortality. First, there is the *statistical* method, by which we arrange the available data in tables according to age and sex. This method permits us to draw conclusions concerning what has already happened. It is applicable only to certain populations.

Second, there is the *demographic* method, which employs theoretical population models based on such statistics as are available. According to the structure and dynamic characteristics of an actual population, it is adjudged to belong to one or another model or type of population, and thus it becomes possible to gain some idea of that population's prospects for the future. This method is more satisfactory than the statistical method in dealing with such populations as those of Africa and Asia, where statistical data are for the most part scanty.

Life Expectancy. Preferable to raw data and crude mortality rates is the measure of life expectancy which can be deduced from them. Life expectancy is the average number of years the inhabitant of a particular country can look forward to at any given age. In the discussion which follows, "life expectancy" is to be understood as the expectation of life at birth.

One of the advantages of this demographic concept is that it is valid for all members of a population, regardless of the variations of natality and mortality to be found among the different segments of that population. It is a more precise measure of population development than crude death rates. Thus, for example, it is possible for a population that is aging and whose mortality rate is climbing to have, nonetheless, a longer life expectancy than a population with a lower mortality.

The UN population study No. 22, entitled *Age and Sex Patterns of Mortality,* contains forty theoretical models of mortality tables expressed in figures indicating life expectancy. These are applied to fifty countries and for different periods in each case. The 158 tables are, of course, theoretical or formal calculations, but they take account of such statistical information as is possessed for each country.

Life expectancy is expressed graphically by a U-shaped curve, and so with the aid of the theoretical models it is possible to plot the curves of populations for which available data are incomplete.

Mortality and World Population. Alfred Sauvy, who has studied the main causes of death over the centuries—famine, epidemic disease, and violence—states that they have helped to keep the balance between natality and mortality for millenia, so that it was never necessary to increase food production to any great extent.[3] It was in the nineteenth century that mortality rates began to decline, first in North America, then in northern and western Europe. The crude death rate was about 30 per 1,000 in this part of Europe at the beginning of the last century, while in eastern Europe it was still about 40 per 1,000.[4] In the same period, notable improvements were being made in the economic potential, such that the increased population found employment in an expanding industry. This development went on all over Europe and speeded up after 1880.

In consequence, the traditional causes of mortality have ceased to have the importance they formerly had for these populations. The loss of millions of lives in war produces relatively slight, temporary effects which the populations recover from rapidly, thanks to the great excess of births over deaths in peacetime in the Western countries. In TABLE 42 we notice how wide is the spread between mortality rates in the Western countries and elsewhere in the world.

TABLE 42

Death Rates and Length of Life in Continents and Sub-Continents
(estimates) *

	Crude Death Rate		*Life Expectancy in years*
	1937	1956–60	1955–58
World total	24–27	18	50–60
Africa	*30–35*	25	*under 40*
North Africa		23	
Tropical & Southern Africa		27	
Americas		*13*	
Northern America	11	9	70
Middle America		15	
South America	20–25	19	50–55
Asia	*30–35*	22	*40–45*
South West Asia		22	
South Central Asia		24	
South East Asia		21	

East Asia	20	
Europe	*14*	*11*	*68*
North & West Europe		11	
Central Europe		11	
Southern Europe		10	
Oceania	*11*	*9*	*68*
U.S.S.R.	*18*	*8*	*68*

* UN, *1963 World Social Situation*, p. 20, Table 3.
———, *Population Bulletin No. 6*, p. 17, Table III.1.

At the same time, the Western countries have been successful in cutting down mortality due to exogenous causes (infectious diseases) to such an extent that the majority of people today die of endogenous causes: cancer, heart disease, old age. Little by little the average expectation of life has climbed toward 80 years. Sauvy gives a survival table comparing France's crude death rate in 1958 with the "biological death rate," that is, with what he considers to be the maximum life expectancy.[5] (See TABLE 43.)

TABLE 43

Mortality in France, Actual and Potential, 1958
(number of survivors per 1,000 births)

Age (Yrs.)	Biological Death Rate	Actual Death Rate
1	989	960
20	987	940
40	977	901
60	904	754
80	500	298
90	169	40

Life Expectancy and World Population. Life expectancy in Northwestern Europe, North America, Oceania, and the U.S.S.R. is now nearing 75 years, after up to one hundred years of struggle against death, but the process of prolonging life has only very recently been extended to some of the underdeveloped countries. Some of them are still little affected by it. TABLE 44 gives life expectancies (in years) for outstanding countries in various parts of the world:

TABLE 44
Life Expectancy in Contrasting Countries, Recorded or Estimated*
1955–1958 and c. 1900–1920†

Advanced Countries		*Backward Countries*	
The Country with Highest Recent Life Expectancy in Each Continent & Sub-continent	*Years of Life Expectancy*	*The Country with the Lowest Known Recent Life Expectancy in Each Continent & Sub-continent*	*Years of Life Expectancy*
Americas			
Canada	70 (45–50)	Haiti	35–45?
North America:			
Canada	70	Mexico	55–60 (33)
Middle America:			
Puerto Rico	65 (39)	Haiti	35–45?
South America:			
Argentina	60	Bolivia	35–45?
Asia			
Israel	70	India	35–45 (27)
South West Asia:			
Cyprus	70	Arabias	35–45?
South Central Asia:			
Ceylon	55 (32)	Pakistan	35–45?
South East Asia:			
Malaysia	55	Cambodia	35–45
East Asia:			
Japan	65 (43)	China (mainland)	45–55?
Europe & U.S.S.R.			
Norway	75 (56)	Albania	60 (30–40)
North & West Europe:			
Netherlands	75 (52)	Belgium	65 (47)
Central Europe & U.S.S.R.			
Switzerland	70 (51)	Poland	60 (30–40)
Southern Europe:			
Italy	70 (45)	Spain	60 (35)
Oceania			
Australia	70 (57)	Papua-New Guinea	30–40?

* Estimates are expressed as ranges. Those estimates followed by a question mark are no more than informed guesses. Statistics for the earliest life expectancy calculated shortly before World War I for Western countries, or calculated shortly after World War I for Asian and Latin American countries, are given in parentheses if available.

† UN, *1963 World Social Situation,* pp. 29–30, Table 5, and *Population Bulletin No. 6,* pp. 17–48.

The basically different trend of mortality that exists between the underdeveloped and the advanced countries is exemplified in TABLE 45. A curve has been drawn showing the life expectancy rate of Sweden, an advanced country, between 1760 and 1960; against this rate is shown the life expectancy rates of a few underdeveloped countries.

TABLE 45

Recent Mortality Trends in Various Underdeveloped Countries Compared with the Secular Mortality Trend in Sweden*

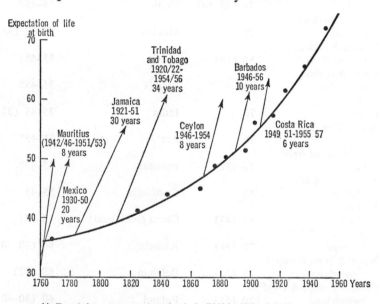

(a) The unbroken curve represents a free hand smoothing of the trend of expectation of life at birth for both sexes in Sweden from 1760 to the present day. (The black dots correspond to the Swedish life tables.)

(b) For each country, a representative period, which is shown in calendar years below the name of the country, has been selected, and the life expectancy at the beginning and that at the end of the period have been compared (for instance, in the case of Trinidad and Tobago, the life expectancy in 1920-1922 is compared with the life expectancy in 1954-1956).

(c) For each country, there is an arrow which starts from the curve for Sweden at the level of life expectancy attained by the country in question at the beginning of the selected period. (For instance, in 1920-1922,

Trinidad and Tobago had a life expectancy of 38.8 years, the level reached by Sweden in 1810. The arrow for Trinidad and Tobago therefore starts at the point for 1810 on the Swedish curve.) On the Y-axis, the head of the arrow is at the level of life expectancy attained at the end of the selected period. Its position on the X-axis has been determined by adding to the point at which the arrow originates the number of years corresponding to the length of the selected period. The length of this period is indicated underneath the calendar years representing the beginning and end of the period. (For instance, Trinidad and Tobago in 1954-1956 had an expectation of life at birth of 61.4 years, and the length of the selected period is 34 years. The head of the arrow for Trinidad and Tobago is at 61.4 years on the Y-axis and at 1810 + 34 = 1844 on the X-axis.)

*UN, Population Bulletin No. 6, p. 50, Fig. IV. 1.

Little progress in prolonging life expectancy took place until the last century, apart from very exceptional cases of effective quarantine and avoidance of catastrophes such as famine. The bourgeoisie of Geneva and other specially favored enclaves in northwestern Europe probably made considerable gains in life expectancy between the Renaissance and the nineteenth century. But the population at large in even the most prosperous countries cannot have enjoyed a life expectancy of much more than 35 years at the best of times. No large population surpassed a life expectancy of 40 years until the mid-nineteenth century. These were the countries in the van of industrialization and trade, that is, northwestern Europe, North America, Australia, and New Zealand. Before that time, medical care was ineffectual, if not positively lethal; public health and environmental sanitation were non-existent; and the growth of squalid cities, with even higher death rates than the countryside, counteracted the benefits brought by the elimination of famine. Before the nineteenth century, only an upper limit can be estimated for life expectancy since waves of epidemics brought this figure lower at least once in every generation. Dense tropical populations and primitive jungle dwellers probably all suffered from an expectation of life below 30, quite apart from waves of epidemics. Thus, while some populations did manage to increase gradually in the long run, numerous groups shrank in size, at least temporarily, between the Middle Ages and the diffusion of modern medicine and public health.

Before the Second World War, only those countries which industrialized rapidly or took up a strong trading position made the greatest progress in reducing mortality. In addition to northwestern and central Europe, North America, and Australasia, Argentina, Uruguay, Italy, Czechoslovakia, U.S.S.R., Japan, and Singapore stood in the van.

In some countries of Asia, Latin America, and Africa, the expectation of life of new-born infants has been lengthened by 15 to 20 years or even more since the pre-war period. For instance, the records show an increase in expectation of life at birth in Mexico from 33 years in 1930 to 50 years in 1949–1951; in Mauritius from 33 years in 1942–1946 to 51 years in 1951–1953; in Ceylon from 46 years in 1945–1947 to 60 years in 1954; in Japan from 48 years in 1935–1936 to 67 years in 1958. Some of these countries are now not far behind the most advanced countries of Europe, Northern America, and Oceania so far as the expectation of life is concerned. . . . It is true that some of the less developed countries which face greater obstacles to rapid improvement of health conditions for the masses of their population have not yet achieved such spectacular successes in reduction of mortality. In India, for example, the expectation of life at birth for the average of 1941–1950 was estimated at only 32 years, a gain of five years over the estimate for 1921–1930, but available evidence indicates that greater gains have been scored in India during the 1950's.

In most of the countries of Europe, and in Northern America, Australia, and New Zealand, which had already achieved relatively low mortality rates before the Second World War, the recent gains in expectation of life have been, in general, smaller than those of the Asian, African, and Latin American countries. Among the European countries, those which were previously below the average of this region in expectation of life have generally made the largest gains in this respect since the pre-war years. Most countries of southern and eastern Europe had expectations of life at birth between 50 and 60 years before the war; on the average, it is estimated that they gained about 10 years in expectation of life between 1935–1939 and 1955–1958, considerably narrowing the gap between them and the leaders in expectation of life among the countries of northwestern Europe, Northern America, and Oceania. The gain in the U.S.S.R. was particularly impressive, amounting to a 24-year increase in the expectation of life between 1926 and 1957–1958.

Meanwhile, the countries which had previously reached the highest levels of expectation of life, including most of those in northern and western Europe, Canada, the United States, Australia, and New Zealand, made some further gains during the post-war period, but these gains were relatively modest. These countries faced increasing difficulties in efforts to reduce their mortality rates further, owing to the intractability of many of the diseases, such as cancer and heart diseases, which now account for a major share of deaths in low-mortality countries. The relative importance of such diseases and their influence in determining the general level of mortality is magnified by the rising proportion of the elderly population in these countries.

The statistics show that the age-old inequality of the rich and the poor in the chances of survival still exists in the world, but it is diminishing. The levelling of disparities between richer and poorer nations, and between social and economic classes of the population within the same country, is a result of modern measures of health protection and cure of disease, which are becoming available to all. The low death rate, which was formerly the privilege of economically advanced countries, is now within the reach of an increasing number of underdeveloped countries: the difference between the average mortality levels of advanced and underdeveloped countries has narrowed, and it will narrow further in the future. Indeed, a number of underdeveloped areas such as Costa Rica, Jamaica, Puerto Rico, Singapore, China (Taiwan), and Venezuela, now have crude death rates equal to or lower than those of some of the most advanced countries in the world; but their low death rates are due partly to the youthful age composition of the population, which is characteristic of underdeveloped countries. When their mortality is measured by life expectancy to avoid the effects of age structure of the population, it is found that they still lag behind the most advanced countries.[6]

Alfred Sauvy has drawn a graph comparing birth rates and death rates for a typical European population and for a typical underdeveloped country, the former from 1805 to 1955, the latter from 1905 to 1955.[7] (See TABLE 46.)

It can readily be seen how the abrupt drop in the death rate in the underdeveloped country has resulted in a sizable population increase and at the same time prompted a notable rise in life expectancy. In Europe the same process has gone on more gradually and thus has not presented such urgent economic and social problems.

At the present day, no question is more pressing. Is the world prepared economically to assimilate the so-called "population explosion" which is going on among the still-backward, long-for-

TABLE 46

Comparison of Birth and Death Rate in a European Population
and in an Underdeveloped Population, Placed One Century Back

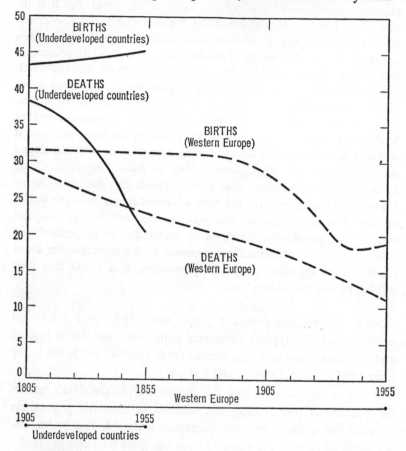

gotten, hitherto "unimportant" peoples? We say "world" deliberately, for it is up to the world as a whole to solve the problem. Not
just because it has created the conditions of health and sanitation
without which the phenomenon would never have occurred, but
also—and most importantly—because the underdeveloped coun-

tries are not themselves capable of assimilating their own increased populations. Europe would never have been able to assimilate *its* increased population in the course of the nineteenth century, had it not been for the wealth it extracted from many of these more "backward" parts of the world, which were its colonies at the time.

In Java during the period of Dutch rule, a population explosion occurred very like what is going on right now in so many parts of the world. Medical services and public health measures between them produced a sizable and steadily mounting population increase among the natives. What happened? The plots of arable land had to be divided up again and again into ever smaller sections. In 1940 these averaged from five to seven acres. Attempts were made to remedy the situation by crop improvement and more skillful utilization of the soil, but they could not keep pace with the growing needs of the growing population.

Ceylon experienced the same thing. When malaria was exterminated by D.D.T. spraying in 1947, mortality dropped suddenly.

Since that time, the birth rate has remained generally high. TABLE 47 indicates the trends in the rate of life expectancy at birth in three Asian countries—Japan, Ceylon, and India—and the swift decline in Ceylonese mortality since 1946.

It is an illusion to suppose that these populations can solve by themselves the problems which arise from such vast alterations in their demographic structure.

When they do get outside help and population increase keeps on apace, the people in the economically active ages are hemmed in by more and more non-productive mouths to feed; many more children as well as more persons of advanced years. Moreover, they have to keep redividing the land and working the soil all the harder, for like the people of Java, the people of Ceylon are primarily farmers. Some young people find employment in industry, if industry springs up with the assistance of the richer countries.

For centuries, everywhere in the world, mortality has regulated the balance between births and the means of subsistence. Human intervention in this age-old play of forces has brought about ever

TABLE 47

Trends in the Expectation of Life at Birth in Three Asian
Countries. The Rapid Decline in Ceylonese Mortality
since 1946*

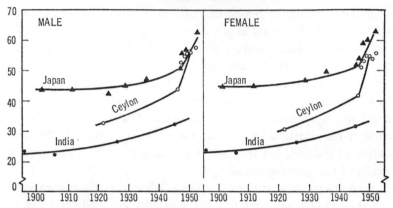

* UN, *Age and Sex Patterns of Mortality; Model Life Tables for Under-developed Countries* (1955), Fig. 13, p. 28.

more efficient control of mortality, so that it is man himself who is at the bottom of the recent increase in human reproductive powers. Because he is a rational animal, he will react consciously to the phenomenon he has himself brought about. We have seen this happen already in the West. The situation in the underdeveloped countries is harder and more complex, for the latter are handicapped culturally and spiritually. The technological revolution was produced elsewhere, in a very different framework of thought and feeling. To the peoples of the underdeveloped countries, adapting to Western civilization constitutes a real break with their own pasts. They face an unknown future, but there is no question but that they are preparing to face it.

Sauvy has studied the spread between life expectancy and the standard of living in the underdeveloped countries today, using as his basis of comparison the European figures for 1938. That is, the following figures for standards of living are percentages of the European level just before the outbreak of World War II:[8]

	Standard of Living	Life Expectancy
Europe (1870)	40	40 years
Asia (1960)	10	40–45 years
Africa (1960)	12	40 years
Latin America (1960)	35	50–55 years

These figures, approximate though they must be, show clearly that Africa's situation in 1960 is far less—some four times less—favorable than was Europe's in 1870. Moreover, with the steady, continuing drop in the mortality rate, the gap is widening further every day. However, it would be a mistake to suppose that this spread or gap has only a numerical, economic significance. It is up to man to bridge the gap between population increase and the standard of living. To achieve this, he has at his disposal his characteristically human faculties of will and intelligence. He is not the slave of purely biological laws. As for the stimuli that spur his behavior, they can rarely be measured on a scale of purely numerical values. More often, we must look to the speed with which a phenomenon develops, to its rate of acceleration; it scarcely seems likely, for example, that there is any correlation between living standards and patterns of behavior. Rather, we should look to a correlation between behavior patterns and the differential coefficients (speed, rate of acceleration) with which the standard of living develops.

Infant Mortality. Modern medical progress has reduced mortality within every age group, but the most spectacular victory over death has been won for children in the first five years of life. It was in this age group that mortality had always been highest.

Lowering infant mortality has had an important bearing upon natality, because now an ever-growing number of babies succeed in reaching adulthood and procreating.

A classic example of the medical progress made in the Western countries is Sweden's rate of infant mortality:

1750–1800	200 per 1,000 live births
1800–1830	160 " " " "
1850–1900	100 " " " "
1900–1950	20 " " " "

Northern and western Europe has for a long time now had a low rate of infant mortality. Southern and eastern Europe, including Czechoslovakia, did not achieve a rate lower than 100 per 1,000, until after the Second World War. At the end of the Second World War, most Latin American countries and almost all African and Asian countries had an infant mortality rate of 150 per 1,000 births or higher.

For the underdeveloped countries, the data are incomplete on infant mortality, although sample surveys have been taken in some cases.

It is extremely probable that 250 and more infants die for every 1,000 live births in rural Africa. In the underdeveloped countries generally, some 40 per cent of live births will not live to the age of 15, and it is quite likely that this rate goes as high as 50 per cent in certain times and places. In Guinea infant mortality in the towns is lower (190 per 1,000) than in the interior of the country (220 per 1,000). The over-all death rate also ranges between 29 and 40 per 1,000, between the two parts of the country.[9] The rural death rate corresponds to a life expectancy at birth of 25 years. In this case, the number of children who die between birth and the age of 5 constitutes more than 50 per cent of all the deaths among the total population every year.

The following table is taken from the UN *Population Study No. 13*. The figures show the percentage of a country's total deaths that is constituted by the death of children between birth and the age of five. The table ranges from highly advanced countries, to some less advanced, and finally to a few underdeveloped ones.

TABLE 48
Percentage of Total Deaths, 1936–1945, for Children
Aged 0 and 1–5 Years

	Infancy*	1–5†
Australia	7.1	9.2
Ceylon	25.4	41.4
Egypt	24.4	52.5
Germany	10.4	12.8
India	23.8	42.4
Italy	17.1	24.7
Japan	17.5	19.2
Latin America	32.5	45.2
Norway	6.2	8.2
United Kingdom	7.1	8.1
United States	8.0	9.9

* First year.
† Second through fourth year.

Modern medical progress, which is at the bottom of the increase in life expectancy, illustrates very clearly the dramatic changes which are taking place today in the underdeveloped countries: today 80 per cent, instead of only 60 per cent, of the population will live to adulthood, and this gain will have been made over a period of 50 years, instead of 150 years. However, all indications are that there will be no such speed-up in the production of foodstuffs, and that thus the spread or gap between the two developments may grow wider than it already is.

The Western world has no right to sit on its hands while all this is going on, and wait for catastrophe on the Malthusian scale to occur. Nor can it refuse aid on the grounds that the situation can only get worse in the long run, in any case. The problem of the underdeveloped countries is a world-wide problem, the solution of which demands enormous effort on all sides, employing every variety of means and bringing to bear every existing force that can be exerted. To solve it, the West may even be obliged to postpone further rises in its own standard of living. As all parts of the world come closer and closer together, the prospect of devising truly effective assistance for a problem of this scale is no longer visionary. Moreover, to do something about it is in the interest of us all.

THE EFFECTS OF MEDICAL PROGRESS

Founding of the World Health Organization. There are different causes for the very appreciable lowering of the death rate in all the more developed countries since the beginning of this century. However, the most spectacular factor has unquestionably been the government-sponsored campaigns against communicable diseases, supported by international organizations.

From the end of the nineteenth century on, the Western countries extended to their colonies the medical advances then being made in the mother country. The big agricultural and industrial ventures were concerned, first, to look after the health of their European employees, but gradually medical care was extended to native labor and finally to the population as a whole.

What for long hindered the efforts of the authorities along these lines was the sheer scale of the public health measures which had to be taken, their cost, and the antagonism or apathy of the populations involved. It is all too true that there is more to public health than just the medical aspect.

During the interwar years, valuable experience was acquired by traveling medical teams composed of a variety of experts: general practitioners, dieticians, midwives, sanitation specialists, etc. They did not limit themselves to cleaning up particular problems, but made a special effort to get at the underlying causes for ill health in particular areas. Thus, for example, they considered such matters as environmental defects, undernourishment, and malnutrition. Being, however, only doctors, they could hardly solve such problems as recurrent bad harvests, nor could they do much in the way of increasing agricultural production.

The World Health Organization (WHO) was founded April 7, 1948, a successor organization to the old World Health Office founded in Geneva in 1923. Working in close collaboration with the other UN agencies and the UN Secretariat under the supervision of the General Assembly, the principal activity of WHO has been to assist the governments of interested countries to wage all-out war on communicable diseases. Profiting from experience gained earlier in these fields, WHO has given priority to making fundamental improvements in nutrition, hygiene, and public health. WHO's budget and certain projects receive support from other UN agencies, such as UNICEF, FAO, the Joint Technical Assistance Program, and also from the Ford Foundation. Given the magnitude of the problems, most of the funds have been earmarked so far for the eradication of epidemic diseases.

There have been some spectacular results already, but how lasting may be their effects depends on the ability of the countries involved to support the social cost. Peoples whose standard of living is at the bare subsistence level and who, thanks to medical progress, have seen or can foresee their populations doubling in less than thirty years, are faced with the dire necessity of discovering additional resources if they are to survive. Their only alternative is widespread and mounting pauperization.

What WHO Does. The principal role of WHO is to promote, coordinate and assist the carrying out of both short-term and long-term programs of public health. Its sphere of operations is thus very broad. It gives grants-in-aid (10,000 of them between 1947 and 1960), it attempts to standardize the world supply of drugs and medicines, it provides elementary instruction in hygiene and the use of medicines, it advises governments on public health problems, and it wages campaigns to stamp out disease, unhealthy environmental conditions, etc.

The most remarkable successes have been in the battle against mortality from exogenous causes: the communicable diseases. Before analyzing the results on mortality rates and enhanced life expectancy, it would be well to notice the sort of large-scale campaigns which have been undertaken. Medical research, both during and after World War II, made discoveries which have permitted the low-cost treatment of some of the deadliest diseases. Thus, in the United States treatment of malaria was brought down to 50 cents per capita per year, the treatment of tuberculosis to 2 dollars per capita (for a full cure), the cure of yaws to 10 cents per capita, and that of leprosy to 30 cents per capita per year.

Successive international conferences have led to a number of campaigns against malaria: at Kampala (Uganda) in 1950, at Bangkok in 1953. A five-year plan for Asia was drawn up in 1958, with an initial $150 million in funds made available. In December, 1959, some malariologists and their staffs gathered at Jaipur in India to plan eradication of the disease in that country.

In a number of countries, such as Italy, Ceylon, and Corsica, such campaigns have been wholly successful and all that is any longer needed is a small inspection staff. In some countries, such as Mexico and some of the larger African territories, similar campaigns take longer to carry out, due to problems of terrain or such climatic special conditions as an excessively prolonged rainy season. Around the Sahara and through the Middle East, there is the special problem of keeping up with the movements of nomad tribes.

Hundreds of thousands of square miles have been covered so far in the anti-malaria campaign, and hundreds of millions of human beings have been protected from the disease, which little more than ten years ago killed one and a half million persons every year. Little by little it is being crossed off the list of the deadly diseases, thanks to this concerted world-wide effort to stamp it out.

In the underdeveloped countries, the campaign against tuberculosis is still to some extent in its preliminary stages. Enormous areas of the world have been covered by wandering teams in the effort to determine the precise extent to which the disease has spread. There have been appreciable improvements in arriving at the most efficient medicines, and the most suitable methods of prevention as well as of treatment. Studies carried out at Madras in India in 1956 have established a method of treatment that works well without requiring patients to stay in sanitoriums. On this basis, India has launched a country-wide campaign which involves visits to 25 million individuals every year and the vaccination of 10 million. Here we have tangible evidence of how medical research, working hand in hand with government authorities, can dispense with hospital treatment and make medical progress available to an entire nation. This had been India's problem: an estimated 2.5 million sufferers from tuberculosis, and only 23,000 hospital beds!

The fight against yaws has also been a great success. Especially large-scale campaigns have been waged in Indonesia, Liberia, Nigeria, Sierra Leone, and Thailand, where today whole vast areas no longer suffer from the disease. Between 1950 and 1958 some 75 million persons were examined and an additional 85 million examined twice, the second visit usually sufficing for complete cure. It is hard to realize what the campaign has meant to a country like Haiti, for example, where 37 per cent of the total population of 3.5 million was seriously afflicted with this skin disease. It is hoped that another ten years will see yaws completely wiped out.

Smallpox, cholera, and plague are treated wherever they reach epidemic proportions. For example, Pakistan in 1958 received 2 million units of anti-smallpox vaccine as soon as a small outbreak was reported. The same year 500,000 units of anti-cholera serum were sent to Thailand as soon as requested. The 15,000 cases of plague recorded in 1951 had been reduced to 514 in 1957. Of the 8,230 cases in India alone, only 44 remained in 1947. In 1953, DDT brought back to health 350,000 natives of Afghanistan who had been suffering from typhoid fever.

Sleeping sickness (Trypanosomiasis) has for centuries decimated the African populations south of the Sahara. The first measures taken to control it were not very rewarding: attempts to destroy the wild animals from which the tsetse fly picks up the infection that it then transmits to human beings. Only when new medicines were introduced was real progress made toward stamping out this disease.

Riverblindness is carried by tiny flies which breed in the rivers and streams of central Africa. In Kenya nearly 40 per cent of the children under 6 were afflicted with this disease. After wholesale sprayings of DDT throughout the region, by 1953 not a single case was reported among children of this age group.

The fight against elephantiasis is carried on in the same way. It is hoped that in the near future 250 million persons will have been effectually protected against these diseases.

In many countries of Asia and Africa, and in the islands of the Pacific, some 250 million persons have been treated for yaws and for syphilis.

And yet all these campaigns are of no avail unless they are integrated with plans for global development. The man who has been cured of yaws or malaria, but is subject to malnutrition or inadequate nutrition, will spend the rest of his life diminished in vitality and unable to be very productive economically. Since 1955, WHO has been building up its resources against Kwashiorkor, an illness or total disability caused by insufficient protein in the diet. Here medicine comes up against the problems of nutrition and agricultural economy in the underdeveloped countries, and it is clear that health improvements must go hand in hand with improvements in the standard of living.

The fall of mortality has been especially striking in areas with thorough anti-malaria campaigns like Ceylon, Mauritius, and large tracts of India, Pakistan, Southwest Asia, and around the Caribbean. Infant mortality has shared in this decline. In Mexico and Jamaica, as in the Philippines and Thailand—to mention outstanding but not exceptional examples—the death rate has fallen from 20 and 30 per 1,000 to 10 or less since the Second World War, but the birth rate remains near 40, if not over 50, Consequently, the rate of natural increase is in the order of 3 per cent per annum.

The efficacy of concerted programs to combat diseases like malaria, smallpox, cholera, syphilis, tuberculosis, typhus, and typhoid is best demonstrated by the fact that areas which have benefited least suffer from the world's highest mortality. Away from urban centers, Haiti, several tropical African countries, much of Southwest and Southeast Asia, as well as Papua-New Guinea, undoubtedly still suffer from that high mortality which was typical of the underdeveloped world three decades ago, and was typical of the whole world little more than one hundred years ago.

Life Expectancy. For countries with satisfactory statistics, it is easy to show the death rate for the various age groups and to calculate the average number of years a person of any given age may expect to live. Thus in France at the beginning of the century, a man of 60 could look forward to 14 more years. By 1950 such a man could look forward to 17 more years. Expectation of life at birth is figured in the same way. In countries with extremely low death rates, like Sweden, the Netherlands, and New Zealand, it had reached 66 years in 1936–39 and 72 years in 1951–55. Until the middle of the nineteenth century no large population had enjoyed more than half this life expectancy.

We noted above how in a number of countries life expectancy has come close to Sauvy's "biological limit," namely, the figure of 78 years. At the same time, however, the ever-increasing number of deaths by accident is an appreciable check on this trend.

It is much harder to arrive at life expectancy figures when vital statistics are incomplete or unreliable, as they are for most of the underdeveloped countries. Here one must rely on over-all death rates and the infant and early childhood mortality rates (ages 0 through 4 years), which are not based on complete records but arrived at via samplings and estimates. These results are then compared with theoretical population models broken down by sex and age group, which were constructed according to actual data collected in the European countries.[10]

The average life expectancy in an underdeveloped country is determined from the theoretical model which best corresponds to such data as are available—data for infant mortality, for example. There is a consistent trend in the correlation between infant mortality and life expectancy, depending on the general level of mortality. In the underdeveloped countries, death rates have dropped and are dropping much faster than they ever did in any Western country, and economic progress has not kept up with the decline. We can anticipate the course of this downward trend in each age group, including infancy, by extrapolating on the basis of previous European experience.

TABLE 49

Recent Crude Death Rates and Natural Increase Rates
for Selected Countries*

	Date	Death Rate	Rate of Natural Increase
Africa			
Congo (Leopoldville)	1955–58	20	23
Guinea	1955	40	22
Mali	1960	30	26
Mauritius ex. dep.	1960	11.3	28.3
Sudan	1956	19	33
Tunisia	1959	26	18.9
Uganda	1959	20	22
America			
Northern America			
Canada	1961	7.7	18.3
United States	1961	9.3	14.1
Middle America			
Costa Rica	1960	8.6	41.6
El Salvador	1961	11.4	38.2
Guatemala	1960	17.5	32.0
Jamaica	1960	8.9	33.8
Mexico	1960	11.4	33.6
Puerto Rico	1960	6.7	24.3
South America			
Argentina	1960	8.1	14.2
Brazil	1950	20.6	22.4
British Guiana	1960	9.5	33.5
Chile	1960	11.9	23.5
Asia			
Southwest Asia			
Cyprus	1960	5.7	20.1
Iran	1959	25	20
Israel	1961	5.7	16.3

Central South Asia

India	1958	19.2	19.9
Nepal	1954	30	15

Southeast Asia

Federation of Malaya	1960	9.5	31.4
Indonesia	1953–54	20	20
Singapore	1961	5.9	29.6
Thailand	1955	18.0	30.9

East Asia

China (mainland)	1957	11	23
Hong Kong	1961	5.9	28.4
Japan	1961	7.4	9.4

Europe

Northern and Western Europe

Belgium	1960	12.9	4.0
France	1961	11.0	7.4
Netherlands	1961	7.6	13.6
Sweden	1961	9.8	4.1
United Kingdom	1961	12	5.8

Central Europe

Austria	1961	12.0	6.5
Czechoslovakia	1961	9.2	6.6
Hungary	1961	9.6	4.4
Poland	1961	7.6	13.1
Switzerland	1961	9.3	8.8

Southern Europe

Bulgaria	1960	8.1	9.7
Italy	1961	9.4	9.4
Portugal	1961	10.7	12.9
Rumania	1961	8.7	8.8
Spain	1961	8.6	12.7
Yugoslavia	1961	9.0	13.6

Oceania

Australia	1961	8.5	14.3
New Zealand	1961	9.0	18.1

* UN, *1963 World Social Situation*, Chap. II, Part II, Table 4.

In Russia, the crude death rate was about 30 per 1,000 in 1913, and 20 in 1926. From 18 per 1,000 on the eve of the war, it dropped to 9 in the early 1950's. It now stands at 7. Russia developed her public health system much later than other countries, and hence the drop in her death rate and extension of life expectancy have come about much more quickly. There, however, economic development has kept pace with both alterations in the population picture. Population increase could be neutralized, as it were, by progressive stages of economic advance. In this connection, India might be compared with Russia earlier in the century. India has indeed launched a program of industrialization and has plans for large-scale agricultural reform and development, but we may question whether these measures are as yet sufficient to absorb fully the extremely rapid population increase. Specifically, we wonder whether the country is going to be able to create the conditions of life necessary to lower mortality among adults and old people at as fast a rate as has occurred elsewhere.

Practically all the underdeveloped countries are presently faced with this very problem, and it is impossible to predict the speed with which any particular country may be able to solve it.

In Ceylon, in most countries in and around the Caribbean—such as British Guiana and Puerto Rico—the death rates have all declined to the European level—i.e., around 10 per 1,000 or less—but for the reasons outlined above we cannot infer therefrom that there has been a corresponding rise in life expectancy in those countries to somewhere between 65 and 72 years. Nor, in the case of countries like Mexico and Malaysia, where the death rates are just a bit higher than in Europe (about 15 per 1,000), can we expect a recapitulation of the advances in life expectancy as was achieved in Europe and the U.S.S.R. in the past. The recent appearance of Kwashiorkor on the scene should suffice to inspire caution on this score. The success of medical progress in all these countries is indisputable, but economic advance is required to make it permanent.

NUTRITION AND MORTALITY

The really killing hunger is known as famine, an extreme lack of foodstuffs. From what is known of world history, we learn that famines have occurred again and again and innumerable millions have perished of hunger. It is certain that there have been many more famines than we have record of.[11] The earliest known famine occurred in the Nile valley around 4,000 B.C. Chinese annals, which run from 108 B.C. down to 1911, mention, in all, 1,828 famines—an average of 91 a century. In the 70 years just before A.D. 1,000, France had 48 famines. In 120 years of the eleventh and twelfth centuries, there were 33 famines, and in each of the next two centuries 10 instances of widespread want and scarcity. The fifteenth and sixteenth centuries had 13 each, the seventeenth 11, the eighteenth 16, and even the nineteenth had 10. The most terrible famines in the history of the world have occurred in India.

The numbers of human beings who have perished in the worst famines known stagger the imagination. In 1877, 9 million people are reported to have perished in China, and 5 million in southern India. In 1770, when some 168,000 are known to have died of hunger in Russia, Bohemia and Poland, and 120,000 died in France, no less than one-third of the total population perished in the single Indian state of Bengal.

It is estimated that half a million Russians died in the famine of 1600–02. Six years earlier, 100,000 Parisians died of hunger in a three-month period.

Famine, however, does not just afflict highly populated areas. Sparsely settled areas of Brazil, Iran, and Mongolia have also known it. And famine, strictly speaking, is not the worst of the mass-killers. Merely insufficient nutrition (as opposed to no food at all) produces conditions of physiological impoverishment which are responsible for millions of premature deaths. Men are progressively undermined by afflictions they have little or no resistance against.

Wherever and whenever nutrition is at the bare subsistence level, expectation of life at birth runs as low as 30 years. It rises gradually

176 HOW POPULATION DEVELOPS

to around 70 years where and when food becomes more abundant and the diet better balanced. The graph in TABLE 50 shows very clearly the correlation between life expectancy and the nutritional level.[12]

TABLE 50

Correlation between Nutritional Level and Male Life Expectancy in Some Countries

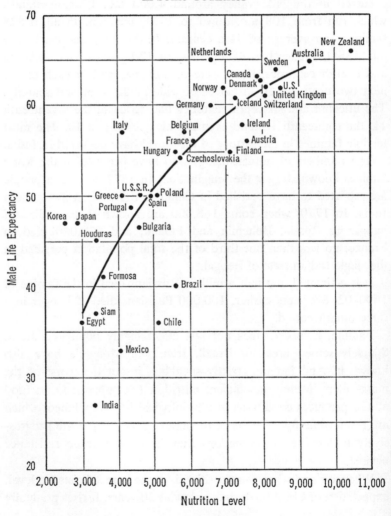

As the nutrition level improves, infant mortality drops from between 150 and 250 (or more) to less than 20 per 1,000. A child in rural India is ten times as likely to die in the first twelve months of life as is a child in New Zealand, and is at twenty times the risk of a baby in the Netherlands. Newsholme states flatly that "The rate of infantile mortality is regarded as a most reliable test of the sanitary condition of a district. . . ."[13] The inverse correlation to be observed between the average nutrition level and infant mortality certainly seems to bear out this view. Of course, it may be objected that malnutrition and undernourishment are not the sole factors in the public health situation. The number of doctors, for example, has an important bearing in the struggle against death. Nonetheless, so far as statistics go, they suggest that there is tighter correlation between nutrition and health than between the number of available doctors and health.[14]

TABLES 51, 52 lead us to make two sorts of observations. On the one hand, it is clear that the extreme nutritional levels of the three countries, Argentina, Uruguay, and Paraguay, are due to an exceptional consumption of meat—something like 200 pounds per person per year—and that this in no way bears upon infant mortality. On the other hand, in countries with a high rate of infant mortality, allowance must be made for the arbitrariness of statistical practice:

The statistical definition of infant mortality was drawn up in the Western world, and is limited to the death of children under the age of 1 year, out of all live births. . . . One of the consequences of this definition is that it conceals the mortality among infants who are nursed longer than one calendar year and who die as soon as nursing is discontinued.[15]

Actually, the "sensitive index" that Newsholme saw in infant mortality, and the importance of children's deaths at weaning, should together make us look more closely into the differences of life expectancy between birth and the age of five. In underdeveloped countries, it must be remembered, high mortality cuts a great

TABLE 51
Correlation between Infant Mortality (per 1,000 population) and the Nutritional Level in Certain Countries
(in vegetable calories, as of 1937–38)

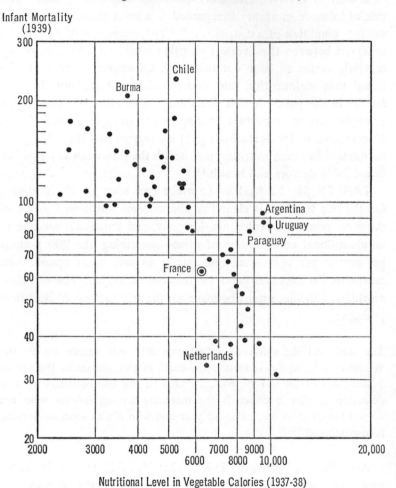

Nutritional Level in Vegetable Calories (1937-38)

TABLE 52

Correlation between Infant Mortality (per 1,000 population)
and Number of Inhabitants per Doctor

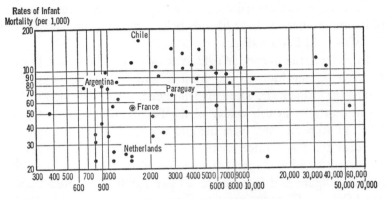

Number of Inhabitants per Doctor

swathe not only among infants but also among all children. Now, among all the diseases that afflict humanity, Kwashiorkor is undoubtedly—in Prof. R. Debré's words—"the gravest of all epidemics between the first and the fifth year." It is intimately related to the cessation of breast feeding and the consequent withdrawal of animal proteins from the child.

What we have so far learned about diseases of nutrition in children, and especially about Kwashiorkor since its existence was made known—a terrible affliction in the undernourished countries, from which perhaps as many as 8 out of 10 children suffer as soon as breast feeding ceases—throws light on other aspects of "the pathology of hunger," including its economic and social consequences. Those who survive Kwashiorkor are by no means winners in the race of "natural selection." On the contrary, they are weakened for the rest of their lives—which may be long, but are sure to be wretched. "There is just no provision for the nutritional transition," Professor Pales tells us, speaking of typical African patterns of life, "between breast feeding and the normal adolescent diet. Instead, there is a nutritional gulf which all do not manage to cross."

Recognition of the seriousness of the problem of supplying a more suitable diet for children after they have been weaned—and of its importance for later life—is behind many of the activities of UNICEF and FAO today.

In France, the Second World War helped to bring out the importance of nutrition in the Mother and Child Care Center at Tourcoing, which Dr. Dron had founded. On his death in 1930, infant mortality in this center of the French woolen industry had fallen to 80 per 1,000, from the 200 per 1,000 at the beginning of the century. The Center continued operations during World War II, though it had to suspend distribution of milk. By 1945 the infant mortality figure had mounted to 99 per 1,000 (compared with 94 per 1,000 for Lille, 98 per 1,000 for Roubaix, cities belonging to the same industrial complex). Once distribution of milk was resumed, the figure declined again to 54 per 1,000 between September 1, 1956 and November 1, 1947. However, among the 602 babies who received milk from the Center, mortality dropped to 8 per 1,000—which means that the other babies in Tourcoing accounted for 76 per 1,000 of the deaths, much the same as the figures for Lille and Roubaix in the same period. Milk alone thus reduces to one-tenth the chances of infant mortality in the first year of life, for the babies fortunate enough to get it.

Similarly, it has been by distribution of milk to babies that Strasbourg has managed to bring down its rate of infant mortality from the highest in France to the lowest.

And yet, however important infant mortality is in itself, and especially when recognition is made as well of deaths at the termination of the nursing period, more is involved than we have mentioned so far. When mothers suffer from a deficiency disease (even prior to the child's birth), the child may suffer its consequences for the rest of his life. Xerophthalmia is not unheard of, by any means, among newborn babies even in the Western countries. Rickets and bone fractures have been observed in the foetus. A. Giroud has written:

For anomalies to be produced, the deficiency diseases must be acute at the most crucial moments of embryological development. When this is the case, the results are irreversible: no vitamin or mineral supplements, no administration of fatty or amino acids, will be of the slightest avail. . . . Our studies and observations permit us to conclude that nutritional deficiency is of most serious consequence in the first phase of gestation, that is, in man the first three months in the womb.

We may note in passing that this is also the time when infectious diseases in the mother have the most serious consequence for her child's future. The sequelae of German measles, for example, are well known.

Later on, undernourishment, and still more, malnutrition—what Josué de Castro has so aptly termed "the specific hungers"—have serious consequences both for the mother and for her child because of the physical weakness they bring on. Jack Drummond wrote:

More than thirty years of research and experiment have convinced me that health is threatened every bit as much by a badly balanced or defective diet as it is by microbes, viruses, and the other agents of infection.

Human beings do not have equal chances in the face of death. This was brought out in 1920 by L. Hersh in a study of the different quarters of Paris, but it is also true of the various nations with respect to each other. To a great extent this form of inequality results from inequality in the face of hunger. What is true for space is true as well for time: far more than the gradual disappearance of famine, it has been the steady rise in nutritional levels that accounts, for example, for "the rise of life expectancy in Sweden from about 34 years in the mid-eighteenth century to 73 years in 1960."[16]

We may then, perhaps, conclude that undernourishment and

malnutrition are factors in mortality, especially in the youngest age group. This is the time when nutritional deficiencies are most serious for later life, too. Hunger cripples more people than it kills.

WAR AND DISEASE

Cannot much the same be said of war and disease? Some writers, including Malthus himself, have looked upon war and disease, along with famine, as "natural" regulators of population increase. It was not so long ago that Henri Bergson said, in much the same spirit, "Leave Venus to her own devices, and Mars will be loosed among you." More recently G. Bouthoul has claimed that war is the only alternative to large-scale demographic and economic "planning," as a practical remedy to the world's overpopulation.[17] Though war and disease can be engendered by hunger, so too can hunger and disease be brought on by war. Surely nobody today needs to be persuaded on this score. The Three Horsemen of the Apocalypse work hand in hand at their common goal of bringing about universal destruction.

But how can anyone think of any of their efforts as a *solution?* Today wars wound and cripple far more people than they kill, and, by the deaths they cause, destroy far more natural resources than they spare. It is possible, even probable, that in former times war did not always have these consequences—this would especially seem to have been the case with tribal wars. And yet, as we have seen, the human race learned at a fairly early date to think of fellow men as sources of wealth to exploit, rather than as competitors, once some of them had been subjected to the power of others.

In his famous pamphlet of 1729, *A Modest Proposal for Preventing the children of Poor People in Ireland from being a burden to their Parents or Country, and for Making them Beneficial to the Public,* Jonathan Swift suggested that the children of the poor should be butchered and sold for food. He thus carried to its most extreme logical consequence, the kind of thinking that regards high mortality among the lower classes—and especially a high rate of infant mortality—as some kind of "salvation" (the term is W. Vogt's), an indispensable safeguard to the standard of living of the wealthy. Swift exposed with ferocious sardonicism the underlying hypocrisy of this attitude:

I grant this food will be somewhat dear, and therefore very proper for landlords, who, as they have already devoured most of the parents, seem to have the best title to the children.

The author of *Gulliver's Travels* might almost have been speaking for the prisoner of war whose life is spared so as to sell him into slavery, or the man in an underdeveloped country today whose right to found a family is questioned:

I desire those politicians who dislike my overture, and may perhaps be so bold as to attempt an answer, that they will first ask the parents of these mortals, whether they would not at this day think it a great happiness to have been sold for food at a year old in the manner I prescribe, and thereby have avoided such a perpetual scene of misfortunes as they have since gone through by the oppression of landlords, the impossibility of paying rent without money or trade, the want of common sustenance, with neither house nor clothes to cover them from the inclemencies of the weather, and the most inevitable prospect of entailing the like or greater miseries upon their breed for ever.

No more than war does disease—to the extent it, too, cripples more than it kills—supply any sort of solution to the problem of an alleged "overpopulation." We have seen this in the case of Kwashiorkor. Consequently, to claim that the struggle against infectious diseases has worsened the demographic situation is to jump to an overhasty conclusion. Measures taken against plague and cholera do, indeed, keep alive human beings who would otherwise die. But medical progress does not just keep people from dying, it preserves the health and productivity of men who would not otherwise (however long their lives) be able to support themselves and their families, not even to feed them.

It is true that the population of northern Iran has doubled since malaria was stamped out, but it has also quadrupled food production there. This is a case where the correlation of population with the means of subsistence has been improved. Here we are merely noting the fact, not attempting to draw conclusions from it. Especially can we not attempt anything of the kind until we have looked into the matter of how the make-up of a population affects its production of foodstuffs.

NATALITY: WHAT ARE THE FACTS?

As we saw in the first of our preliminary chapters, world population doubled twice between 1650 and 1950, from 545 million to 1,175 million and then to 2,475 million. However, while the first doubling required two centuries—from 1650 to 1850—one century sufficed for the second. There is, then, every likelihood that it will have doubled again before the year 2,000—that is, in less than 50 years.

So remarkable a historical development, characterized by constant acceleration, is primarily accounted for by the reduction in mortality. By and large, birth rates lag behind the declining death rates. It is as though populations tried implicitly to find a balance between the two. Thus, the cause for the rapid population growth is to be found in the historical gap or differential between the two rates.

In this section of the chapter, we shall look into what has been happening to the birth rates in the various parts of the world, and we shall try to discern fundamental trends with the aid of a few figures. The remaining two sections will be devoted to systematic studies, respectively, of the biological factors in natality and of the social and cultural factors which bear upon fertility and the birth rate.

The crude birth rate relates the number of recorded births to the total population figure. It is, of course, possible to arrive at a theoretical maximum, assuming no checks on fertility and no deaths before the age of 50 on the part of the female population. More often we are content to note that the highest birth rates so far recorded in large populations scarcely exceed 55 per 1,000. Rarely have these figures been exceeded, and we may consider them as reflecting natural fertility. Such extremely high fertility prevailed in Quebec, Russia, and the United States until the mid-nineteenth century, and is now found in West Africa and Central America. No Asian country of appreciable area or population tops a birth rate of 55. If we consider 35 or more births per 1,000 as high fertility, the most common frequencies within this band lie between 40 and 50.

The lowest birth rates in large populations have rarely fallen below 10 persistently, even in the depths of war or depression. Certain European countries come close to this—Sweden, for example. Most of the countries of western Europe have birth rates lower than 20 per 1,000.

It can be seen, then, that a country whose birth rate approaches 50 per 1,000 has a birth rate from four to five times that of a country where the figure is around 10 per 1,000. As we draw up the tables for groups of countries, or by continents, we find that the actual rates run from two to three times the lowest rates.

By Climatic Zones. When we divide the world into two climatic zones—tropical and temperate—we find that the countries with the highest birth rates fall within the tropical zone without exception. Here birth rates range between 30 and 55 per 1,000. Indeed, most tropical countries have birth rates between 40 and 55. China, Korea, Nepal, and Taiwan, all countries of high birth rate, extend into the temperate zone.

As for the temperate zone, here birth rates range from average (over broad continental areas like North America where the rate is between 20 and 30 per 1,000), to countries of the lowest birth rates, in western Europe and Japan.[18]

While this tie-in with features of the natural environment is noteworthy, its importance should not be exaggerated. The disparity is not just one of climate, but also of economic development and type of civilization.

Countries where birth is surrounded by the most elaborate care for mother and child, and where expectation of life at birth is longest, are also countries where twice as few children are born as in countries where birth is a perilous adventure and chances of survival are slim.[19]

The countries with the lowest birth rates are the richest and most highly industrialized countries, with the highest levels of educational attainment, where contraception and the regulation of births have gradually been extended to every stratum of the population. They are the countries in which the aging of the population has gone farthest.

By Continents—Europe. In most of the underdeveloped countries today, birth rates are higher than they have been in western Europe since comprehensive vital statistics were first collected— that is, in the eighteenth century, if not before. The generally lower fertility there can be accounted for only in terms of a basic cultural fact: "Western man, who is far less closely integrated within a 'family' thought of in the broadest sense, has far more than other men the responsibility for his children's well-being, both material and spiritual."[20] There is supplementary evidence for this cultural fact in the newer countries colonized by European immigrants:* North America, Australia, and New Zealand. In those countries, birth rates of about 25 per 1,000 are certainly higher than those of Europe, but they are much lower than those of the non-European peoples.

A partial explanation for the fact that the European birth rate was lower at the beginning of the industrial revolution than it is in

---

* The countries which are only today at the beginning of their "demographic revolution" have not as yet enjoyed, as Europe has, this advantage of mass emigration to other continents.

non-industrialized countries today, may be found in the fact that Europe was to some extent already urbanized. In any case, the rural folk of western Europe were wont to delay marriage when a couple could not set up house on their own. Consequently, large proportions of the population *never* married. Similarly, when harvests were bad, nuptiality and natality fell.

Between 1800 and 1880 in western Europe, two Catholic countries led all the rest in lowering birth rates. These were France and Ireland, and they launched the trend in the earliest years of the nineteenth century.

It was only toward 1870 and 1880 that the other countries of western Europe, such as England, Belgium, and Germany, began to show a markedly declining birth rate. The decline in mortality had begun earlier, but was as yet very gradual. In this part of the world, the expectation of life at birth went from 40 years in 1840 to 44 years in 1880.[21]

It was at the beginning of the twentieth century that the greatest spread was recorded between births and deaths, about 10 per 1,000 of the population.

The lowest birth rates in western Europe were reached between 1930 and 1940. From France to the Scandinavian countries during this period, rates ranged from 10 to 17 per 1,000. Central and southern Europe continued to record rates of slightly over 20 per 1,000. Among these were Spain, Italy (especially in the southern provinces), Yugoslavia, Rumania, and Poland. These may be thought of as countries on the periphery of the region where the trend to lower birth rates was most marked. A few of these peripheral countries, such as Bulgaria, Czechoslovakia and Hungary, also saw their birth rates drop below 20 per 1,000.

In confirmation of the above, TABLE 53 traces how the birth rates have changed over the past eighty or ninety years in a number of western European countries.[22]

Now, it would be a great mistake to interpret this trend to fewer and fewer births as simply the result of the widespread availability of contraceptive devices. As we shall demonstrate in a later section,

TABLE 53
Changing Birth Rates, 1871–1960

Country	1871–1880	1881–1900	1900	1913	1930	1939	1947	1955	1960
Western Europe	34	32	29	26	21	19	21	18	19
France	25	24	21	19	18	15	21	19	18
Germany	39	37	36	28	18	20	17	16	17
Ireland	27	23	22	23	20	19	23	21	21
Italy	37	38	33	32	27	24	22	18	18
Portugal	—	33	31	33	30	26	25	24	24
Spain	38	36	33	31	28	17	22	21	22
U.S.S.R.	—	—	—	47.0	—	31.3	—	26	24

use of contraceptives or "family planning" presupposes a "contraceptive mentality," the appearance of which in history is tied in with a great many varied conditions and causes.

Since World War II, birth rates in a number of countries have picked up again. Although this was at first attributed to temporary factors such as the war itself, today it seems certain that other more lasting factors are at work. Not all countries exhibit this reversal of trend, but the major countries of western Europe do. Those on the periphery, meanwhile, are continuing the pre-war trend, even deliberately encouraging it as in the case of Yugoslavia. In Spain and Portugal, where no political support or encouragement is given, birth rates have gradually continued to drop and now stand near 20 per 1,000.

The Other Continents. In the absence of complete and accurate statistics, we cannot trace actual historical developments very far back, though we may in general say that birth rates have always been very high. Where the drop in mortality has been sudden and marked, there has scarcely been time for any decline in natality to make itself felt.

As we have already seen, birth rates and death rates alike, in the underdeveloped countries, are for the most part higher than they were in Europe or North America at the start of the industrial revolution. And not only are they higher "to begin with," as it were, birth rates in some of these underdeveloped countries have increased slightly. The same medical advances which have reduced mortality have also made childbirth safer, and the results in the underdeveloped countries show up most clearly in the birth rate. The spread between births and deaths thus becomes rapidly and progressively wider, with the drop in the latter coinciding historically with an increase in the former. Japan, whose contraceptive policies are well known, is an exception.

In any case, the world birth rate very definitely went up in the period 1937–1950. According to UN estimates, it ranged between 34 per 1,000 and 38 per 1,000 in 1937. TABLE 54 breaks this down for the principal geographical regions as of that date, together with figures showing total population.[23]

By 1950, the world birth rate was believed to have reached 39 per 1,000, and there has been a decline since to 36 per 1,000 as

TABLE 54

Estimated World Population and Birth Rate, 1937

	Estimated Population (in millions)	Estimated Birth Rate (per 1,000)
Africa	169	40–45
America (total)	266	—
Canada and U.S.	140	17
Latin America	126	40–45
Asia (total)*	1,141	—
Near East	66	40–45
South Asia	378	40–45
Japan	71	28
Remainder of Far East	626	40–45
Europe (total)	560	40–45
North, Central, Western Europe	195	17
South Europe	83	23
Eastern Europe†	282	30–34
Oceania	11	20
World Total	2,147	34–38

* Not including Asian U.S.S.R.
† Including Asian U.S.S.R.

of 1957–60.[24] The 1950 increase is attributed to the post-war "baby boom" in the advanced countries and to better records revealing higher birth rates in underdeveloped countries than previously estimated.

Recorded birth rates in the *Demographic Yearbook 1962*, together with the UN estimates for 1975, allow us to expect further decline. At the same time, however, this decline in future fertility will remain much slighter than the current decline in mortality and much smaller than the estimates of future mortality allow us to expect. World population will thus continue to increase, and at a rate some observers have qualified as "explosive."

In any case, as TABLE 55 indicates, in 1950 the world areas with birth rates higher than 30 per 1,000 accounted for about 1,700 million of the world's population, whereas the areas with birth rates between 20 and 30 per 1,000 accounted for only 600 million.[25]

TABLE 55

Estimated World Population Growth and Birth Rates,
1950–1975

	1950		*1975*	
	Total Population (millions)	*Birth Rate (per 1,000)*	*Total Population (millions)*	*Birth Rate (per 1,000)*
Africa	199	47	303	44
North America	219	22	240	18
South America	112	40	303	32
Asia	1,380	46	2,110	35
Europe	393 }574	20	— }751	15
U.S.S.R.	181	25	—	19
Oceania	13	26	21	24
World	2,500	39	3,828	30

Thus, a slight decline in birth rates is anticipated by 1975, but the world areas with birth rates higher than 30 per 1,000 will account for more than 2.7 billion of the world population, while those with birth rates lower than 30 per 1,000 will not have reached one billion. This demographic shift in the scales will bear down heaviest on the areas least well equipped to meet the economic, social, and cultural challenge.

It seems very likely, if the world remains at peace, and if present aid to underdeveloped countries is maintained or even increased many times over, that we shall be faced with the following population picture:

1) A more rapid drop in mortality, such as went on in Europe over the period 1850–1950, with consequent increase in life expectancy.

2) A more or less speedy reciprocal influence between births and deaths, with possibly a more abrupt decline in the birth rate than occurred in Europe. This is especially likely if a rapid falling off in infant mortality has the effect (as we know it has had) of discouraging childbearing.

3) However, the spread or discrepancy between deaths and births may continue for some time, mainly among marginal groups who resist any decline in the birth rate, while at the same time urging on continuing decline in the death rate. The situation will be analogous to what we find when we contrast northern Europe and southern Europe over the last one hundred years.

It is our opinion that both when it comes to defining the problem and when it comes to drawing up forecasts for the future, greater allowance should be made for the various peoples' capacity for going their own ways. Certainly, European developments are full of instances of national deviations from the over-all pattern at any given moment. France and Ireland are cases in point, and so, to a less spectacular degree, have been recent developments in Spain, Portugal, Italy, and the Netherlands, where the birth rate has dropped far below 30 per 1,000. Also, there is the matter of the higher birth rates in the European-settled regions outside Europe. Japan proves an exception to the Asian norm, and Argentina and Uruguay to the general Latin American trends.

We may note with surprise how brief, if not altogether superficial, have been the effects of populationist policies sponsored by modern governments. Under Hitler, Germany's fertility rose slightly until the Second World War, but there is no sign that Mussolini or Stalin were able to raise fertility in Italy or the U.S.S.R. Perhaps we shall also have occasion to be surprised by the results actually achieved by governmental policies for checking population growth if people do remain free to act as they will in these matters. In his *Traité de démographie,* Landry gave more importance to this imponderable factor than is usually done in publications of the type. It might be a good thing if the press and molders of public opinion generally called attention to it more frequently than they do.

BIOLOGICAL CAUSES OF
THE FALLING BIRTH RATE

As is well known, natality began to decline first in the most advanced countries of the world and among the upper classes of those countries. Physiologists have sought a physiological explanation for the phenomenon, moralists and sociologists a moral or sociological explanation—in the last-named category, Landry's "demographic revolution" has had the widest currency.

Nutrition. Since it is undeniable that nutrition plays a part in reproductive processes, it has occurred to some to try to simplify the problem by viewing reproduction as a function of food consumption: fertility (or potency) would rise or fall with the "alimentary level."

Actually, the opposite seems to be the case, when we compare birth rates and consumption measured in vegetable (i.e., primary or original) calories. We note that the birth rate dips as we approach the 6,000 calory mark (per capita and per diem), and then drops off from there to a negligible point as consumption increases. This would be the point where, basic caloric needs satisfied, luxury products (especially animal products) replace the cheaper foodstuffs (for the most part of vegetable origin). Observations of this kind have given rise to two theories as to how food consumption becomes a check upon the birth rate. The first of these, presented in the mid-nineteenth century by Fourier in France and by Doubleday in England, directly links abundance of food with a falling birth rate. Others have pointed to excessive weight (in men or animals) as a check upon the reproductive faculty.

It was part of Fourier's plans for his Phalanstery that its members should be overfed, to check population growth. Folk wisdom has always held that "a fighting cock is never fat." Livestock breeders observed long since that certain animals become sterile when they have been fattened up, and that when their consumption is curtailed for a certain time, fertility returns. However, as Josué de Castro has remarked, this is an empirical finding which has had little importance in scientific circles. The opposite observation is just as true: a temporarily sterile animal tends to put on weight. In any case, raisers of livestock often castrate the animals they want to fatten for market.

We need not press the point that analogous observations hold true for the human species. It was among the best-fed classes that the birth rate first began to decline in the nineteenth century, at a time when the richer foodstuffs were not as yet so widely available as they are today, and when the bulk of the population still followed a simple diet. It seems only natural to turn to this sort of explanation, but we must admit that the situation described corresponds to the first part of the curve on the graph given above. Births decline less rapidly than deaths as food consumption increases.

Animal Protein. Such an explanation will not do in the mid-twentieth century, and Josué de Castro has suggested another. It may seem in flat contradiction with the foregoing, but then there may be no necessary connection between them at all. In biological investigation it is often necessary to recognize the side-by-side existence of seemingly contradictory facts.

According to de Castro, it is the quantity of animal protein in the diet that acts as a check on fertility. This view would be in agreement with the graph shown above, and in particular would throw light on the second part of the curve. In de Castro's view, his hypothesis deserves to be recognized as a biological law.

In 1925–28, J. R. Slonaker published in *The American Journal of Physiology* a series of sensational experiments on groups of rats brought up for six generations on diets of different protein content. Sterility increased as soon as protein made up more than 18 per cent of the total calory count, the fertility period in the females was delayed, and there were fewer and smaller litters.

TABLE 56
Relation between Protein Percentage in Diet and Fertility in Rats

Rations with Protein Percentage of	Sterility Males	Sterility Females	Average Number of Young per Rat
10	5%	6%	23.3
18	22%	23%	17.4
22	40%	38%	13.8

It can only be concluded that, despite greater resistance on the part of the young and a higher percentage of survivors (F. C. Russel and I. Leitch, 1948), the reproductive capacity is lowered as the diet is made richer in protein.

Experiments conducted at the University of Chicago (*American Journal of Physiology,* 1950) by Anton Carlson and Frederick Hoelzel reported highest sterility (76 per cent for males, 75 per cent for females) among rats given a rich and copious diet, lowest sterility (19 per cent for males, 27 per cent for females) among rats given a poor, scanty diet. M. A. Rudzinska's experiments on a protozoan at New York University (*Science,* 1951) and those on egg-laying hens by O. B. Kent tend to show that the same relation obtains throughout the animal kingdom.

But on the Other Hand. Does the human race constitute an exception to the law? It would scarcely seem so. L. Henry's studies in this connection (INED, 1956–58) are not enough to prove the contrary, though they do justify pointing out that more than a biological law is at stake and that it cannot by itself explain the phenomenon of depopulation in populations that are well nourished.

Without taking count of mortality (of one or the other marriage partners) or of age at marriage, Henry calculates the total fertility rate and estimates the number of children a couple would have had from age 20, in various population groups that (so far as is known) had no recourse to contraceptive practices. His results are as follows:

Hutterites	Marriages, 1921–30	10.9
	Marriages before 1921	9.8
Canada (marriages 1700–29)		10.8
Geneva Middle Class		
	Men born 1600–49	9.4
	Men born before 1600	7.5
Crulai (a parish in Normandy)		
	Marriages, 1674–1742	8.2
Iranian Villages (1940–50)		7.5

"Are we to conclude from this that conditions of physiological deficiency bring about a reduction in fertility?" The question is Alfred Sauvy's, and his answer is that this is probable, adding:

However, other factors are involved: sexual habits, length of nursing period, in-breeding and genetic factors, climate, way of life, etc. Lengthy, patient research would be necessary to discriminate in these matters.

Why, then, in view of the fact that Henry drops food consumption from his list of six important factors, does Sauvy conclude that his figures, ". . . Not only contradict J. de Castro's hypothesis, but also the widespread superstition to the effect that fertility declines with the passing of time and the development of civilization"?

These few figures are, indeed, hard to compare, and too many other factors enter in for any very sweeping conclusion to be drawn. It is doubtful that they have more than a monographic value. Not that this is negligible: it is merely that no theory that does not account for all the facts can be expected to be of wider relevance. So long as a single feature fails to conform to our hypotheses, fuller research is called for.

In particular, we know too little of the food habits of various groups to rule out the applicability of de Castro's hypothesis, and for two cases, at least—the Hutterites of North America and the Iranian peasants—research on this score ought to be feasible.

Moreover, de Castro himself has a number of recent cases to cite in support of his theory, and they too should be taken into consideration. There is the matter of the sheer drop in the Puerto Rican birth rate from 1937 on. It had been over 40 per 1,000 since the beginning of this century, but it had dropped to 35 per 1,000 in 1954 and to the low 30's in subsequent years. Was it, as has been claimed, a triumph for Neo-Malthusian propaganda, or is it rather to be explained as de Castro suggested (in 1956) as

in great part due to the fact that since Puerto Rico's new political orientation in 1947, the traditional diet of the region, always one of the world's most nutritionally deficient and uncertain, has been undergoing modifications.

When the first world survey of food consumption was made, Puerto Rico had an average per person per day consumption of 2,219 calories, 366 of these of animal origin. In terms of vegetable (primary or original) calories, the total is 4,415. Discussion is far from closed on this score, but de Castro claims:

The most dramatic single confirmation as to the decisive influence of diet upon fertility is to be found in the report (published by the Smithsonian Institute, Washington, D.C., 1955) of researches conducted by Prof. MacGinitie of the California Institute of Technology.

MacGinitie carried out his researches at the U.S. Naval Arctic Research Laboratory at Point Barrow, Alaska. They brought out the extremely significant fact that the Eskimos in this part of the world, whose traditional diet (wholly of animal origin) has these past few years been modified by admixtures of vegetable origin, have practically tripled their fertility.

Undoubtedly, such findings give weight to the thesis de Castro drew up in 1952 on the basis of Lynn Smith's statistics in *Population Analysis* (1948) and the FAO information on world protein consumption. (See TABLE 57.)

TABLE 57
Birth Rates and Protein Consumption per Head

	Birth Rates (per 1,000)	Daily Animal Protein Consumption (grams)
Formosa	45.6	4.7
Malaysia	39.7	7.5
India	33.0	8.7
Japan	27.0	9.7
Yugoslavia	25.9	11.2
Greece	23.5	15.2
Italy	23.4	15.2
Bulgaria	22.2	16.8
Germany	30.0	37.3
Ireland	19.1	46.7
Denmark	18.1	56.1
Australia	18.0	59.9
United States	17.9	61.4
Sweden	15.0	62.6

Other Factors. There may well be other factors involved. Within the animal proteins, it is possible that certain amino acids play a special role in the phenomena we are dealing with. Also, to change from a cereal diet rich in vitamin E to a supposedly "richer" diet without that vitamin, could lead to lessened fertility. Cereals can be deprived of the vitamin by certain processes used in the preparation of cereal products. There is the matter of the "ordinary" honey in the cells that hatch the drones and the "royal jelly" in the cells that hatch queen bees. Nothing in the female larvae produces the difference: switch them around, and the bee which is hatched will be a drone or a queen depending on the nourishment it has had.

Food consumption thus has unquestionably some influence over procreative capacity, and it may produce very different results. We know too little about just how diet has such contradictory effects to be able to opt for one theory or another. A number of lines of research, however, are clearly indicated and ought to be followed up.

What Is It Safe to Say? Widespread evidence to the effect that the most ill-nourished peoples are by and large the most prolific permits us to go along with Webster Johnson and Raleigh Barlowe:

A disturbing fact is that in those parts of the world where the population increase has been most rapid, the people have a diet of only around 2,000 calories per day. It also seems that an inadequate diet is associated with the fecundity of man.[26]

The observation accords with what we have already mentioned, the "great biological law" that Thomas Doubleday expressed in the following terms:

The GREAT GENERAL LAW then, which, as it seems, really regulates the increase or decrease both of vegetable and of animal life, is this, that whenever a *species* or *genus* is endangered, a corresponding effort is invariably made by nature for its preservation and continuance, by an increase of fecundity or fertility; and that this especially takes place whenever such danger arises from a diminution of proper nourishment or food, so that consequently the state of depletion, or the deplethoric state, is favorable to fertility; and on the other hand, the plethoric state, or state of repletion, is unfavorable to fertility, in the ratio or intensity of each state, and this probably throughout nature universally, in the vegetable as well as in the animal world; further, that as applied to mankind this law produces the following consequences, and acts thus:

There is in all societies a constant increase going on amongst that portion of it which is the worst supplied with food; in short, amongst the poorest.

Amongst those in the state of affluence, and well supplied with food and luxuries, a constant decrease goes on.[27]

A Possibly Fruitful Distinction. Before examining the studies that may throw light on processes still poorly understood, we should like to advance a supplementary hypothesis inspired by analogies from the development of present-day knowledge concerning blood pressure, pulse, and respiration (studies by Heymans and Gand), and also by analogies from certain things which have long been known about the physiology of starvation. We have to distinguish between hunger and appetite, and to recall that anorexia (lack of appetite) is one of the symptoms of extreme hunger. Where reproduction is concerned, reproductive *capacity* is not necessarily involved. Especially where the male sex is concerned, fertility seems to be more immediately linked with strength of sexual appetite than with that of the reproductive faculty.

Teitelbaum's and Grant's experiments at the Pavlov Laboratory of Johns Hopkins University (*Science,* 1956) scarcely seem to us to lend support to de Castro's thesis. The number of spermatozoa per cubic centimeter of sperm may well vary without affecting fertility to any important extent. It is well known that there are always many more male cells than are required to assure fertility. More to the point would be studies of the analogous phenomena in females, or studies of how differences in food consumption affect sexual reflexes.

It seems quite possible that an individual's reproductive faculty (whether male or female) is not affected by a state of somatic well-being, but that desires may be rendered less urgent then, the individual's reflexes being controlled at the level of the nerve-centers and never reaching consciousness. The contrary might occur in a state of somatic distress, even in an individual whose reproductive faculty is weaker. On this hypothesis, what Hesnard called a state of "serene continence" should be possible for a perfectly healthy person, so long as no toxins disturb his reflexes and his will does not dictate use of his procreative faculty.

And so we are bound to acknowledge that "the plethoric state" can conduce to great fertility or can check it, that deficiencies of diet no less than dietary sufficiency can act as a check on fertility—in both cases in seemingly contradictory ways. It is not unusual in biological studies, when we carry them far enough, to find that the phenomena are more rather than less complex than they seemed at first, even to some extent "ambivalent" in character. And when our findings are such, we dare not rule out the phenomena simply because we do not yet understand them fully.

To Sum Up. We must attempt some evaluation of the scattered researches so far undertaken in this field. May we not state it as a principle, that no form of control that arises from mutilation of the human person—even were the mutilation self-willed—can be countenanced, or, to be more precise, is to be employed save to avoid a greater evil? Hippocrates' *primum non nocere* is at one with Christian respect for the integrity of the human person. Does this mean doctors are never to make use of poisons? Surely not, though there are doctors who carry their respect for the letter of the Hippocratic oath this far. In no case, however, can the sick person or those around him—let alone any external agency—take responsibility for so dangerous a procedure. The individual who would make use of any means to alter the integrity of his own person—a fortiori the integrity of his fellow man—without the concurrence of "the physician of souls," would be presumptuous indeed.

On the other hand, whatever serves to enhance physical and moral health and thereby to bring about a more serene continence —that is, to limit fertility more immediately—ought, at first glimpse, to be considered a sound use of natural laws.

De Castro's theory proposes a way of checking female fertility through a diet rich in animal protein. We may compare this with the procedures involved in the search for "the sterilizing pill." Both methods are actually based upon a hormone-theory of fertility. De Castro writes:

Biologically, fertility depends on the functioning of organs whose action is regulated, in large part, by hormones, which are the secretions of certain ductless glands. Fecundation in women is closely related to the functioning of the ovaries, to the production of their hormones, particularly the estrogens, and to the quantity of these substances present in the blood and internal organs.

It is known that there is a direct connection between the functioning of the liver and the ovaries, the role of the liver being to inactivate the excess estrogens which the ovaries throw into the blood stream. Fatty degeneration of the liver and the tendency to cirrhosis are, as we have previously seen, among the characteristic results of protein deficiency, and are very common in the Far East and in certain tropical areas of other continents. When degeneration of the liver occurs it begins to operate less efficiently, and is less effective at its job of inactivating excess estrogens. The result is a marked increase in the woman's reproductive capacity.[28]

A pharmacological procedure has been invented to prevent formation of the estrogens, a sort of "sterilization" through the use of male hormones. The consequences to mental and physical health are highly suspect. The processes involved are more obscure than surgical sterilization, though its advocates claim that they can control the effects. All the same, a true mutilation is involved.

On the other hand, de Castro's suggestion scarcely seems open to objection: the indirect consequence to fertility through diet does not interfere (according to de Castro) with the normal working of the liver and the carrying out of its internal functions. The health of the organism would not be affected. Should science come up with a hypothetical substance whose only effect was to increase the capacity of the liver to inactivate the estrogens, without improving the other functions of the organ or the general health, then the moralist would have to face a problem that goes far beyond biological questions.

Yet, sufficient unto the day the evil thereof. We have touched on the ethical aspect of the problem to bring out better its biological aspects. That was the sole object of this chapter.

SOCIAL AND CULTURAL INFLUENCES ON FERTILITY AND BIRTH

The slower pace of population increase in Europe and North America is corollary to the fact that the spread or discrepancy between births and deaths never went beyond certain limits. In the older, richer countries, decline in the birth rate ran relatively parallel to decline in the death rate, after a lag of a few decades. In any case, fertility declined before mortality in France and the

United States. Moreover, the developments proceeded gradually, for the most part. In the countries which are just setting out on their modern development, the falling off in mortality is being accomplished at a very rapid rate. With very few exceptions, there has as yet been no corresponding falling off in natality.

Medical progress, the introduction of public health programs, cheaper methods of treating disease, all came about over a relatively short period to effect a sharp reduction of deaths in the underdeveloped countries. Moreover, the improved social order that conducted campaigns against epidemic disease also reduced deaths from famine and tribal warfare.

Now, all these factors which have gone to produce so notable a lowering of mortality, operate more or less independently of the particular environment where they are introduced. Other features of social and cultural advance, however—urbanization, industrialization, the raising of living standards—take a good deal longer to be achieved. And these are the factors which lead to a lowering of the birth rate.

Thus, if we are to account for the phenomena of population change, for the shifting birth and death figures over any period of time in a country's or a continent's history, we have to take account of social and cultural developments, as well as medical and biological developments.

The Importance of Sociology. The four principal factors in population change, within a single country or a continent, are natality, mortality, immigration, and emigration, the last two being of secondary importance. All four are determined by developments in the spheres of medicine and biology, psychology, economics, sociology, and culture.

Although many demographers, sociologists, and anthropologists have been aware that socio-cultural factors play an important role in population matters, few systematic studies have been made.[29] In particular, too little attention has been paid to how the various social groups within a population change within themselves and with relation to each other, and to how the value-structures of all or part of the population are affected. In other words, population growth and change may be analyzed in terms of a particular group of changing sub-groups with reference to the values, both old and new, that inspire them and the individuals who compose them.[30] However, such studies as have been undertaken along these lines remain limited, and it is scarcely possible to say that there as yet exists a sociological theory adequate to the study of demographic developments. If such a theory is to be worked out, it must be able to show how fundamental alterations in social conditions and social relations derive from, or lead to, parallel alterations in norms and value systems—and how these two forms of social change combine to influence the four principal factors in population growth and decline: births, deaths, immigration, emigration.

Though the study of socio-cultural causes is today not very far advanced, there is every reason to hope that progress will be made. In the not too distant future, causes of this type may turn out to be the key elements of population development in the various parts of the world. This is apparent to all who grant that the final explanation for the diversity of population development is to be sought in the types and conceptions of life that characterize the various societies and the various groups that make up each of them.

At the same time, socio-cultural explanations cannot take account of only one or two causal factors. We have already in this study noticed the disadvantages of overrigid, absolute theories or "laws" of population development. In searching for a more realistic explanation, we would do well to rely on theories that allow for a great many more variables, at once interdependent and interacting.

Biological and Sociological Factors in Natality. When we compare the birth rates and fertility rates of one part of the world with those of other parts, we find important differences. In some places they are three times what they are in other places, a difference that corresponds more or less to the degree of the region's development. Interregional differences between birth rates are far greater than differences between death rates.

When we go farther, and examine the historical background of the present situation, we find that for a very long time now the birth rates have been declining in all the richest countries, whereas in the poorer countries (apart from such exceptions as Japan, where contraception, abortion, and sterilization have been encouraged) the birth rates have remained relatively high. Of the former countries, it can be said that the birth rate has reached and passed its "low point of the century," and that the future trend will be upwards. Certainly that is the case in most of the European countries, in the United States, and in other countries of European settlement, where increases have indeed already occurred. Paradoxically, this reversal of trend has been most notable in highly urbanized areas.[31] At the same time, however, it scarcely seems likely that the birth rates in these countries will ever regain the high levels which prevailed until the late nineteenth century.

Biological Fertility. Biologically, the peoples of the world are not, perhaps, less fertile than they used to be, but more so. However, changes in birth rates are far from being influenced solely by biological factors. In accounting for natality, they rather tend to take on secondary importance, despite the efforts of various authors to show that fertility and fecundity tend to decline as the standard of living rises. In a previous part of this chapter, we discussed the arguments for reducing fertility by physiological means. Moreover, there are many studies of reproductive capacity that show how improvements in food consumption, public health, and medical care increase that capacity.

What needs to be emphasized is that the medical improvements which have so effectively reduced mortality even in environments where social and economic conditions are unfavorable, also have effects which are life-enhancing with respect to natality and reproductive capacity. Sterility due solely to biological causes can very often today be overcome. Some miscarriages can be avoided, and the number of stillbirths and deaths in childbirth can be reduced.

There are other factors which operate more indirectly upon fertility and fecundity: for example, giving up the habit of breast feeding in certain countries, the decline of polygamy in others.

Obviously, medical techniques can also be employed—and in some countries are employed—to check fertility through sterilization, abortion, and contraception. However, to the degree that such practices are prohibited or condemned—or simply are not made use of—especially under the influence of socio-cultural factors, it is not possible to say that the reproductive capacity of the human race is declining from the strictly physiological point of view.

Hence we may claim that the lessened fertility of the wealthier countries does not arise from any increase in sterility. Quite to the contrary: sterility due to biological causes is on the decrease, and what keeps the birth rates between 15 and 25 per 1,000 is the practice of birth control or "planned fertility."*

In the countries of the West, including the so-called Catholic countries of Europe, some sort of limitation or control of births is a fact in the overwhelming majority of families. We know this is so because the average number of children—also, the most frequently found number of children per family—is between two and three.

In many minds, the notion of any restriction or regulation of births is linked with that of sexual perversity. And of course it is true that it is not most often the proper and decent means of checking births that are employed. However, the fact that means of checking births are so widely employed today—proper and decent ones along with others—arises, in the first place, out of the new biological conditions under which life is transmitted, and secondly, out of new social conditions characteristic of our industrialized, mechanized, urban civilization.

It is so much easier to transmit life than it ever was before. For some decades now, for the purpose of assuring a family's continuation over generations with approximately the same number of individuals, a progressively smaller level of natality has sufficed. This has been due to the steady decline in mortality. In particular, there has been a spectacular drop in infant mortality and in deaths of children generally. Thanks to medical progress, it is no longer necessary to bring 6 and 8 children into the world to see 3 grow up.

* So-called "family planning" may be a true "planning," or it may simply be a going-along with current social practices.

Besides, fewer women die in childbirth and fewer marriages are childless for reasons of physiological sterility. A family can survive generation by generation with far fewer births than ever before.

Parents today may be no less eager to pass on the gift of life, no less generous or affectionate than their ancestors, and no less desirous of continuing the family line, and yet wish to spare themselves the expense of having as many children.[32] Even in the traditionally most prolific country regions, among farmers and farm workers, people today are seeking means of planning and limiting births.

Some writers have pointed out how the percentage of married persons has been increased in recent times by an ever freer choice of partners, by a devaluation of bachelorhood and spinsterhood, by early marriage, and by increased longevity. If this is indeed the case, it would be a further reason for families having fewer children, for with more households, fewer children in each would still keep up the total population. Of course, in most European countries the marriage age is still comparatively late compared to the underdeveloped countries generally, but interregional differences are now slight, as far as their effect on fertility is concerned. The age of marriage has gone down in the West since the 1930's, while some underdeveloped countries, particularly in the Far East, have recently exhibited a later age of marriage.

The Sociological Explanation. In accounting for changes in birth rates, social and cultural factors are at least as important as biological factors. More and more, sociologists are looking to them to account for the differing fertility of different populations. In this connection, sociological analysis has probably gone farther than it has with any other demographic phenomenon.[33] So far, at least, that today social and cultural factors are recognized to have an almost primary importance in accounting for changes in fertility rates and birth rates.

Actually, whether the changes take the form of a rise or a decline, they are at least as much due to changes in people's attitudes and motivations as they are to advances in medicine and surgery. How important they can be is also shown by studies of the introduction and use of birth control methods. How willingly these are adopted varies greatly with the socio-cultural group and its religious beliefs.

Frank Lorimer, for one, examining the conditions of fertility in many different societies with a team of researchers, was able to conclude that a population's fertility does not depend just on biological factors, but also on various aspects of its social structure and on the value system obtaining in it.[34]

The social structure and the value system may favor a population's fecundity or they may discourage it. To grasp the attitudes of families and social groups toward fertility, in whatever society, such attitudes must be viewed in the full context of the other social phenomena. Changing attitudes must be seen against the background of changing social structures and the fundamental transformations in the society which they imply.

In the last analysis, every form of social behavior and every observable change in it—especially in regard to fertility—is a reaction to a complex set of conditions and relations which are today in rapid process of change. The reaction is determined with reference to norms and scales of value accepted by individuals and by groups. And not only do values differ from group to group, they differ from society to society according to its level of development.

In a rapidly changing society, there is a parallel change of outlook. Institutional changes set up new goals and new methods of attaining them. As the goals change, together with the values that define them, the means or the norms which define the means also, inescapably, change. A case in point is how modern urban, industrial societies came to consider profit as at once a value and a norm, a goal and a criterion of rationality. It can also be shown how new opportunities for rising in the social scale created the desire to improve one's own and one's children's social status, even as the cost of having children and raising them sharply increased.

The changing status of woman in society, and her changing role in the home, has likewise brought about aspirations for further changes, and still other roles.

To sum up, new conditions of life and work bring about changes in the social structure and in the value system or hierarchy of values. Any attempt to explain why some people have more children than others within the same society, or why some societies are more prolific than others, must take account of socio-cultural factors.

How the Sociological Approach Works. Studies of the factors which influence fecundity and the birth rate may be divided into two categories. First, there are the studies that stress social groups and their interrelations in time, against the background of changing familial structures. Then there are the studies that stress one or several elements of the cultural pattern, in terms of their permanence and change. No doubt the two categories cannot always be sharply differentiated, but they correspond to the two types of sociological analysis: that which addresses itself to such *concrete structures* as social groups and groupings, and that which addresses itself to *theoretical structures,* most notably to norms and values, customs, traditions, and other cultural models of individual and group behavior.

NATALITY AND SOCIAL ORGANIZATION

Social Categories and the Birth Rate. A great many studies have been made of how fertility and natality vary from group to group, from one social category to another. The phenomena have been analyzed in terms of socio-economic classes, in terms of income bracket, in terms of occupational categories, levels of education, age groups, political and religious affiliations, as well as in the broader terms of whether people live in the country or in the city, whether they are engaged in agriculture or industry, etc.[35]

From the earliest times, and in more than one country, it has been observed that the upper classes reproduce less rapidly than the lower classes, though there have been quite a number of exceptions in certain times and places. What this shows is that the relation between fertility and membership in one or another social group or category is not a rigid one. The facts have to be analyzed and supplemented with reference to cultural considerations. Similar groups or social categories do not necessarily behave the same, as between one country and another, nor do they have the same norms and value systems.

It is probable that the ruling classes of ancient Greece and Rome became extinct by failing to reproduce. In the Middle Ages the privileged orders were more prolific, very much as in China prior to modern times, where the richer and better educated families tended to have more children than those less fortunate. On the other hand, it has been established that in England between 1850 and 1910 there was very little difference on this score between the social classes. The same holds for Germany and the Netherlands in the interwar years of this century. Studies of the Stockholm population indicate that members of the professions especially, and of the upper classes generally, have the highest fertility rate.[36]

Fertility by Occupational Categories. Only since the appearance of industrial civilization have clear-cut differences in fertility been remarked between the socio-economic classes and among the various employment categories. In present-day urban, industrial societies, ever larger numbers of people fall within the high income brackets. Sometimes as much as one-fourth of an area's population falls within the management or upper employee class. This group generally had an extremely low fertility rate compared to the rest of the population, until the Second World War.[37] There are a number of cases where this group has been so unprolific as to be unable to replace its own numbers—a factor that enhances the social mobility characteristics of modern industrial societies.

Thus, although a steady decline in the birth rate is an over-all feature of latter-day urban, industrial societies, the decline actually has occurred mainly in certain economic and social groups. Sauvy, on the basis of a breakdown of occupational categories into primary, secondary and tertiary, has analyzed this matter and finds fertility weakest in families belonging to the last of these categories.[38] In his view, the steady shift of the population away from the primary occupations to the secondary and tertiary occupations characteristic of modern business and industry, is at every social level accompanied by a progressive drop in the number of births per family. The basic explanation for differences in fertility between the various economic and occupational sectors seems to lie in the fact that the growth of secondary and tertiary occupations is an index of the growing refinement of needs, compared with the needs of a society mainly engaged in primary occupations.[39] These last, age-old, predominately agricultural activities create no new needs such as cannot be satisfied within their own scope: food, protective clothing, shelter, and heat. A population that has gone on to the secondary occupations, however, needs manufactured products: vehicles, machines of various sorts, furnishings, household appliances, etc. A population that includes the tertiary occupations has still more things to spend its money on: personal services, books, plays and theaters, art objects, insurance, travel, cosmetics, regular medical attention, and luxury goods of every sort.

We may still ask ourselves, however, whether occupational categories have a truly determinative influence on the behavior of individuals and families with respect to their fertility. At least theoretically, manufactured goods and services are available to all, and thus Sauvy's classification may draw too sharp a distinction between population groups. The style of life of persons involved in the tertiary occupations, especially, is not limited to or defined by the particular character of the kind of production they are engaged in. Also, persons engaged in primary occupations are perfectly capable of enjoying the goods and services produced by the other social sectors. The kind of life they choose to lead, the purchases they do or do not make, are not all so rigidly bound up with the occupational category to which they belong.

Fertility by Geographical Areas—Rural vs. *Urban.* A number of authors have broken down populations in terms of residence in, or affiliation with, rural areas and urban areas. The distinction is an important one, for the modern drop in the birth rate seems to have been preceded or accompanied by a very sizable movement of population—of country people to the cities and of city people from place to place within the same and different cities. Even within a single country, the difference between the two birth rates has become very marked, to the point where it can be said that the bigger the city, the lower its birth rate.[40] However, this correlation is not an absolute one, in the sense that it works only one way. In the United States, for example, the size of the city has little connection with the fertility of its population; this may mean only that the urban mentality and way of life have spread fairly widely throughout the country.[41] Rural groups may, on occasion, let urban standards guide them. On the other hand, in the rapidly growing cities of the less advanced countries, the birth rate is sometimes as high as in the rural regions of the same country. What detailed analyses of fertility rates in rural regions have shown, is that there are marked differences from one place to another. Not all forms of agriculture or stockbreeding conduce to large families.[42]

And just as rural, agricultural communities do not necessarily all have the same birth rate, so might we expect to find similar variations among urban groups. To begin with, recent authors have had to distinguish between urban areas proper, and suburban areas, for there are notable differences in fertility between them. It is much higher in suburban areas, either because the families that live there are more interested in having children or because those who can afford to live in suburban areas are in a better position to raise a family.

All of which is enough to permit the conclusion that, whatever the social category we single out for study, and whatever regroupings may have taken place, it is not enough to measure or confirm differences in fertility and birth rates to explain how and why the widespread present-day practice of birth control, voluntary parenthood, or "planned fertility" has come about. To get to the bottom of the falling birth rate and the different variations in it, we have to define the whole set of new conditions and ways of life which, in the cities, have brought about a change in family attitudes and motivations respecting fecundity.[43]

Actually, the growing wealth of the populations, the development of secondary and tertiary forms of economic activity, just like the urbanization of the populations and the tendency of big cities to get still bigger, at bottom reflect the social division of labor, a mounting degree of "specialization" which is tied in with technological advances. Such developments would be incomprehensible without a high degree of mobility, both socio-economic and geographical. In the end, it is the way of life—the nature and conditions of employment—that determine the low birth and fertility rates.

If the birth rates are everywhere falling—in rural areas as well as in urban areas, in one profession or occupation no less than in another—this can only be attributed to the fact that family ways of life have changed radically. Growing specialization in every line of work, agricultural as well as industrial, the influence of the mass media, and much else today act as so many centripetal forces upon the family. Naturally—for what could be more normal?—in these conditions of constant change, persons in differently changing occupations or in movement from one place to another are differently affected at any given moment. Not everyone's way of life has as yet fully adjusted to the standards of urban, industrial society.

And even if all this shuffling around were to cease—both the "vertical" (or socio-economic) movement, and the "horizontal" (or geographical) movement—it is not likely there would occur any very perceptible rise in the birth rate. Urban, industrial society has its own way of life, which is irreversible, just as it is unlike earlier ways of life. The present slight rise in the birth rates of a number of Western countries has various causes. The insecurity of life in the thirties has become a thing of the past, and the threat of war has greatly lessened, though some authors attribute the baby boom and its sequel to a revaluation of family values. According to them, the Depression years and the Second World War brought about lessened respect for purely economic standards of security. Moreover, government assistance to families has become more widespread.

Fertility by Educational Levels and Religious Affiliations. Research has also been made along these lines, breaking down the populations of the various countries according to degree of education. Here too sharp differences appear with respect to fecundity. Until the last two decades, the higher the educational level, the lower the birth rate, was the rule. Undoubtedly the fact that prolonged education tends to postpone marriage has something to do with this, but it is also possible that advanced learning encourages different ways of life and thought, including deliberately different views on fecundity. At the same time, highly educated persons are generally endowed with particular gifts for social mobility, and this would also go to explain why they have fewer children. This correlation has been partly reversed in some North Atlantic countries. Since the Second World War, the least educated members of the urban population have had the lowest fertility in some of the most advanced countries.

Studies have also been made of fertility in relation to people's religious affiliations, occasionally correlating this data with population breakdowns by economic status, job or occupation, level of education, etc. One interesting finding has been that there is no radical difference between believers and nonbelievers in any of the various categories. Nor should this be hard to understand, to the degree that believers and nonbelievers in the various categories are subject to the same patterns of social, economic, cultural, regional, and national conditions. The very slight difference to be observed in the figures does not, however, imply that the groups are identical, either with respect to ends or to means. When all extraneous factors are put aside, the most careful and serious studies have shown that religious affiliation can have a positive bearing on fertility and births.[44] This, of course, shows up most clearly in countries where there are large proportions of Catholics and Protestants, and both denominations are well represented in all socio-economic categories, as, for example, in the United States. Although, in general, there is a tendency among Catholics in the United States to marry later than others, they have a slight edge over Protestants when birth rates are compared for equivalent socio-economic categories.

However, the data show that the difference has become smaller over the years.

There seems to be no data available for meticulously comparing the fertility of Catholics with Orthodox Christians or Muslims in those parts of the world, such as Lebanon and Yugoslavia, where large proportions of each live side by side, for the few studies undertaken do not make refined distinctions among their various socio-economic strata.

Fertility and Migration. Some authors have accounted for the decline in fertility in terms of the enhanced mobility of people in recent generations: whether within their own countries (social mobility or internal migration) or to other countries. Unquestionably, it has been a determining factor in the social disorganization of some communities when too many newcomers have poured in too quickly for adequate assimilation. When this happens, basic community structures are undermined and may be shattered, especially if the newcomers are not only numerous but also (as often happens) of diverse origins. Social controls at the point of immigration break down, while the social controls brought with them by the immigrants are weakened by the move. Really massive population shifts can provoke increases in delinquency, prostitution, divorce, and various forms of vice.[45] A perceptible lowering of the birth rate is the normal accompaniment to migrations of this type.[46]

But is such a consequence inevitable? In certain African towns which have in recent years witnessed a very great influx of new inhabitants, there is no such indication that fertility decline necessarily results from the disorder of population movements.

One theory, which minimizes the problem of social disorganization, holds that the fertility of immigrant groups normally tends to adjust to the standards of the new community. Thus, if the people among whom they now find themselves have a high fertility rate, they will have high fertility, and low fertility if there is a low fertility in their new home. (An instance of the latter adjustment is provided by the Italian families who have settled in Belgium.) In other words, fertility differences between immigrant and native populations depend upon the degree of assimilation achieved by the former. However, assimilation does not always take place on this score. Immigrants may cling to the standards of the communities they have come from. Some groups are more traditionalist than others—and some circumstances are more favorable to such an attitude than others.

Ever since A. Dumont, various authors have accounted for the decline in fertility in terms of social mobility or "internal migration,"[47] people's aspirations to rise in the world and their opportunities for doing so.

According to this theory, the greater the amount of socioeconomic (or "vertical") movement of this kind going on in a given population, the lower its rates of fertility. Although the studies on this score are very interesting, we may ask whether social mobility alone provides an adequate explanation for the phenomenon in question. It should follow from this theory that once opportunities slackened in a particular society, then the birth rate must rise or at least stop declining. There have been many discussions of attempts to establish such a correlation, but there have rarely been separate studies of the individual who is himself trying to rise in the world and the individual who is content to prepare for his children's rise. Motivations and attitudes on the score of fecundity may well differ widely in the two instances.[48]

Meanwhile, recent studies have demonstrated that "socially mobile" persons adapt their standards in this matter to those of the groups they aspire to belong to. This may lead them to have more children, or fewer children, depending on whether the class above them is prolific or not. Here we have proof that social mobility cannot of itself be considered the cause of lowered fertility. The problem becomes, in other words, not so much that of showing that people who are "moving up in the world" tend to have fewer children, but that of explaining why they adapt their standards and behavior in this way and why the groups to which they are drawn in present-day societies have the lowest fertility and birth rates.

There is no question, as Kiser and Whelpton have expressed it, but that the greater the spread between the actual standard of living and that which is aspired to, the more likely it is that the family will practice contraception. At the same time, however, allowance should be made for societies where the wealthy look upon children as an index of success and prestige. It is not at all certain that in such a society the "socially mobile" would still exhibit lowered fertility. In the case both of the internal migrant and the international migrant, the most important determinant of fecundity would seem to be the group they look to as setting standards for them, and this can be either the new group or the old group. Moreover, there have been some studies that associate a low level of fertility with a stationary social order or, even, with various forms of social decay.[49] It would be proper to conclude that there are no simple theories in this connection.

NATALITY AND FAMILY STRUCTURES

While the historical changes in fertility are related to the social categories of a given population and to the way families are distributed among them, they are also related to familial structures. World-wide social and economic developments have had a bearing upon the latter, and it is changes in them that also go to account for the decline in fertility.

In the pre-industrial ages, families themselves produced most of the goods they needed. With technical specialization and the social division of labor, an economy has developed in which secondary and tertiary production figures importantly. Families are no longer producers, in the primary sense, and tend to become consumer groups. More and more of all production activities go on outside the family circle, and individuals are involved in an ever greater number of transactions in their new consumer role. The family has been subjected to centrifugal forces which are all the greater under the conditions of urban life as the family rises in the income brackets.

What has taken place is a fundamental transformation of the

social structure at all levels, and its effect upon the family has been to make its members look outward, beyond the family circle, not just in producer-consumer relationships but also in social and cultural activities.

So far we have been examining fertility in terms of what might be called the "macrostructure" of society. Now we have to look into the family unit itself, the "microstructure," and see what bearing it has upon fertility. Of course its development is at least partly related to what has been going on in society as a whole. Davis has shown that fertility may be affected both positively and negatively as families branch out and form new ties of blood.[50]

In primitive agrarian societies, such as the underdeveloped countries of the present-day, the conjugal family belongs to a very broad structure of blood relationships which is not without bearing upon how it resolves the problem of fecundity. According to Davis, within such extended family structures the parents are spared some smaller or greater part of the economic burden of raising the child, caring for it, and educating it. Childbearing is neither so expensive nor does it demand such sacrifices of the parents as in our societies. Consequently, the marriage age is very much earlier. In general the man and the woman alike are eager to have a child very soon, though the social structure and the views of the wider clan on this score have to be allowed for. In all such societies there is a very distinct differentiation between the man's and the woman's role. The latter remains close to the home and occupies herself with family responsibilities. These are all conditions that make for a high birth rate.[51]

In our urban, industrial civilization, however, families in their wider extension and ramifications are broken up by the fact that they no longer constitute the basic social unit of production. Consequently, the role of the woman has undergone fundamental change. There are a great many things she can do outside the home, and this dispersion of attention is reflected in declining fertility.

According to some authors, the principal cause for the breakup of the family from a multicellular to a single-celled unit has been the complete individualization of the wage-earner, characteristic of capitalism in its liberal stage. This is not necessarily characteristic of present-day urban, industrial life.

Others besides K. Davis and A. W. Lewis have judged that the weakening and breaking up of family ties are a result of increased social mobility. It is true that under present-day conditions the various members of a family tend to rise or fall to different social strata.[52]

Still other writers claim that the single-celled family tends to prevail in Western civilization, for the reason that it was long since considered to be the ideal family.[53]

And lastly, it has been pointed out that in certain countries housing conditions favor the development of small family units.[54] However, even where this seems to have been the case, other larger types of family have managed to survive.[55]

All in all, it seems safe to say that, everything else being equal, the small family unit will tend to show a falling off in fertility. It is a fact that this is not the cheapest way to live. Expenses are high, not just because of the urban environment, but because each member requires his or her own outfitting, starting from scratch, and has to meet certain fixed fees the total of which is shared among fewer persons. In the small family the generations aid one another less and less, and social security systems fail to come up to the standards which formerly obtained in larger family groupings. The child's entire expenses fall upon a single generation, a circumstance which may, however, confer a number of psychological and emotional benefits. In any case, in view of the economic disadvantages, it is not sure that all families look with favor upon the single-celled type.

It would seem that in the years to come sociologists might well address themselves to the study of how family structures have been changing under urban, industrial conditions, and what alterations they have gone through in the past and in different types of cultures.

To the degree that observable differences in fertility are tied in with the type of family structure, in the various countries, corresponding to the degree reached in the social division of labor and the number of functions carried on outside the home,[56] it ought to be possible to analyze more systematically the various correlations which occur among these various phenomena.

In our opinion, the narrowing down of the family structure has not been so much due to the ideological or cultural superstructure as to the changed conditions of life in urban, industrial society. However, until more systematic study has been given this question, it remains an open one.

Further, it is not beyond the bounds of possibility that the fertility of small family units might yet increase, either through attainment of higher income brackets or through such community assistance measures as nurseries for working mothers. Indeed, it could happen without warning, as we have seen recently in suburban areas settled by families of the single-celled type. Family fertility is linked, moreover, with an enormous range of socio-cultural attitudes and traditions which we have as yet scarcely touched on.

NATALITY AND CULTURAL SYSTEMS

Cultural Change and the Birth Rate. When we break down a population by social category and trace the differences in fertility thereby revealed, we have still not accounted for those differences, nor have we established the fundamental causes for the decline which has been going on at every social level, though in varying degree. Similarly, when we notice the differences to be observed on this score between families of the multicellular and single-celled type, we have still not found any explanation of the over-all decline in fertility nor of the ways in which it has come about.

It is surely useful to show that fertility varies in inverse ratio with the degree of wealth attained, and that it also varies with occupational category, religious affiliation, degree of social mobility, urban residence as opposed to rural residence, and also according to the type of family structure. What all such observations go to show is that fertility tends to diminish as the economic well-being of the population increases, as the secondary and tertiary modes of production increase in importance, and as the different generations of a family begin to live apart. Further, it is possible to show that all these developments reflect the social division of labor which is expressed in the mounting specialization of technological employment. These are conditions that make for social mobility within each country and for the movements of people to other countries. More and more activities go on outside the family circle, and people's needs are constantly being stimulated by advertising and the mass media.

There is no question but that all these different measures of change with respect to human fertility touch on the underlying cause: namely, the development of an urban, industrial civilization which has radically altered family life.

When we interpret the results of all these studies, we find it easy to understand why it is at any given moment that persons within all these various social categories and structural groupings are differently affected by the changing times. The degree of integration within urban, industrial ways of life is not uniform.

Similarly, this gives us a basis for supposing that even were the present social trends to be arrested at some future date, there would still be no particularly notable rise in the birth rate. The new modes of life are here to stay, with all their enormous differences from earlier ways of life. Moreover, though there has been a real renewal of respect for family values in recent years, the rise in the birth rates of the Western countries has been slight. It has come about as a reaction to the disappearance of the insecurity of the Depression years and to the relaxation of international tensions. Government assistance to families has also played a part.

However, the fact is that in many countries births are far from having reached the biological maximum. According to P. Vincent, out of any 100 families in which procreation was allowed to take its natural course, with the women marrying at age twenty, nearly half would have 8, 9, or 10 children.[57] Thus, it is clear that in urban industrial areas where the average family has from 2 to 3 children (and where the majority of families have 2 or 3 children), some sort of family planning or birth control is being practiced. It is a great paradox that the richest countries should be among the least fertile. But we might carry the paradox further by observing that in these same countries it is not the wealthiest families, nor the most highly educated ones, that have the biggest families.

In this connection, it has been advanced by certain writers that successive generations within the same family exhibit a "law of alternating behavior patterns." That is, children born into big families will tend to have fewer children themselves, while children born into small families will tend to have more children.[58] Nonetheless, the decline in fertility has been going on for several generations now in the most advanced countries; the trend has scarcely been interrupted for a century.

There are various causes for the declining birth rate. One of them, paradoxically enough, has been the reduction in mortality. Another is that in the advanced countries small families—limited to 2 or 3 children—represent the ideal to a great many people. We might ask this question: why has this come to be characteristic of highly industrialized, urban societies?

The explanation is to be sought, first of all, in the cultural changes which have accompanied the fundamental transformations of society. As it becomes more complex, civilization sets up a conflict between procreation and other goals. And even in matters of procreation, conflict is set up between extensive and intensive goals —that is, between numbers and quality.

All too many studies of human fertility have neglected to take into account the changes that have been going on in people's attitudes with respect to goals, or ends. Too often the falling birth rate has been explained by the spread of contraceptive devices to ever wider reaches of the population, for the purpose of limiting or spacing births. Now this explanation will not do, for although certain birth-control methods are of recent origin, there are others which go back so far that their origin is unknown. Why should it be only quite recently that their use has become so widespread? In other words, the fact that means of birth control exist does not imply that they must necessarily be employed. For this to occur, there has had to come about a willingness to prevent conception, at the least a desire to space births. What needs to be gone into, to account for such a development, are the causes for this new attitude and the conditions under which it has come about.

Doubtless the existence of new contraceptive devices has spurred on such a radical turnabout of attitude in the countries of urban, industrial development. But there have also been profound alterations in social objectives and in the forms or modes of "social control." In the following paragraphs we shall try to analyze what has been going on at the level of ends and means, and in the forms of social control.

The Multiplication of Goals. In the moral and cultural spheres, the individual who loses himself in the variety of big-city life can choose among a great many modes of behavior and can pretty well decide for himself who his friends shall be and what kind of life he will lead.

Meanwhile, he is beckoned on every hand by advertisements which cater to his tastes and attempt to create new needs in him. Little by little, the mediums of mass communication impose upon him the conviction that, if he is to be like other men, he must have the things other men have. This constant appeal to his pocketbook is one reason for keeping families small: the more children there are, the less money there is for other things.

In the course of daily life, nearly everything that goes on goes on outside the home; as consumers as well as producers, the members of the family are forever being called elsewhere. Nor is this solely a matter of the frivolous pursuit of pleasure: the really vital necessities have to be worked for outside the family circle, and what is earned is also to a large extent spent outside it.

There have been a great many studies showing how hard it is, with a big family, to keep up in cultural matters and other activities requiring leisure, and to take proper part in matters of political and social concern. Vacations are more expensive, and needs for recreation suffer. Sports activities require equipment, and cultural development involves paying for goods and services. When we study the figures of what families spend on books, magazines, newspapers, records, etc., we can verify that the amounts spent get smaller as the size of the family increases.

Marriage involves a lowered standard of living for many parents, and when the children come they are tied down in ways that have drastic effects upon their former social and cultural interests. Also, to families with young children, the environment of the city has many drawbacks: lack of fresh air, crowded living quarters, noise, undesirable contacts, physical danger. Such have been the consequences of the anarchic fashion in which the big modern cities grew up. They are what drive families with children to live in outlying quarters or, when possible, in the suburbs.

This is the environment in which the cultural, economic, and social emancipation of women was effected. Precisely to the degree that she hopes to realize herself in one or another of these spheres, the modern woman must not let herself be tied down with children. Studies have shown that her aspirations along these lines are the greater, the better educated she is. If she would take an equal part with men in the intellectual, cultural, and social activities of a big city as they exist today, she can only do so by spending less time at home and by keeping a tight rein on herself during the childbearing years.

Moreover, in urban, industrial civilization women can and do take jobs outside the home. Housework is felt to be a dreary chore, as unskilled—and unpaid—labor. To the best qualified, best educated women there is serious frustration in the way they must cut down on all other activities in order to raise a family—a frustration only partly compensated for by the love they bear their children.

Also, in the most technologically advanced societies it is important to keep rising in the social scale. The desire to do so becomes very great, but involves special expense in the way of getting the best education, getting to know the right people, and acquiring the particular goods and services which bespeak a further refinement upon human needs.

Lastly, the urban environment offers too wide a range of choices to the individual as it does, because older forms of social control have disappeared. In the cities, the influence of the family, even of the neighborhood have dwindled. Formerly they served as a check upon individual behavior, and their censure was a serious matter.

To sum up, we might say that urban, industrial society is characterized by the way it has multiplied human goals and aims, often at the expense of procreation and child-rearing. Moreover, the values which inspire the choice of goals today under such conditions, are often as various as the different groups and behavior patterns which the city affords. It is this that limits the effectiveness of some forms of social control.

The Ends of Marriage. Union of man and woman in marriage has two essential ends or goals: the growth and development of the married couple as persons and as partners in marriage, and the expression of this union in procreation.

There is no doubt about it, the married couple's growth and development as such have been accorded ever greater importance over the past few decades, with the result that many have come to think of it as the sole and unique end in itself. This point of view runs contrary to Catholic morals. The theme has been sufficiently treated in contemporary literature so that there is no need to insist upon it here. The fertility of a marriage can be limited, out of respect for the woman, by the practice of a continence not injurious to health. However, the widespread dissemination of civilization's erotic features can lead to another kind of limitation of fertility: the separation of sexuality from procreation altogether. The love of man and wife upon which procreation depends, may also have the goal of encouraging their joint pursuit of certain forms of social, political and religious vocation.

It has been observed that couples are engaged in activities that involve a wider community than the family circle. There are choices of behavior which are not necessarily outlets for egoism. A few want to know if love and marriage cannot be made to serve broader purposes than procreation alone. The problem arises particularly in marriages that must remain childless. In any case, it is clear that the objective end of marriage has much sharper competition today than formerly from the pursuit of vocations in marriage.

The development of a right to happiness distinct from the duty to procreate, which may take a number of directions, obviously derives from the series of discoveries which have culminated in the human ability to separate love from its objective end: namely, procreation. This is not to say that love cannot, in this manner, serve as a powerful means of bringing the couple closer together. The attempt to find an end in marriage apart from procreation poses a problem only when it is too narrowly pursued.

We have left behind us the day when fertility was an essentially organic phenomenon, and have arrived at a time when it is more and more within the powers of the human intelligence to determine. To a hitherto unprecedented degree, couples may decide for themselves to pass on the gift of life in accord with their condition in life and their convictions.[59]

There is no reason to suppose that, so long as the means employed are honorable, they may not now be able to realize their capacities for childbearing without sacrificing a variety of other values.

Numbers vs. Quality. Urban, industrial civilization has made it much more expensive to have children. Children are forbidden to work, and young people can take jobs only under carefully regulated conditions. The return on the parents' investment becomes ever smaller and of shorter duration. At the same time, care of the child has become more and more elaborate and fussier, especially in matters of feeding and medical attention. The education of girls has become nearly as extensive as that of boys. All these developments mean that, besides being less of an investment than they used to be, children cost a great deal more to raise today. Moreover, in a society where commercial transactions have become so complex and involve an ever-increasing number of goods and services, where—in a word—everything is bought and sold, it is hardly surprising that the cost of having children should come to be thought out in the closest detail and in advance.* The fact that this is done today may well make having children seem a more expensive proposition than formerly. And yet, even allowing for some psychological exaggeration, it is clear that parents do have to invest more than they used to in each child, in the knowledge that there will be less and less of a return to them on the investment.

All this has tended to make the two family tasks of procreation and education seem to conflict with each other. When a family chooses to remain small, this is not just because there are so many other things to do outside the home, but because the smaller it is, the more it will be able to do in the way of preparing the children for life.

In other words, the small family does not necessarily imply selfishness or lack of love. People may have fewer children than they used to because they spend more time on those they have, and because—precisely for this reason—they feel the weight of responsibility more keenly.[60] It is not going too far to say that the day has passed when parents simply remained the object of their children's love and respect, and that what we have now come to is the family in which the children are the parents' main preoccupation.

At the same time, recalling our observations above on how the costs and care of the children are no longer shared by grandparents and other relatives, it is less and less surprising that families today hesitate to give full rein to their procreative capacities. The single-celled family runs more and more risks, the bigger it gets: among others, unemployment, the sickness of one or other parent, their divorce, or their death.

All of which doubtless bears upon the low fertility and birth rates characteristic of the modern single-celled family. Writers like Frank Lorimer have pointed to this reduction of the family to husband, wife, and children, as explaining the difference between Western societies' birth rates and those of the rest of the world,

* State aid to encourage bigger families includes education in economic matters. See the discussion of the French system below.

where the family constitutes a broader unit. Western man is the sole material and moral support of his children, and it is not surprising that the marriage age should also be later for him than elsewhere in the world.

Lastly, Western culture's emphasis upon the man-and-wife relationship as the core of the family seems to have also played a role in keeping the birth rate low, both through postponing the marriage age and through checking fertility in marriage.[61]

Lorimer cites among the possible causes of the different conceptions of the family in Western Europe (compared with Asia, for example), the influence of Christianity. It is hostile to ancestor worship, and it insists on the sacredness of marriage. By making marriage a sacrament and by regarding the union of man and woman as indissoluble, once freely embarked upon, Catholicism consecrates the conjugal family as it does no other social grouping. Thus there is a sense in which it can be said that the modern concept of the family is that of Christianity,[62] notwithstanding the fact that there seems to be conflict between the Church's commandments and family attitudes to fertility.

State Aid to Families (in France). Although social security systems in most countries came in only after 1930, France had Family Allowances from 1920 on. Only on the eve of World War II had they been extended to all wage earners, however, and it was only after liberation that they were made available to the population as a whole.

For a long time, few even among the wage-earners in business and industry were eligible for Family Allowances. In 1920 there were only 6 offices making disbursements to 50,000 wage earners. The next year there were 57 offices for 500,000 wage earners, and by 1930 there were 232 offices for 1,820,000 wage earners. How the plan has grown since is shown in TABLE 58.

The fact that from 1942 on the French birth rate began to rise for the first time in a century, has often been attributed to this policy of encouraging larger families through a system of Family Allowances.

TABLE 58

Development of Family Disbursement Offices in France,
1931–1945

Year	Number of Disbursement Offices	Total Wage-earners Served
1931	230	1,850,000
1932	244	1,850,000
1933	255	2,425,000
1934	186	2,425,000
1935	210	3,750,000
1936	222	4,238,000
1937	222	4,803,000
1938	228	5,315,000
1939	229	5,400,000
—	—	—
1943	389	5,475,000
1944	399	5,666,000
1945	399	6,316,000

France has, in fact, had a population upsurge since 1942, but this is characterized by a drop in mortality after 1945 as well as by a rise in the number of births. As of that date, for the first time in a decade there were more births than deaths. However, let us look into this development more closely. From the prewar low in fertility to the postwar years, France has really been the only country in Europe that has experienced an appreciable and prolonged increase in fertility. Thus it stands also with Australia, Canada, New Zealand, and the United States.

Countries where there was little or no system of state aid to families, particularly the United States, attribute their increase to the prolonged post-war "baby boom"—a complex phenomenon. However, most European countries have not had any appreciable and prolonged post-war increase in fertility, although they nearly all dispense large family support subsidies. Moreover, compared to the United States, the immediate effects of the "baby boom" wore off in France much more quickly. (This comparison with America would also hold with all the other European countries as well, for most of them went through a classic baby boom in the immediate post-war years.)

At the same time, we must note that the drop between 1947 and 1958, a period of 12 years, had occurred previously in only 8 years, between 1931 and 1938 in France. Thus, the French birth rate was declining more slowly than it had in the pre-war period. However, we may note also that between 1902 and 1913, another twelve-year period, the birth rate fell from 22 to 18 per 1,000.

Ought we to conclude from the above that state aid to families in France has had no effect on the birth rate? That would be going too far.

Sauvy has written: "No married couple has children for pay." That is putting the matter crudely, and experience teaches that often it just isn't so. It is harder not to have children than to have them, and though the birth rate was low enough before the war, still a certain number of children who were born had not been wanted. The policy of state aid to families, in the event, served to lower resistance rather than to "sell" couples on having more children. This would seem to be the best way of evaluating such a policy in a country where the birth rate had long been declining. In any case, more is involved than Sauvy allows for when he writes:

However, the rise in the birth rate may not be permanent. Younger generations may take the Family Allowances for granted, without anything of the psychological shock felt by those who first benefited from the system.

The Family Allowances teach people who had never done so before to think about how much it costs to have a child. In some countries, Spain for instance, state aid of this type actually speeds decline in the birth rate. In the Oran district of Algeria, the same phenomenon has also been noted. It seems that in countries, or in classes of the population, already tempted by the "economic man" psychology, a policy of state aid to families strengthens Malthusian tendencies. While in French peasant families of especially low income the Family Allowances still have an encouraging effect, in urban surroundings the psychological appeal soon wears off, and the calculation of costs which the policy inspires is already producing opposite results.

Does this mean that Family Allowances in particular, and the French social security system in general, have had no more than a transient effect on the country's population recovery? Actually, the system deserves part of the credit (just how much, however, is hard to say) for the decline in mortality and, therefore, for the fact there is once again an excess of births over deaths in France. The progressive decline in infant mortality over the period 1930–1959 is especially characteristic. Between 1930 and 1939 it dropped from 78 per 1,000 live births, that is, by 22 per cent, to 64. Between 1950 and 1959 it dropped from 47 to 25, a further 88 per cent. The fact that children are today better fed and cared for in France, and that their economic status has been strengthened, is—we repeat—not so much due to the system of Family Allowances as such, as to the way in which that system has (as we said above) "lowered resistance."

The national income is today far better distributed for meeting basic human needs, and most notably those of children. The French population as a whole has benefited from the social security system, even though the populationist aims behind the policy of Family Allowances have not been realized.

Customs and Traditions. Fundamental changes in the conditions of life and in human attitudes over the past few generations, are what have persuaded people to have fewer children than formerly. They are, thus, behind the development and use of the various contraceptive measures, as well as behind the rise of the "family planning" point of view. New technical devices for outwitting nature have, of course, strengthened the will as well as the desire to control and regulate births. That is to say, the ends give rise to the means, and the means encourage and act upon the ends.

All the same, it does not necessarily follow that the use of contraceptive measures alone accounts for a falling birth rate. Actually, a population's vital statistics may undergo notable change through the operation of other factors entirely.

Davis and Blake have assembled evidence for the possible role of particular cultural factors in human fertility.[63] Taking an essentially physiological approach, they divide the reproductive process into the following stages: sexual relations, conception, gestation, and parturition. Then, for each of these stages, they have tried to find cultural factors that could be of determinative importance.

Among the cultural factors affecting sexual relations, they introduce a subdivision: those which have to do with how marriages and other unions are entered into and dissolved, and those which have to do with the frequency of sexual relations within such unions.

Under the first heading they list: age at marriage, the number of unmarried women (including those vowed to chastity on religious grounds), the lapse of time between successive marriages or other unions (whatever the cause or origin of the remarriage—divorce, separation, desertion, or death of one partner). In ways that differ from society to society, all these factors influence fertility.

There are primitive societies in which widows are discouraged from remarrying. Whether unions are monogamous or polygamous is a matter of importance, too. In polygamous unions, wives no longer young may be abandoned, and the male may exhaust his reproductive capacities.

In other words, the age at which marriage or other unions are contracted, the extent to which celibacy is practiced, how enduring marriages are, and whether or not remarriage or extra-conjugal union is permitted, are all indisputably matters that vary according to a given society's customs and traditions. They obviously bear upon a country's fertility and birth rates.

Under the second heading, Davis and Blake list the factors governing sexual relations in marriage: voluntary abstinence, impotence and disease, psychological depression, living arrangements (does the couple live under the same roof?), and frequency of intercourse. A number of societies observe various sexual taboos in marriage. African peoples, for example, generally forbid intercourse while the child is being nursed.[64] The same taboo was formerly observed in parts of France (Brittany, for example), where it was the custom for the nursing mother to sleep with her mother or her eldest daughter. It would seem at least possible that the frequency of sexual relations may vary from society to society according to custom and religious ordinance.

Next, Davis and Blake turn to the cultural factors which have a bearing upon conception. Temporary sterility varies in duration and frequency according to whether breast-feeding is practiced or not. Sterility from other causes may be more or less prevalent according to the availability of medical care, training in personal hygiene, etc. In regions where venereal diseases are prevalent, both fertility and the birth rate may be seriously affected. One or another variety of sterilization may be practiced on either sex. Just to what extent any of these factors is operative differs widely from place to place and from time to time, but any one of them can have a real bearing upon the sterility or fertility of couples.

Other cultural factors to be considered, of course, have to do with the extent and kind of contraception that may be practiced, as well as with other efforts to check or limit births. Here, Davis and Blake distinguish between chemical and mechanical devices and practices of another character entirely, such as utilization of knowledge concerning the menstrual cycle, or such practices as might fall under the head of sexual perversion—coitus interruptus, for example. It is clear that where and when such factors enter into the picture, they are of determinative importance to fertility.

Lastly, the writers group the factors that bear upon the hazards of gestation and successful delivery of the child. Accidents during pregnancy can be fatal, and may be caused by particular physical exertions of the mother. The availability of medical care and the habit of making use of it differ widely from place to place and can be of crucial importance to the birth rate. Similarly, societies vary enormously on the score of abortion, both in the matter of practicing it or not practicing it and in the matter of tolerating or condemning it.[65]

The foregoing list of cultural factors capable of playing a crucial role in the reproductive process is doubtless not exhaustive—nor was it intended to be. Its usefulness is that it suggests just how purely cultural factors can enter into the picture. It helps us to some notion of the very various ways in which different societies may go about what we call "birth control" or "family planning." Cultural factors intervene at one or another particular stage of the reproductive process and vary greatly with the degree of civilization attained by a particular society. In comparison with the pre-industrial societies, the more highly developed ones appear to have brought a more systematic approach to certain stages of the reproductive process and to have followed procedures peculiarly their own. Davis and Blake claim that, with reference to the whole range of possible methods of controlling the reproductive process, the industrial societies have chosen those which involve as little institutional reorganization as possible and as slight a human cost as possible,[66] namely, contraceptive methods in the main. There is no denying that sterilization and abortion cost dearly. However, the conclusion is a hasty one, for objectively the exhaustive study of the cultural factors in fertility shows that the problem of fertility cannot be reduced to contraceptive devices, sterilization, and abortion—not in any society. A more acceptable conclusion would be that the fertility and birth rates in any society are determined by a combination of the variable factors listed, and that which of them happen to be of determinative consequence also varies. Moreover, such is K. Davis' opinion.

What needs more systematic study is the way each society thinks about the spacing of births and birth control.[67] Ideas and attitudes are constantly undergoing change on this score.

The factors which make for lessened fertility at one stage of urban, industrial development may no longer be of a determinative effect once a subsequent stage of development has been reached. Now other factors may make their appearance and affect attitudes and behavior. Thus, for example, it is possible that when income is well above the subsistence level and urbanization no longer is accompanied by grave social shortcomings, then cultural differentiations make themselves felt all the more unmistakably in every area of behavior and specifically in matters touching fertility, although their influence previously had been almost imperceptible. Until the most recent decades, the greater part of the population in industrial cities suffered from severe poverty and social disorganization. Burgeoning aspirations for a better life meant long and bitter striving for the urban masses and lower middle class. But this is no longer so. The poor and the socially mobile no longer need feel forced to forego children. So, instead of industrial-urban fertility being related mainly to class differences, it is likely to be associated with other dimensions of social differentiation. This would apply to the religious factor, which up to now has scarcely seemed to have had any very overwhelming effect in this domain. Under improved conditions of urban, industrial civilization, this factor could well make for new modes of behavior on the score of fertility.[68]

When the whole complex of cultural factors influencing fertility is carefully examined, it becomes more comprehensible how offensive the introduction of birth control devices and practices can be, not just from a religious point of view, but also from moral or merely aesthetic points of view. Once we become aware of the full cultural context, we shall be less likely to embark on all-out campaigns or crusades in favor of contraception.[69]

Moreover, it has been observed that, in a number of countries, not all families exercise the same sort of "family planning." When it comes to the matter of which contraceptive measures are employed, it is clear that social and cultural factors play an important role. Freedman's study in the United States has brought out the difference between Protestants and Catholics on this score: 50 per cent of the latter employ the rhythm method. This study brings out as well the fact that the measures couples have recourse to change over the years, as the marriage progresses.[70]

Hill has made a study of the population of Puerto Rico which is also interesting in this connection. He has a great deal of data concerning which measures of birth control and family planning are known and used, and their relative accessibility.[71]

Such studies illustrate how useful it can be to concentrate on single factors within the whole complex of social, cultural influences on fertility: in this case, on the factor of contraception. They help us to see the problem in a new light, and if we had more of them we would perhaps appreciate better than we do that there are still many peoples of the world to whom having children is a thoroughly attractive idea. Better appreciation of such facts could only lead to greater caution in the promulgation of birth-control measures. The young, as yet undeveloped countries might well view any such crusade in their midst as a hedge against their demographic expansion undertaken by the rich countries out of motives of self-interest.

The Competition for Women's Time and Attention. Stycos has made an even fuller study than Davis and Blake of the cultural factors that conceivably have a bearing upon human fertility.[72] He points out the advantages and the disadvantages which go with woman's role as progenetrix. Having children, and especially many children, involves some physical discomfort, danger to her health, and loss of beauty. There are besides more long-term problems connected with the care and raising of children. Whether, and to what extent, she can feel that the disadvantages are offset by the advantages, depends upon how the society in which she lives defines, respects, ennobles, and rewards her for carrying out her role as progenetrix and mother. Different societies, and different groups within the same society, vary in how they treat a pregnant woman. Even the pains of childbirth may be presented in such a way that she is less, rather than more, fearful in anticipation. It would be of the very greatest importance to have a really comprehensive study of the different ways the different cultures envisage the problems and discomforts attendant to woman's essential function as the bearer of human life.

As for woman's own view of these matters, it does not depend just on her personal attitudes, on her particular feelings and desires, but also on (1) the judgment of the other members of hers and her husband's family, on how they have been brought up on this score, and whether they think of the female role as a burden or as a blessing; as well as on (2) how the less immediate reaches of her society have come to view wives and mothers, the degree of consideration customarily shown to women, and the values they ascribe to the bearing of life.[73]

In our own society, where women are so much more than merely wives and mothers, it can happen that a woman finds herself torn between one and another of the very many demands upon her time and attention. Besides the demands entailed by marriage and a family, there are many opportunities for work outside the home and for a great many other activities of a variously cultural, social, political, educational, or merely recreational character. The emancipation of women has been one of the fundamental revolutions of our era, and has developed apace on the juridical, political, cultural, and social levels. Parallel with it has gone a progressive freeing of the female from the more onerous aspects of domestic labor and housekeeping. What has happened is that activities outside the home have taken on ever greater value and importance, while nearly everything to do with the household has come to seem less and less rewarding. And after all it is perfectly true that, even transfigured by the love of a mother and the devotion of a wife, household tasks are a variety of hard, unskilled labor.

The ambiguity of woman's position in urban, industrial societies has been the subject of many excellent studies.[74] We have ourselves touched on aspects of the matter elsewhere in these pages. In view of the importance which has been attached to such problems as "the working mother," it might be interesting here to pose in some detail the problem of just how fertility is affected by female employment outside the home, though this is but one aspect of the many claims today made upon woman's time and attention. More and more, they are finding themselves obliged to reconcile individual and family needs with ever more numerous "outside interests."

Hence the ambiguousness of their position today. Quite apart from actual employment, as society has assumed more and more of the functions formerly filled by the family, women find more and more activities appealing to their interests and talents.

However, precisely because more and more outlets for feminine skills are being found, we ought to take a closer look at how human fertility is being affected by female employment in business and industry. Though it is very hard to prove statistically, it does seem likely that the effect is negative. At the same time, however, we must be careful not to exaggerate on this score. It is far from having been demonstrated that the countries with the highest percentages of women employed are those with the lowest fertility. In areas largely given over to the textile industry, for example, an industry which employs many women, it has been shown that there was no particular effect upon fertility as compared with other areas. What ought to be gone into more carefully, however, in connection with such studies, is whether or not the areas in question had not preserved a semi-rural character such as is known to be favorable to a high fertility rate.

Statistically speaking, married women who work outside the home are younger, as a group, than married women who are not so employed. When we compare the average fertility rates of the two groups, the differences we find are not necessarily significant because, being younger, the married women who work probably number fewer individuals who have passed the age of childbearing.

Further, though it may be possible one day to prove that women who work are in general less fertile than those who do not, still we should not be able to conclude from such a study that they are at greater pains to avoid having children. It would be necessary, first, to determine whether jobs in business and industry do not have a special appeal for women who are by nature less fertile than others. We may note here that jobs which involve any very strenuous labor, especially when taken on in addition to regular household tasks, are likely to produce more accidents during pregnancy.

It has occasionally been argued that women who are extremely fertile by nature (as well as women who are less than averagely so) are particularly drawn to seek employment outside the home. In this case, they would be motivated by the need and desire to contribute to the family exchequer.

In conclusion, we can only affirm that no study has as yet been carried far enough to permit us to measure the bearing of female employment on human fertility in properly objective, scientific terms. Public opinion surveys have shown that there are more proponents of birth control among women who work than among women who do not.[75] However, such an attitude may reflect simply an especially keen ambition on the part of such women to help insure their family's rise in the social scale, added opportunities for their children, etc.[76] It must not be supposed that such an attitude necessarily goes with female employment in business and industry. There are a number of ways in which jobs for married women can be kept from becoming an obstacle to fertility: part-time employment, for example, and "maternity leave," on the military model.

GENERAL CONCLUSIONS

The social and cultural factors are most important of all in their bearing upon fertility. Any form of state aid to encourage bigger families must be quite clear on this score. Certainly the proponents of birth control have grasped this point firmly and have allowed it to inform every aspect of their publicity and public relations. Indeed, we can at this point do no better than quote a few of their guiding principles:

1. Increase the frequency of friendly contacts between people knowing about the techniques and those who do not. Thus, not only would doctors, public health nurses, pharmacists, and midwives be bearers of the initial information, but older women (perhaps designated as "practical nurses"), scribes, and soldiers could be quickly indoctrinated and brought into the program for the spread of the knowledge.

2. The information accompanying the drugs, as represented by the printing on the package and in circulars, must be carefully tested in field studies so that the intended meaning is clearly conveyed and all common objections that come to mind are answered. These precautions tend to increase the effectiveness of the personal contacts mentioned above.

3. The cost of the contraceptive materials to the persons intending to employ them should be just sufficient to make sure that the products will not be scandalously wasted. . . .

4. The educational systems can be quickly advised on advantages to the family, the community, and the nation when the family size is small. . . .

5. The archaic ideologies that in the main oppose the rapid adoption of family planning can be superseded by a dedication to the common welfare and by nationalism. . . .

6. In order to optimize the rate of spread, a coordinating and research organization is likely to be set up. . . . This approach is strictly analogous to the market research and sales engineering employed by modern corporations in expanding the distribution of their products.[77]

Further on, it is urged that the various mediums of mass communication should be made use of, including advertisements over radio and TV as well as in magazines. It is also pointed out that propaganda should be especially directed to those portions of the population whose standard of living is rising.

Today more and more scientific studies are being made of the factors which are more or less favorable to the employment of the various contraceptive methods. Such matters as what leads families to practice contraception, how much they know about it, and which methods they prefer or could be persuaded to try, have all been gone into. In view of the scientific spirit which informs these studies, and the forthrightness with which the public is being indoctrinated, we may ask whether the moment has not come for the Catholic Church to undertake a systematic co-ordination of its efforts in this connection. The task is not at all one of raising bastions against the evil, in the expectation of confining it, but one of finding worthwhile solutions in time for very present world-wide population problems.

With the enormous progress already made toward reducing the causes of death and with the enormous explosion of new life now going on in many parts of the planet, the first solution we must try to find is obviously to the economic problem. How are the world's vast resources and technical knowledge[78] to be developed to their full potential, and how are we to arrive at a more equitable distribution of the world's wealth on the international level? It would be a shame if we were in this connection to show ourselves lacking in daring, in inventive genius, or in generosity.[79] The second task before us is that of insuring that modern medicine, and Catholic medicine in particular, contributes all its skill, its science, and its energies to the discovery and improvement of methods for regulating the appearance of new life in accordance with our morals and with the laws of nature. For is it not true that "We have no right to demand of mankind that it obey the law, unless at the same time we do all that it is in our power to do, to make obedience possible"?[80] It would be very expensive, not just in material terms but also in moral terms, to expect contraceptive devices, abortion, or sterilization, to solve this problem. Moreover, any sudden checking of population growth, any abrupt falling off in the birth rate, must lead to further problems—among others, the rapid aging of populations. The solution proposed by the Catholic Church appears the most humane.

Lastly, the Church's message must be made more widely and correctly known. If it is to reach great numbers of widely scattered and extremely various socio-cultural groups, that message will have to be adapted to them. There must be the courage to say out loud that, while the Church indeed frowns on certain contraceptive practices, it frowns no less on the mindless, instinctive, unbridled proliferation of new life.[81]

No doubt the Church's essential message in this context is self-mastery and fidelity to the will of God.[82] Obviously, it is not only in this context that self-mastery is required. Doctors do not hesitate to urge it on their patients for their own well-being. Is it, however, practical where large numbers of people are concerned?

Periodic continence has to be justified on solid social and economic grounds, or on grounds of health—whether the health of the mother or that of her progeny. What this means is that, where passing on the gift of life is concerned, man must know what his responsibilities are and understand them clearly, taking into consideration not just the physical and psychological well-being of the parents, but also that of the children, the family, and the whole human community.

And so the Church's mission, first of all, is to educate the parents —not to train them in contraceptive practices, but rather to prepare them to take on great responsibilities.[83] By their very nature, these involve taking account of personal, family, and social conditions, the conditions necessary to the well-being of the group and of the nation. Unfortunately, the Christian message is too often passed on with too little emphasis upon all that is attractive and perfectly sound in it, though there have been some praiseworthy efforts along these lines.[84]

NOTES

1. UN, *Population Bulletin No. 6—1962*, p. 13, Table I, 1.
2. UN, *Demographic Yearbook 1962*, pp. 1–2.
3. Sauvy, *Fertility and Survival*, pp. 26–38.
4. Gustav Sundbärg, *Bevölkerungsstatistik Schwedens 1750–1900*, quoted in *Determinants and Consequences* (UN), p. 51.
5. Sauvy, *op. cit.*, p. 43.
6. UN, *Population Bulletin No. 6*, p. 10.
7. Sauvy, *op. cit.*, p. 57.
8. *Ibid.*, p. 47.
9. R. Blanc and G. Théodore, "Les Populations d'Afrique noire et de Madagascar," *Population* (June, 1960), p. 422.
10. United Nations, *Age and Sex Patterns of Mortality: Model Life-Tables for Under-Developed Countries* (New York, 1955).

11. Michel Cépède and Maurice Lengellé, *Economie alimentaire du globe* (Paris: Librairie de Médicis, 1953).
12. *Ibid.,* p. 283.
13. Arthur Newsholme, *The Elements of Vital Statistics,* 3d ed. (London: Sonnenschein, 1899), p. 120.
14. Cépède and Lengellé, *op. cit.,* pp. 280–81.
15. Michel Cépède, *La faim* (Geneva: 1960).
16. Halvor Gille, "Demographic History of Northern European Countries in the Eighteenth Century," *Population Studies,* III, 1 (June, 1949).
17. Georges Bouthoul, *La surpopulation dans le monde* (Paris: Payot, 1959).
18. Pierre George, *Questions de géographie de la population* (Paris: Presses Universitaires, 1959), pp. 38–39. This is Cahier no. 34 in the INED series "Travaux et Documents."
19. *Ibid.,* p. 39.
20. Louis Henry, "Caractéristiques démographiques des pays sous-développés" in *Le "Tiers-Monde",* p. 166.
21. *Determinants and Consequences* (UN), p. 54 (Table 8).
22. "Low Birth Rates of European Catholic Countries," *Population Bulletin,* XVIII (March, 1962), 25.
23. *World Population Trends, 1920–1947* (New York: United Nations, 1949), pp. 3 (Table 1), 10 (Table 2).
24. United Nations, *1963 Report on the World Social Situation,* Chap. II, Part c.
25. *The Future Growth of World Population* (UN), pp. 2 (Table 2), 33 (Table 13).
26. V. Webster Johnson and Raleigh Barlowe, *Land Problems and Policies* (New York: McGraw-Hill, 1954), p. 379.
27. Thomas Doubleday, *The True Law of Population, Shewn to be Connected with the Food of the People,* 2d ed. (London: E. Wilson, 1843), pp. 5–6.
28. Josué de Castro, *The Geography of Hunger* (New York: Little, Brown, 1952), p. 163.
29. The state of sociological analysis of fertility has not greatly improved since the UN's *Determinants and Consequences* and Lorimer's *Culture and Human Fertility.* Freedman's, Kiser's, and Nag's recent surveys of this subject may herald an approaching synthesis of this yet disjointed field, however: Ronald Freedman, "The Sociology of Human Fertility," *Current Sociology* (Oxford), 10/11, 2 (1961–62); Clyde V. Kiser (ed.), *Research in Family Planning* (Princeton: Princeton U. Press, 1962); Moni Nag, *Factors Affecting Fertility in Non-Industrial Societies* (New Haven: Yale U. Press, 1962). The United Nations has issued a brief preliminary report on the subject, *The World Demographic Situation with Special Reference to Fertility,* especially Sec. 5.

30. Florian Znaniecki, *Cultural Sciences* (Urbana: U. of Illinois Press, 1952), quoted in Joseph J. Spengler and Otis Dudley Duncan (eds.), *Population Theory and Policy* (Glencoe, Ill.: The Free Press, 1956), p. 369.

31. Charles F. Westoff, Robert G. Potter, Jr., Philip C. Sagi, and Elliot G. Mishler, *Family Growth in Metropolitan America* (Princeton: Princeton U. Press, 1961).

32. Clément Mertens, S.J., "Données démographiques et économiques des problèmes de population," *Saint-Luc-Médical*, XXXIII (1961), 122.

33. Frank Lorimer et al., *Culture and Human Fertility: A Study of the Relation of Cultural Conditions to Fertility in Non-Industrialized and Transitional Societies* (Paris: UNESCO, 1954), 510 pp. E. T. Hiller, "A Culture Theory of Population Trends" in Spengler and Duncan, *op. cit.*, pp. 371–90. Kingsley Davis and Judith Blake, "Social Structure and Fertility: An Analytic Framework," *Economic Development and Cultural Change* (Chicago), IV (April, 1956), 211–35. Alfred Sauvy, *Théorie générale de la population*, 2 vols. (Paris: Presses Universitaires, 1952–54), II, chaps. 6 & 7: "Les facteurs sociaux de la fécondité" and "La stérilité volontaire." Clyde V. Kiser and Pascal K. Whelpton, "Resume of the Indianapolis Study of Social and Psychological Factors Affecting Fertility" in Joseph J. Spengler and Otis Dudley Duncan (eds.), *Demographic Analysis* (Glencoe, Ill.: The Free Press, 1956), pp. 256–71. Reuben Hill, J. Mayone Stycos, and Kurt W. Back, *The Family and Population Control: A Puerto Rican Experiment in Social Change* (Chapel Hill: U. of North Carolina Press, 1956), 481 pp. Westoff, Potter, Sagi, and Mishler, *op. cit.*, 433 pp.

34. F. Lorimer et al., *Culture and Human Fertility, op. cit.*

35. See, for example, Clyde V. Kiser, "Fertility Trends and Differentials in the United States" in Spengler and Duncan, *Demographic Analysis*, pp. 162–83.

36. E. T. Hiller, *op. cit.*, pp. 378, 384–90 (bibliography).

37. Frank W. Notestein, "Class Differences in Fertility" in Reinhard Bendix and Seymour M. Lipset (eds.), *Class, Status, and Power: A Reader in Social Stratification*, 3d ed. (Glencoe, Ill.: The Free Press, 1957), pp. 271–81.

38. Alfred Sauvy, "Progrès technique et répartition professionelle de la population," *Population* (April/June, 1949), p. 307.

39. On this subject, see especially Pedro Calderan Beltrão, S.J., *Vers une politique de bien-être familial* (Louvain: Institut de Recherches économiques et sociales, 1957), p. 100.

40. Ronald Freedman, Gerhard Baumert, and Martin Bolte, "Expected Family Size and Family Size Values in West Germany," *Population Studies*, XXXVII, 2 (Nov. 1959), p. 146.

41. G. Baumert, "Some New Aspects of Rural-Urban Differentials in Family Values and Family Structures in the Sociology of Family," *Current Sociology*, XII, 1 (1963–64), pp. 46–54.

42. Michel Cépède, *Du prix de revient au produit net en agriculture* (Paris: Presses Universitaires, 1946), pp. 113–22.

43. *Determinants and Consequences* (UN), esp. chap. 5, "Economic and Social Factors Affecting Fertility," pp. 71–97.

44. Hill, Stycos, and Back, *op. cit.;* Hugh E. Brooks and Franklin J. Henry, "An Empirical Study of the Relationships of Catholic Practice and Occupational Mobility to Fertility," The Milbank Memorial Fund *Quarterly,* XXXVI, 3 (1958), 222–81. See also Ronald Freedman, Pascal K. Whelpton, and J. W. Smit, "Socio-Economic Factors in Religious Differentials in Fertility," *American Sociological Review,* XXVI, 4 (Aug. 1961), 608–14; Westoff, Potter, Sagi, and Mishler, *op. cit.*

45. Mabel A. Elliot and Francis E. Merrill, *Social Disorganization,* 3d ed. (New York: Harper, 1950), esp. chap. 22, "The Concept of Community Disorganization," pp. 473 ff.

46. Frank Lorimer, "Culture and Human Fertility: Conclusions" in Spengler and Duncan (eds.), *Population Theory and Policy,* pp. 395–99.

47. Beltrão, *op. cit.,* pp. 87 ff.

48. Two small studies lend support to this contention: H. Y. Tien, "The Social Mobility/Fertility Hypothesis Considered," *American Sociological Review,* 26, 2 (April, 1961), pp. 247–57, and Richard Tomasson, "Social Mobility and Family Size among Younger University of Illinois Faculty," *Population Index,* 29, 3 (July, 1963), pp. 219 ff.

49. Kiser and Whelpton, *op. cit.* (See n. 33, above.)

50. Kingsley Davis, "Institutional Patterns Favoring Fertility in Undeveloped Areas" in Lyle W. Shannon (ed.), *Underdeveloped Areas: A Book of Readings and Research* (New York: Harper, 1957), pp. 88–95. See also J. C. Ridley, "Number of Children Expected in Relation to Non-Familial Activities of Wife," The Milbank Memorial Fund *Quarterly,* XXXVII, 3 (July, 1959), pp. 277–96.

51. Later studies have supported this contention, such as Ronald Freedman, "The Sociology of Fertility," *Current Sociology* (Oxford), 10/11, 2 (1961–62).

52. William Arthur Lewis, *The Theory of Economic Growth* (London: Allen & Unwin, 1955), pp. 113–20; Kingsley Davis, *Human Society* (New York: Macmillan, 1950), p. 423.

53. S. M. Greenfield, "Industrialization and the Family in Sociological Theory," *American Journal of Sociology,* LXVII, 3 (Nov. 1961), pp. 312–22.

54. Michael Young and Peter Willmott, *Family and Kinship in East London* (London: Routledge & Kegan Paul, 1959), p. 232.

55. John M. Mogey, *Family and Neighbourhood: Two Studies in Oxford* (London: Oxford U. Press, 1956), p. 181; E. Litwak, "Occupational Mobility and Family Cohesion," *American Sociological Review,* XXV, 1 (Feb. 1960), pp. 9–20.

56. Ronald Freedman, quoted by Ridley, *op. cit.,* pp. 277–78.

57. Paul Vincent, "Recherches sur la fécondité biologique: Etude d'un groupe de familles nombreuses," *Population*, 1 (Jan./March 1961), pp. 105–112.

58. James H. S. Bossard, *The Large Family System* (U. of Pennsylvania Press, 1956), pp. 282–83.

59. P. S. Shenshaw, *Adaptive Human Fertility* (New York, McGraw Hill), p. 322.

60. Jacques Leclercq, *La famille* (Namur: Wesmael-Charlier, 1944), p. 246.

61. Louis Henry, "Natalité, Nuptialité, Fécondité" in G. Balandier (ed.), *Le "Tiers-Monde": sous-développement et développement* (Paris: Presses Universitaires, 1956), pp. 166–67. This is Cahier 27 in the INED series "Travaux et Documents."

62. *Ibid.*, p. 167.

63. Davis and Blake, *op. cit.*, p. 211 (see n. 33, above). See also Henry, *op. cit.*, pp. 159 ff.

64. Henry, *op. cit.*, p. 164.

65. We have not taken account here either of post-natal infanticide nor of the social and cultural factors involving infant mortality. On this score, a good work to consult is Alain Girard et al., *Facteurs sociaux et culturels de la mortalité infantile* (Paris: Presses Universitaires, 1960). This is Cahier 36 in the INED series "Travaux et Documents."

66. Davis and Blake, *op. cit.*, p. 235.

67. *Ibid.*, p. 236.

68. J. Schachter and W. H. Grabill, "Child Spacing as Measured from the Age of Children in the Household," The Milbank Memorial Fund *Quarterly*, XXXVI, 2 (1958), pp. 75–85. J. Sutter, "Attitudes devant la maternité: Une Enquête à Paris en service hospitalier," *Population*, XVI (April/May 1960), pp. 223–44. Westoff, Potter, Sagi, and Mishler, *op. cit.*, pp. 178–211.

69. Henry, *op. cit.*, pp. 172–73.

70. Ronald Freedman, Pascal K. Whelpton, and Arthur A. Campbell, *Family Planning, Sterility, and Population Growth* (New York: McGraw Hill, 1959), pp. 172–214.

71. Hill, Stycos, and Back, *op. cit.*, pp. 108–62 (see n. 33, above).

72. J. Mayone Stycos, "Some Directions for Research on Fertility Control," The Milbank Memorial Fund *Quarterly*, XXXVI, 2 (April, 1958), p. 139.

73. W. J. Goode, "A Theory of Role Strain," *American Sociological Review*, XXV, 4 (Aug. 1960), p. 489.

74. Among others, see Alva Myrdal and Viola Klein, *Women's Two Roles: Home and Work* (London: Routledge & Kegan Paul, 1956), also Janet Wolff, *What Makes Women Buy* (New York: McGraw Hill, 1958).

75. G. Jacquemyns, *Pour ou contre la limitation des naissances* (Brussels: I.N.S.O.C., 1952), p. 25.

76. J. Morsa, "Travail des femmes et natalité," *Revue de l'Institut de Sociologie Solvay* (Brussels), 2 (1959), pp. 233–63.

77. Richard L. Meier, *Modern Science and the Human Fertility Problem* (New York: John Wiley & Sons, 1959), pp. 142–43.

78. W. S. Woytinsky, "World Resources in Relation to Population" in Philip M. Hauser (ed.), *Population and World Politics* (Glencoe, Ill.: The Free Press, 1958), pp. 46–75.

79. Clément Mertens, *op. cit.*, pp. 114–23. (See n. 32, above.)

80. Msgr. Léon-Joseph Suenens, "Christianisme et Santé," *Collectanea Mechliniensa*, XLIII (Nov. 1958), 578–80.

81. E. Tesson, "Encore le contrôle des naissances," *Etudes*, CCCIX (June, 1961), 370.

82. Msgr. Léon-Joseph Suenens, *Amour et maîtrise de soi* (Bruges: Desclée de Brouwer, 1956), p. 230.

83. "Is the Church Populationist?" *Social Action*, II, 3 (March, 1961), 97–103.

84. Stanislas de Lestapis, S.J., *La limitation des naissances* (Paris: Editions Spes, 1959), p. 315. See *idem*, "Position catholique à l'égard du problème de la population et de limitation des naissances," in the U.I.O.F. (Union Internationale des Organismes Familiaux) Review *Familles dans le monde*, XII (Sept. 1959), 197–202. Clément Mertens, S.J., "Problèmes de la Population et Morale: faisons le point," *Nouvelle Revue Théologique* (Dec. 1959), pp. 1029–1048. William D. Gibbons, S.J., "Fertility Control in the Light of Some Recent Catholic Statements," *Eugenics Quarterly*, III, 82–87. Further references may be found in F. Campbell, "Birth Control and Christian Churches," *Population*, XIV, 2 (Nov. 1960), 131–47.

Chapter 6

How Food Production Has Developed

PRELIMINARY CONSIDERATIONS

METHODS OF MEASUREMENT

AT FIRST GLIMPSE, it must seem easy enough to take an accurate measure of anything so substantial as the food we eat. This is true enough where any single foodstuff or product is concerned, but here our problem is that of arriving at some accurate measure of world food production, so as to be able to judge its adequacy to the needs of the world's populations. Faced with particular quantities of various foodstuffs—wheat, cassava, rice, milk, meat, caviar, or truffles—what we obviously need is a common unit of measurement.

Now, monetary value is no help here. Even for the purpose of charting food production within a single country, prices fluctuate in time as well as from place to place. Economists have found how hard it is to work with such figures, nor are their difficulties solved when they draw a careful distinction between "current" prices and "constant" prices. The bigger the geographical area being studied, or the longer the period of time covered, the less satisfactory are money measures of value. For our purpose here, which is to study food production in relation to human needs, we must rule out this approach entirely.

Ever since Lavoisier made us grasp the analogy between combustion and life processes, we have been measuring the nutritive power of the foods we eat in terms of calories. Let us say that an adult human being of average height, average weight, etc., who does not perform hard physical labor, needs 2,500 calories a day to sustain life. From this we can readily calculate the average food requirements for a year, for any country whose population we know. Or, for that matter, for the whole world. One billion human beings, for example, would require:

$$2,500 \times 365 \times 1,000,000,000 = 9,125 \times 12^{11} \text{ calories.}$$

On the same assumption, even the most optimistic writers on this subject have admitted that from 10 per cent to 15 per cent of the total world population (excluding China) does not get enough to eat. The first attempt at a worldwide survey along these lines was undertaken in 1934–38, and the results were published by FAO in 1946. What it showed was that the average inhabitant in countries representing more than half the world population gets less than 2,250 calories per day. The average inhabitant in countries representing about one-sixth the world population gets between 2,250 and 2,750 calories per day, and somewhat less than one-third of the world population gets more than 2,750.

Living things look to food to supply them with more than combustible materials. Our "motors" just won't run on coal, hydrogen, and petroleum products. Nor is it merely enough for a product to be nontoxic in order to serve as food. Besides the calories, food must contain elements capable of keeping our motors well "lubricated" and in good "repair." Our bodies do not just require fuel, they must be kept in condition to reconstitute the living matter they take in. We owe this further step in our understanding of nutrition to nineteenth-century chemistry.

Viewed in this light, human nutrition embraces a very great number of chemical elements. The human organism is formed out of a certain number of them, which are present in precisely given proportions. As we exert ourselves, we lose a great many of them, and this loss must be made up promptly or the organism is in mortal danger. The list of basic, indispensable chemical elements has been drawn up, and how much the organism loses over a given period, as well as what it must without fail replenish, have both been calculated. As our bodies cannot manufacture these elements, we must supply our bodies with the food that contains them. As for what it should be, this is being spelled out ever more clearly from the chemical point of view.

Right down to the present century, it was believed that the human organism was capable of synthesizing all the molecules of which it is composed. We know better today. *Living things are not chemically self-sustaining.* There are numbers of molecular combinations—amino acids, fatty acids, vitamins—which the body is incapable of producing itself and which can only be supplied in the diet. These particular elements are, moreover, essential to life. A few tenths of a milligram less of any of them, due to insufficient or improper nutrition, and the organism falls sick and dies.[1] From what we know today of nutritional processes, we can readily deduce what a given population requires in the way of a suitable and sufficient diet, if it is to stay healthy and be able to work. Nutritionists today are about to dump an extraordinarily complex problem in the laps of the agronomists. We may, perhaps, risk an attempt to grasp its over-all dimensions.

Those who first advanced the proposition that calories are all that matter in human nutrition should have been rudely awakened by now. The notion that cheap calories in sufficient quantity are all that is needed to feed mankind, held the fancy of chemists who had not gone a step beyond Lavoisier. Did not Denis Papin in 1682, in a very curious work,[2] advance in favor of his pressure cooker that it was a "digestor," capable of making soup out of bones and other leftovers from the tables of the rich, suitable for nourishing the poor? How the apparatus was to be made to work only became clear to him somewhat later, after the Edict of Nantes had been revoked and he settled in Germany.[3] This and other "philanthropic" projects generally are disastrous. Scarcely has "undernourishment," or even "hunger," been theoretically conquered, when we find "malnutrition" making its appearance in the wake of various "deficiencies" and "specific hungers."

It was in connection with the study of certain spectacular diseases like scurvy, pellagra, beri-beri, and rickets, even advanced cases of which occasionally clear up miraculously with changes in the diet, that we first became aware of the "deficiencies" and "specific hungers." Among these are protein deficiencies (or deficiency in certain proteins) and mineral deficiencies (calcium deficiency, phosphorus deficiency). The best known today are the vitamin deficiencies, discovery of which had to wait until vitamins had been isolated in the first quarter of this century. What has only recently been discovered is that even before these diseases make their appearance, the specific undernourishment which causes them has already condemned its victims to a lifetime of diminished vitality.

What holds for adult life holds even more for organisms still in process of formation, or in process of giving life to new organisms. Without the proper food and enough of it these processes are seriously affected. Pregnant and nursing mothers, babies, and adolescents are especially vulnerable to the "specific hungers."*

Stock breeders brought our attention to one of the main "specific hungers": nitrogen deficiency, or, more properly, protein deficiency. Extended to the study of human nutrition, one of the first practical results was that those who are concerned with feeding people as cheaply as possible began to introduce dried vegetables into institutional diets. Peas, beans, and the other legumes now constitute, along with bread and water, the staple diet in such collective feeding places as prisons, armies, boarding schools, and the various sorts of big industrial and agricultural enterprise. That is, at the present stage of our knowledge of nutrition. Disasters still occur, however, for mankind is far less self-sustaining, chemically speaking, than the herbivorous animals. They can synthesize the amino acids within their own tissues, from the protein content in the plants they feed on.

Because we cannot do this, we have to supply these chemical elements from the animal foods which contain them: meat, fish,

* Failure to take account of these nutritional problems is what leads Colin Clark today to deny that two-thirds of the human race is undernourished.

eggs, dairy products. It is the presence or absence of these essential elements in the human diet that chiefly defines the differences between "nutritional levels" in different parts of the world today. Agricultural products do not supply them directly: the cereal grains or green plants must first have been assimilated by animals. We cannot expect to be supplied with the equivalent of a calorie of milk or meat by eating a calorie of the grasses or grains the animals eat.

On the basis of studies made in western Europe, the international organizations devoted to food and agriculture claim that the caloric proportion involved is 1:7. That is, for every calorie of animal products, seven calories of grasses or cereal grains will have been consumed by the animal.

This calculation supplies a basis for measuring agricultural production, or at least that part of it devoted to the raising of animal fodder and grains, in relation to dietary needs. The range of nutritional levels is much wider than had hitherto been recognized, between the extremes of feast and famine, from bounteous "overproduction" to extreme scarcity. The first world-wide survey showed that the average per capita consumption for some 70 countries varied between 1,900 calories and 3,300 calories. It must be noted that as the nutritional level rises, the percentage of calories derived from animal products increases sharply. In the most inadequate diets—around 1,900 calories per person per day—only about 100 come from animal sources. The production required to supply this "diet," breaks down to 1,800 calories of plant and cereal origin directly consumed, and 7 × 100, or 700 more of the same calories consumed by animals. This gives a total of 2,500 vegetable (i.e., primary or original) calories.

In the diets of well-nourished persons—3,600 calories per person per day—as many as 1,100 may be supplied by animal products. Such a diet requires the production of 2,500 vegetable calories consumed directly, plus 7 × 1,100, or 7,700 more calories consumed by animals. A total of 10,200 primary or original calories. In other words, four times the food production is needed to sustain this nutritional level than was needed for the very inadequate one cited above. It is just not true that, "Given enough calories, the rest will take care of itself." There have to be enough calories, but a portion of them must come from animal products. A somewhat better wording would state approximately this: "Given enough primary, vegetable calories, malnutrition and undernourishment will be overcome."

We ourselves showed, in 1953, that calculating in primary, vegetable calories, besides providing a measure of agricultural production, also provides a closer correlation with such elements of human welfare as the sanitary level.[4] This is not illogical, when you reflect that animal products are expensive, as are the other foods rich in those "protective elements" essential to combat malnutrition and the "specific hungers." Naturally, anyone who has managed to obtain a sufficient number of the former will at the same time introduce the latter into his daily diet.

It was when we were drawing up the statistical laws that seem to govern food consumption, from the extreme of feast or plenty to the extreme of scarcity or famine, that we were led to make the following three-fold breakdown of foodstuffs, each of which when graphed displays a different developmental curve:

1. The dry vegetables or pulses (dry beans, dry peas, broad beans, chick-peas, lentils), consumption of which declines as the nutritional level rises;

2. The "expensive" foods: milk, meat, eggs, fish, the oils and fats, and sugar, consumption of which increases as the nutritional level rises;

3. Cereal, grains, and the root vegetables, maximum consumption of which is no greater among the well-nourished than among the most gravely undernourished.[5]

The characteristic curves are illustrated in the graphs of TABLES 59, 59A.

Mankind's earliest concern is to find food in quantitative sufficiency (approximately 2,500 calories as ordinarily figured), including a certain amount of proteins besides those to be obtained

TABLE 59

How the Average Consumption (in calories) of the Principal
Food Products Increases in Relation to Total Food
Consumption (in calories) per Person and per Day

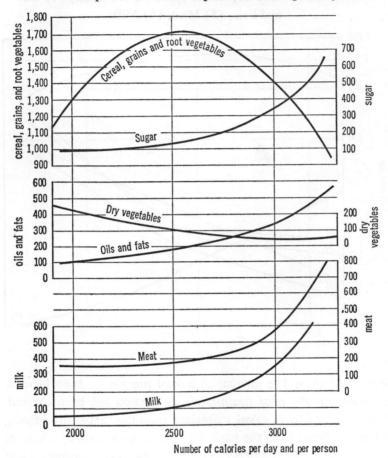

Number of calories per day and per person

TABLE 59A

Transposition of the Consumption Curves Shown in the Preceding
Graph to Semi-Logarithmic Scale: (1) Cereal, Grains and Root
Vegetables, (2) Dry Vegetables (pulses), (3) Sugar, (4) Oils
and Fats, (5) Meat, (6) Milk

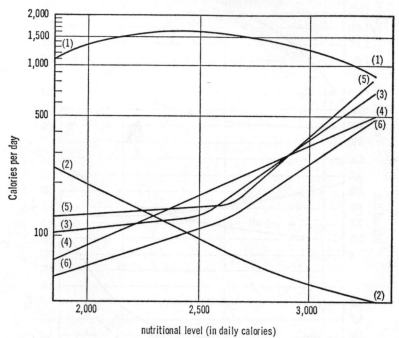

from the pulses. The amount of animal protein tends to increase
the more rapidly once quantitative satisfaction has been assured,
with more and more calories obtained from the "expensive" foods,
fewer and fewer from the basic foodstuffs. In the case of sugar, its
degree of consumption under any circumstances is determined more
by economic than by physiological considerations. When we break
down foodstuffs into three divisions only:

P   animal products (exclusive of butter)
L   oils and fats
G   all other

and draw up a curve of consumption for each on a graph with triangular co-ordinates, there is sufficient alignment to calculate the formula for any diet composed of items from the three groups. Utilizing our data, J. Carrié drew up one such formula:

$$0.01\,G + 1.56\,L - 0.86\,P = 0$$
$$P + L - G = 100$$

Any deviation relative to the average dietary composition which such a formula gives, is highly significant. The proportion of *P* to *L* stays very close to 2 in any average diet, and important changes in the value of *G* do not affect much the proportion of *P* to *L*, so that the measure of nutritional level in primary, vegetable calories would seem at a rough glance to be characteristic. Correlated with data as to health and living standards, this measure gives us the most exact information.

A population's health standards (over-all mortality, diseases and deaths from special causes, expectation of life at birth) are, indeed, much more closely tied in with the nutritional level when the latter is figured in vegetable calories than when it is figured in "final" calories. Take, for example, the diet of a well-to-do, country-dwelling Muslim in North Africa. He consumes 5,000 "final" calories per day, 80 per cent of which come from cereal grains, only 155 calories from animal products. This is a nutritional level of less than 6,000 vegetable calories per day, and not really higher than that of populations among the best-nourished anywhere in the world, also figured in "final" calories. It is close to the nutritional level of countries in western and eastern Europe which, over the years 1934–38, had an average diet of about 6,000 primary or vegetable calories.

P. V. Sukhatme, who heads the statistical branch of FAO, made a study of the different units of measurement proposed for calculating levels of nutrition, and concluded that the vegetable (primary or original) calorie gives the best simple scale, in terms both of food production and of human needs.

VEGETABLE CALORIES

The method is very simple, for it involves no more than adding to the number of calories consumed daily in vegetable products, the number daily consumed in animal products, this last multiplied by any arbitrary coefficient equal to 7.

How many calories from vegetable sources may be required to make one calorie of animal origin varies a great deal. Relatively few are required in the production of milk, pork meat, and fowl. The number increases for beef and is still higher for veal. Depending on a country's stock raising characteristics, it is possible to correlate human consumption with the production of vegetable calories. The correlation is expressed in the formula

$$y = \frac{1}{1 + (k-1)\, x}$$

where x is the fraction of animal calories in the total diet.

Goreux has given examples using a coefficient k taken at random, but equal to 10. For the first world survey of food production we used the coefficient $k = 7$. In a note to the published edition, FAO remarked that the multiplier necessarily "varies, of course, from one class of livestock to another and also among countries, according to differences in the quality of livestock and in feeding practices. Further research is needed on this subject, but the argument is essentially the same whether the multiplier is 4, 7, 10, or some other number."[6]

Not only does the reasoning remain the same, but even with a multiplier chosen arbitrarily, it is possible to establish the various rates of return on stock production and to compare them, whether as between countries or as between differently organized production methods. Here are two examples.

Pre-war Germany required 9.2 vegetable calories to obtain 1 calorie from animal production, while the Netherlands in the same period required 7 vegetable calories. Here are some postwar figures:

	Germany	Netherlands
1954	8.2	6.85
1955	8.7	6.9
1956	8.3	6.85
1957	8.3	6.95
1958	8.5	6.9

Now, the question is, are we in each instance to take the above figures for our multiplier? We believe it is more practical to keep to the arbitrary coefficient of 7, and at the same time to point out how the return from animal production has varied in the two countries:

	Pre-war	1954	1955	1956	1957	1958
Germany	76	85	80	84	84	83
Netherlands	100	102	101.5	102	100.5	101.5

And even if, at some future time, we were able to replace some of the animal products indispensable today with certain vegetable products, so as to bring the diet up to a decent nutritional level, there would still be no need to change the arbitrary multiplier, $k = 7$. It is true that we might just as well have picked another numerical value, but the problem which has seemed to be raised is not really a problem—not any more than choice of the value zero to represent a certain point on the thermometer (Centigrade, Fahrenheit, or Réaumur) poses a real problem.

With the aid of the coefficient 7, we can measure in primary or vegetable calories the agricultural product per acre in all the principal parts of the world.* FAO has worked out the figures for the period before World War II. We can also figure agricultural pro-

* The metric measure *hectare* (2.47 acres) is used in all UN studies. *Transl. note.*

duction in terms of vegetable calories per inhabitant, per agricultural laborer, or, when data are lacking on agricultural production, per unit of the rural population. Such figures bring out differences between (1) intensive and extensive agriculture (high or low yield per hectare) and (2) between "active" agriculture (plentiful labor supply) and "progressive" agriculture (ample capital investment).

For the period prior to World War II, agriculture in the Far East was intensive and active (according to this classification), that in North America extensive and progressive. That of western Europe was intensive and relatively progressive.

We must here call attention to the relativity of notions like Colin Clark's and Fourastié's, as to the number of inhabitants fed by a single agricultural worker. These economists have tried to make this the sole criterion of agricultural productivity. Actually, the notion must vary widely with the nutritional level of the consumer involved.[7]

Period 1934–1938

	North America	Far East	Western Europe
Production (in veg. calories)			
per day per hectare	6,250	13,750	18,750
per day per unit of rural population	39,300	3,270	14,250
per day per capita	10,000	2,750	5,250
Consumption (in veg. calories)			
per day per capita	8,577	2,871	6,845

Number of Inhabitants Fed
(at the prevailing consumption level)

	North America	Far East	Western Europe
1. Per hectare			
North America	0.75	1.6	2.18
Far East	2.18	4.8	6.5
Western Europe	0.91	2.06	2.74
2. Per unit of rural population			
North America	4.6	0.44	1.66
Far East	13.7	1.3	4.95
Western Europe	5.75	0.48	2.08

MAN, PARASITE AND PREDATOR

Darwin claimed that Malthus had inspired his theory of the survival of the fittest, according to which it is a law of life that the proliferating vital powers must be more than a match for the conditions they find themselves in. We have already called attention to Karl Marx's criticism of Darwin in this connection.* Marx observed that Darwin seemed unaware he had invalidated Malthus' theory with his own discovery of the geometrical rate of growth of plants and animals. "Malthus' whole theory consists of opposing to the geometric rate at which the human race multiplies, a chimerical arithmetic rate at which plants and animals multiply." And we showed earlier that Malthus' law does not apply solely to the human species; in effect, it is a special case of biological laws which apply to any group of living things.

As an animal, man appears as a parasite with remarkably little specificity of adaptation. He is capable of going anywhere within the biological continuum, indeed, he has of late even gone outside it entirely. This last point would be of no importance unless there were other environments capable of supporting life elsewhere than on this planet. Because he is not chemically self-sufficient, man must draw his nourishment from his environment, must be able to prey on other living things. Humanity's future, as an animal species, is ruled by the laws of parasitism, though the forms of its mastery over the planet go much farther than any mere predator-prey, host-parasite relationship. With varying degrees of success, mankind extends its dominion over whole plant and animal populations. Even at the simplest stages of human economy, the food-gathering, hunting, and fishing stages, man's use of tools projects his power far afield, beyond the scope of what would seem to be his normal, natural powers. Already his reason and his cognitive capacities are enhancing his mastery of his environment, making it more profitable to him, better organized for his needs.

With the development of agriculture and stock raising, man

* See above, pp. 66–67.

ceases merely to take his prey where he finds it, and assumes control over whole plant and animal populations. Now he is in danger of abusing his powers, of imperiling his own future by destroying the populations under his sway.

However, by respecting them he can also enable his species to overcome the evil fate which seems to preside over other parasitic and predatory species. In any case, he has already shown himself to be less and less confined within the narrowly biological limits which nature seems to impose on his species (one of the least well endowed by purely animal standards). This is "the phenomenon of man," as Teilhard de Chardin phrased it, whose basic orientation it is "to reach Heaven through earthly achievement."[8]

THE HISTORY OF FOOD PRODUCTION

FOOD-GATHERING, HUNTING, AND FISHING

The most primitive forms of human economy consist of merely collecting nature's bounty where it may be found, whether among plant life (food-gathering proper) or among animal life (hunting and fishing). At this stage man is a true predator (a *Wildbeuter,* as the German sociologists put it), who lives off other species of life. He would be at the mercy of the same dangers that threaten other parasites and predators, if he did not bring his reason to bear on the problem of how to make his efforts more productive.

In view of its polyvalence, what a given people eats at the food-gathering stage must vary widely. For a balanced diet, food must be available in sufficient quantity, and this is the chief nutritional problem. Climate is an important factor, with its alternation of hot and cold, dry and rainy seasons. For one part of the year nature is lavish with her gifts, but for another part she supplies little or nothing for men to eat. In this connection, since man is not a narrowly specialized parasite, it might seem that Volterra's laws must apply, and that in poor seasons man would simply turn to other sources of food. However, his environment is much affected by the choices he makes and by the varying degrees of resistance he meets from the species he preys upon. At this stage of human economy, he is not a producer but a destroyer; his labors are purely negative. As soon as his consumption has gone beyond the capacities of the plant and animal world around him to supply his needs, he finds himself working harder and harder and eating less and less well.

What we should expect to happen in these circumstances does happen. The most highly prized species are the first to be destroyed, and so become scarcer and scarcer. There is no longer enough of them to go around, and a policy of dietary discrimination is introduced. The more vulnerable portions of the population begin to exhibit serious deficiencies; rising mortality strikes especially at those who are left behind when the food-gathering expeditions set out. The women, children, and old people will often develop protein deficiencies, most notably, as the tribe finds it necessary to forage farther and farther afield and to be gone for longer and longer periods. And even the hunters and fishermen will find their diets becoming more monotonous and less well balanced, for only so much can be carried with them on a long expedition: they will miss the basic staple foods and vitamins of vegetable origin. The prevalence of scurvy among fishermen long at sea is a case in point.

Moreover, as more and more labor comes to be required in the food-gathering societies, nutritional needs are themselves stepped up for the hardest workers. The sum total of these needs may well rise above the nutritive content of the food gathered for the entire population, as game gets scarcer and there are more mouths to feed from the same trees and plants. Whether the natural resources have been literally exhausted, or merely have become scarcer, the effect is the same. To state the problem as simply as possible, where it had formerly cost 50 calories to gather the equivalent of 100, now the greater exertions involved cost 100 or 150 calories to gather the same amount of food. Under such circumstances, there can only be a slowing down of effort, irrespective of the relative

"exhaustion" of the natural resources. Now, rather than weary himself further, man will simply not bother with the fruit high up in the
tree, the fish in distant, deeper waters, or the game which does not
fall in his nets of itself.

The more primitive the means employed by mankind in the
food-gathering stage, the more likely it is that predation will be
limited by the limitations of the human efforts involved. The environment will not be completely destroyed, so long as people are
not equipped to take more than nature can produce. Under the
circumstances, the numbers of human beings can hardly increase to
any great extent. And yet, can we say that such a check on population growth is caused by insufficiency of the natural resources?
They are available enough, surely, and the fact that they cannot be
utilized is explained rather by insufficient productivity on the part
of the human labor.

Reflecting on these matters, we may be led to conclude that
labor can and should be closely correlated with the nutritional
level, and that when it is not, we may speak of "food shortage."
We can graph the individual's situation on this score, taking into
account his nutritional needs, both to sustain life (maintenance
ration) and to perform work (labor ration). As TABLE 60 shows,
there is a theoretical point at which the volume of needs is balanced
by a food supply just sufficient to meet them.

When we read the graph as applying to an entire population, not
just to an individual, we may think of it as defining at least theoretically a population which is not at all "limited" (a term that
suggests a population maximum, anything less than which must
imply that things would be better), but narrowly determined by the
environment. Active underpopulation, as well as active overpopulation, would on this hypothesis lead to a food shortage. Of course,
where a whole population is involved, the maintenance ration (M)
consists of the total subsistence needs, both of nonactive and active
members, while the labor or production ration (L) consists of the
supplementary requirements of that portion of the population engaged in work. Balance between them, on this definition, would

TABLE 60

Relationship between Nutritional Ration and Labor Ration
and Productivity

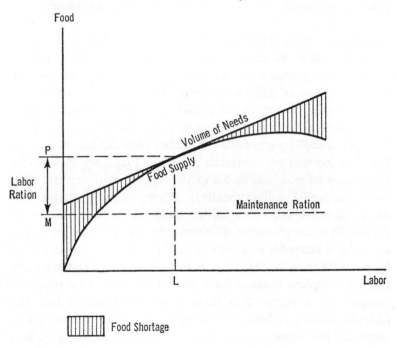

[|||||||] Food Shortage

come about as a result of lowered productivity (with respect to food-gathering), on the one hand, and increased consumption, on the other. However, it may be remarked that seasonal variations, for example, in the correlation of needs with the volume of food gathered, lead to periods of relative abundance and scarcity. We may gain the impression that populations so stabilized are, not at some possible optimum, but already far beyond the maximum limit which it is always tempting to refer to.

In the middle Paleolithic (the age of chipped stone implements), the total population of the globe could hardly have been more than a few hundred thousand, one million at the most, and that of Gaul 50,000 at the most (cf. Cailleux 1951, Nougia 1959). Theirs was still a wretched, poverty-stricken existence. Their ways of exploiting the resources of nature brought them so meager a return that, paradoxically, we may say that the planet was already overpopulated.[9]

This passage from Henri Prat shows to what extent "overpopulation," at least at the stage of human development we are examining, may be a phenomenon altogether independent of the question of the adequacy of natural resources. Rather, it is a consequence of the inability of mankind at certain levels of technological development to make the most of nature's bounty. Moreover, a globe "overpopulated" by one million wretched Neanderthals was to stay like that for tens of thousands of years. Predatory Neanderthal man, *homo faber,* constituted a species whose population was stabilized at around 1 million members. When the environmental conditions changed and *homo sapiens* made his appearance towards the middle of the glaciation of Worms, the species began to die out. It had been incapable of increasing and multiplying, because it had been unable to make the earth its own. We call the successor species *homo sapiens* because from his first appearance he resembled ourselves to a degree that none of his predecessors had (the Chapelle-aux-Saints Man, for example). Were we to meet a Cro-Magnon Man today, dressed like ourselves, in the street or on a bus, we would not find him especially remarkable, but would probably take him for another European, Asiatic, or African.

Of course, *homo sapiens* is a *faber,* too. His reaction to poverty and scarcity was to address himself to the factor which limited his population growth as well as his standard of living, namely, the low level of his own productivity. In two different ways he set out enhance the range of his parasitism, first by bringing new plant and animal species under his dominion, and then by discovering hitherto untapped sources of wealth. Already polyvalent in his parasitism, he would make ever greater efforts to extend that polyvalence and to cut down the number of his specialized dependencies. He it was who gave names to all living things and thereby singled out and took possession of the ones most useful to the satisfaction of his needs. He multiplied (and is still multiplying) the number of technical inventions he inherited. With him, tools will increase the productivity of his labor ever more astonishingly.

What Böhm-Bawerk calls "the capitalist economic detour" is valid enough as a theoretical construction, but is unreal as a description of the process which has occurred. As is known, this Austrian economist's classic example is the fisherman who, rather than devote his energies to "productive" work by going fishing, instead uses his labor power to construct a net, by means of which he will be able to catch many more fish than before with the same expenditure of effort. What is unreal about the notion, is that it fails to take account of one essential element of primitive life. Nobody works all the time; there are occasions that are not suitable, periods when it would be pointless to work. The fisherman does not make a net *instead* of going fishing, he does so when for some reason he *can't* go fishing—or, on analogy from what goes on in many a human community, assigns the chore of making nets to those members who for some reason can't go fishing themselves. Investment in equipment, at so primitive a level of human economy at least, does not represent some *sidetracking* of immediately productive labor power, but rather a supplementing of it with some otherwise unused labor power which is not involved in "production" to begin with. What happens here, this so-called "detour," is to be met with at every stage of economic development.

Before going on to more elaborate stages of human economy, it should be noted that food-gathering activities still play their part in the "system of production," even in the world today, and are not essentially different for the fact that the tools involved have reached a high degree of perfection. Whaling, as it is carried on today by factory-ships equipped with radar and every other twentieth-century device, remains nonetheless a food-gathering activity. Whatever we may have to say about the problems posed by such a form of production applies no less (perhaps rather more) to the modern instance than to primitive ones. Neanderthal men, we have seen, did not pose much of a threat to the life they preyed upon, and Volterra's laws would seem to apply to them, especially the more somber predictions about the fate that lies in store for predatory species. However, as man has perfected his methods of food-gathering, he has become a real threat to the animal and plant populations he exploits. He can destroy them outright, or, what is worse, so far interfere with a so-called "ecological balance" that his environment rapidly is turned into a wasteland.

Nobody can count the numbers of useful plant and animal species which are no more, because man has demanded more of nature's productivity than she can produce. It is characteristic of the food-gathering economy that man does not himself produce, but merely *appropriates.* Nature alone *produces,* because she alone *reproduces.* Though it was seriously misunderstood after them, this was the insight that informed the Physiocrats' theory of "the net product."[10] The best example of a rational food-gathering economy is provided by the "scientific forestry" which is still practiced in only a very small fraction of the world's timber reserves. The principle involved is that of preserving the forest's capacity to reproduce, while at the same time getting a continuous return out of it.

The principle of "continuous return" is at the bottom of scientific forestry. According to Franz Hezke, it was practiced in Germany 1,000 years ago. Sweden was practicing it around 1600, and it was little by little established in France after Philippe IV founded the Services des Eaux et Forêts around 1300. FAO proposed it to all its member states in 1951 as the essence of a forestry policy. The same principle informs international treaties on fishing rights and the successive international conferences since the London conference of 1937–38 for the regulation of the whaling industry.

Scientific forestry can serve as an example of an artificial "balance of nature" more adequate to human needs than the real thing. By means of it, forests can be created which give a much better continuous return from the species desired than any "forest primeval." Of course, this amounts to treating timber as a crop. Similarly, a rational hunting or fishing economy might take steps to assure itself of a "continuous return." But this is not enough: the species adjudged most useful should be protected against the hazards of their environment, that is, should be "raised" or "bred."

But now the discussion is taking us beyond the boundaries of the food-gathering economy, on to new forms of civilization: to *agriculture* and *stockbreeding*. The last-named first takes the form of what is called the "pastoral economy." It might be defined as a special case of the food-gathering economy, which utilizes domesticated animals to transform plant life into animal products such as man in turn "gathers" for his own consumption.

PASTORAL ECONOMY

As we have just defined it, the pastoral economy is that kind of life which was promised the Chosen People in "a land that is all milk and honey" (Deut. 6:3). There had been some domesticated animals in the food-gathering economy, such as hunting dogs, birds used as decoys, pigs for rooting out truffles, etc. Here and there animals were trained to do the actual food-gathering: falcons and hawks, cheetahs in the East, cormorants for fishing, etc. However, what characterizes the pastoral economy is that a higher value is set on the product made by the domesticated animal (meat, milk, eggs, honey, fur, wool, etc.) than on the *uncultivated* products of nature consumed by the animal. The bee is the most perfect example, for it raids a source of wealth in nature which is useless to man until this tiniest of the "domestic animals" has transformed it into honey. The more general case, however, is the nomad shepherd moving his flock or herd from place to place in search of pasture. Again, grass is for the most part a product of nature of no direct utility to man—though China, where it is burned for fuel when wood is unavailable, provides a notable exception.

What is problematical in such an economy is no different in principle from what was problematical in the food-gathering economy. Man has increased his polyvalence through the instrumentality of the domestic animals, by means of which he can prey on additional plant species. Caring for certain animal species at the expense of others, he places nature at the service of his own satisfactions by obliging her to favor the increase of the domestic species. He combats the factors that would limit the increase of their population; especially, since he would be the sole parasite on (and sole predator at the expense of) their population, he destroys species that dispute his possession or would rival it. Now his talent for organization is exercised in the search for good pasture and the best places to water his herd. Whether his techniques derive from magic or from science, they demand knowledge of open country, and the nomad of the steppes, the grasslands, the tundras, and the mountain slopes finds the answer to his problems in the heavens. They guide him and help him to forecast things to come. The nomad shepherd constantly tries to extend the boundaries of his domain, at the expense of the forest which holds his two worst enemies: wild animals and hunters. His weapon against them is fire, which destroys the trees he abhors and which clears new ground for pasture. In the high grass country, periodic fires get rid of predators and improve the quality of the plant life. This is a step toward the agricultural economy proper, for as Jean Brunhes has phrased it, "To till the soil is to modify the carpet of plant life."

The shepherd intervenes as well in the reproductive processes of the domestic species, to keep their numbers up to the maximum which the environment can support or—at least—up to what he supposes that maximum to be. Again, on the score of quantitative considerations, he observes that most species have more males than maximal reproduction requires, and so it will be among the males that he looks to satisfy his personal consumption needs. Considering his future needs, he will castrate a number of the males and keep them with the rest of the herd. Castration is necessary, in this instance, if his own needs are to be met without increasing the population of the herd beyond what he considers the maximal number. Even quite "primitive" hunters learn to kill male animals in preference to the females, the cock pheasants rather than the hens, for example. Similarly the raiser of goats "thins out" the ranks of the he-goats when their numbers become disproportionate to those of the she-goats. On the score of quality, the shepherd is more systematic than the hunter about destroying diseased or ill-favored animals. He does not trust "natural selection" to take care of this for him—which, we may recall, is a process that too often "cripples more than it kills" (René Sand). Indeed, he protects the species he lives off against the hazards of natural selection, thereby bringing into being his own process of "rational selection." Similarly, on the score of genetic quality, man brings his own will to bear on the animal processes of sexual choice, which Charles Darwin saw as the blind agency of "natural selection." His own criteria replace the seeming freedom of animal couplings, in order to produce a breed more in conformity with his own interests or fancy.

Though it seems to us that the means of subsistence constitute the dominant factor, we must not fail to note that the shepherd is influenced by other considerations as well. We mentioned them earlier in discussing populationist ideas in ancient times. To many a shepherd the head-count is the sole criterion; numbers mean more to him than the condition of his beasts. Other shepherds, however, are willing to limit numbers in favor of handsome, healthy animals such as "do them proud." It is rare, before modern capitalism, to find economic return constituting the principal value in stock raising.

At a fairly early stage we find man including other men among the animal species he exploits. Even food-gathering societies may go in for raids on other communities, and hunt down human beings as though they were prey, though this is comparatively rare among truly primitive peoples. Cannibalism in all the animal species, including man, seems to be a phenomenon of group degeneration when it is not simply a reaction to some extreme situation like famine. The more frequent motive for hunting down other men is to rob them of their possessions. Raids for the purpose of getting women appear at a somewhat higher level of society. "Thou shalt not steal," in such groups, applies only within the group, not where outsiders are concerned, and "Thou shalt not take thy neighbor's wife" means "close neighbor," not the members of another tribe. Still later, it is the labor power of other men that is appropriated, or other qualities they possess (as in the slavery of the Greco-Roman world). When we move from the food-gathering to the pastoral economy, the domestic animal becomes man's slave, and the owner of herds thinks of himself as superior to the slave in those "patriarchal" societies most often found among pastoral peoples. The best status the slave can aspire to is to be treated as a child (*puer, paidon*), a status that assumes "paternalism" on the part of his "master." In more attenuated form, this attitude carries over into societies of the hierarchical type—those governed by a single sovereign or by an oligarchy. In them the patrician ruling class looks upon the plebs, the people, much as the shepherd looks upon his flock, as creatures to be looked after. In such societies the temptation is great for those in power to go beyond this—beyond any mere "administering of the goods of the poor" or concern for "the common weal"—and to take a hand in the proliferation of the "flock" or "herd." Policy will most often be populationist on the score of quantity, eugenicist on the score of quality. We have already touched on this matter in an earlier chapter briefly reviewing the history of population theories, but the foregoing analysis of features of the pastoral economy will perhaps cast further light. There have been many societies where the peasants come under the control of "owners" who, though they may themselves be tillers of the soil, think of themselves not as peasants but as "shepherds of peasants." The actual work is done by farm laborers: the helots of Sparta, slaves, the Roman *coloni,* medieval serfs, latterday paid agricultural "hands."

In such societies, "agriculture" is indeed carried on, but decisions remain with a master class of "shepherds." We shall have to come back to this arrangement, but we should not confuse it with the agricultural economy proper, to which we turn now.

AGRICULTURAL ECONOMY

What characterizes an agricultural economy is not just the tilling of the soil, but—to repeat Jean Brunhes' phrase—the modification of "the natural carpet" of plant life. The shepherd who sets fire to the brush or the forest does indeed alter the plant life and is taking a step towards agriculture, but this is not how agriculture begins, especially not "peasant" agriculture. It makes its appearance, rather, among hunting and fishing peoples who live in settled communities, and most often before any animals have been domesticated. It is usually the women who are the first to observe the effect of human occupation on the plant life (through the manuring of the soil). The plant species sought after for food grow more thickly and abundantly close to the village huts than elsewhere. Soon the mystery of the grain and of seeds is plumbed, and the women begin to sow and plant where the ground is most propitious. Once they have learned to turn over the soil at planting time, with the aid of a "digging stick" which can serve both as planting tool and plough, they are in possession of the basic elements of all agriculture. Cato the Elder's words on this score are still valid today: *Quid est agrum bene colere? bene arare. Quid secundum? arare. Quid tertium? stercorare.*

Gradually the clearing in the forest, which at first had been no more than a place to live, becomes a place of tilled fields. Bit by bit it is discovered that working the land is more "productive" than going on food-gathering expeditions. The principal foods can be grown in sufficient quantities close to the place where they are to be consumed. All that is required is human labor, which takes on greater importance here than in other systems of production, especially than in that type Aristotle characterized as distinguished by the "poetic" labor of the decision-making master as opposed to the "servile" labor of those who carry out his decisions. Gradually, over the ages, agricultural efficiency will grow as mankind develops more and better tools. The history of agriculture is summed up in the history of the plough, in the development that one German sociologist has called "From the Hoe to the Plough."[11] Or, as we might put it ourselves: from the digging stick to the mechanical harvester.

From the first, agriculture seems to have been an activity pursued by sedentary peoples, whereas the pastoral economy was naturally conducive to nomadism. With continuous dwelling on the same land comes awareness of how human effort makes "basic improvements" on that land and increases its fertility. Whereas in the food-gathering economy the only investment had been improvements in "harvesting" and "storing" nature's bounty, now it involves something more than invention of tools for more effective parasitism and predation (as in the Austrian economist's example of the fisherman and his net). Now the productiveness of the soil is increased, and the numbers and quality of plants—eventually the numbers and quality of animals as well. Nature's own production is being improved upon. With agriculture, human labor becomes a factor, not just for reaping nature's immediate bounty (food-gathering, hunting, fishing) or former bounty (mining), but a factor in the natural processes of production themselves.

The classic economists who studied these matters almost entirely neglected this essential phenomenon. A sociologist of rural origin would be tempted to put it down to the fact they were all city dwellers. One of the most typical expressions is the theory of "ground rent," as Ricardo presented it. It may be worth bringing up here because it seems to underlie tendencies to take a pessimistic view of humanity's future.

Ricardian rent is based upon the varying fertility of different soils. We might have mentioned it in connection with the food-gathering economy: some regions have more game than other regions, some fishing grounds are better than others, and the plant life people can eat is more abundant in some places than in others. Naturally enough, all other things being equal, mankind prefers to settle in such "earthly paradises."

Again, the basis for the theory turns up also in pastoral economy. Some pastures are greener, can support bigger herds, have a plant life that makes for healthier animals. As the hunter or herdsman population increases beyond the capacity of nature to support it, it may wipe out the plant life or the animal life it lives to exploit. Necessarily the survivors find themselves worse off than the earliest settlers were, perhaps obliged to seek out some new and less promising territory than the "original" one was before mankind's powers of destruction devastated it.

As for the agricultural economy, Ricardo supposed that the earliest inhabitants in any region settled in the most fertile lands, and that those who came later had to be content with less fertile areas where the costs of agricultural production must be higher. Then, once the market price is established—according to this classic economist—on the basis of the highest cost of production, the earliest inhabitants will profit by an "excess" return on their production. This is economic, or Ricardian, rent.

Historically, however, nothing like this takes place. The first lands to be put under cultivation were most often those where it was healthiest to live, those which were easiest to work, or which (in the case of cleared land) involved the least felling of trees, etc. They were not chosen so much for their agricultural potential as for being good places for human settlement. Basic improvements will have increased the fertility of such lands before settlers go out from them and find regions of greater natural fertility, but which because of distance from the settlement involve greater investment of human energies to be put under cultivation in their turn.

Rent, however, in this sense of a return on "the original and indestructible powers of the soil," does not just include an "excess" due to differences in the natural fertility of different lands. Nearly always it includes as well, and to a more important degree of the total, a value due solely to what has been invested in the land. Even in its earliest stages, agriculture was not just conservationist, but also improvement-minded. Technical progress in agricultural methods, as well as "basic improvements," make the concept of fertility ever more complex and changing.

Though we think of fertility as inherent in the land, we must not neglect the function of climate. When the Physiocrats spoke of *la terre*, they meant the whole concatenation of natural factors. Most soils can be improved in quality, but climate sets a limit to what crops can be grown. Of all the ways in which we create "artificial" environments, those we employ to control or improve upon the weather are among the most costly. What has been called "mastery over water" probably represents man's most effective intervention on this score. Control of light and temperature involves heavy investment, too. But even allowing for the role of climate, we have still to arrive at a more precise understanding of the notion of fertility. With respect to any given crop, it may be thought of from three different and frequently contradictory points of view: *a*) Quantity, *b*) Quality, *c*) Uniformity. Let us take viticulture, the cultivation of the grape, as an example to show how conceptions of fertility can differ. Quality production (*b*) is often to be had at the margin of cultivation, that is, in places which neither give a high yield, quantitatively (*a*), nor can be counted upon season after season (*c*). Here the vines are more subject to such hazards as frost and hail, plant diseases, and parasites. Production is uncertain and risky in the extreme. In this connection it could be objected to Ricardo that the return on a vineyard of given fertility (*a, b,* and/or *c*) is not necessarily matched by a given cash value. In a commercial economy, distance from the market is a factor that enters in also, so that economic uncertainty is added to technical risk and uncertainty in this connection.

Let us get back to the topic of investment in "basic improvements." We may note that it is an especially delicate matter, to figure out the exact increase in productivity that results. Besides costs, we have to take into account values often neglected or underestimated, human values in particular. To drain the swamps of the Mitidja (in Algeria), much less money was spent than has since been spent on similar operations elsewhere. You might conclude that it was a relatively "inexpensive" form of basic agricultural improvement, if you leave out of account the deaths due to malaria because of the slowness with which the land was reclaimed. On the other hand, financiers poured money into the French province of Brie to make it a better place to live and to stimulate agriculture there, without getting much of a return. They wrote it off as a "prestige investment." Nonetheless, the economically conscious people who live there today and work the land are doing very well for themselves.

Besides immediate results in the form of increased productivity, basic agricultural improvements involve also such matters as the employment they give (in a country like Italy, for example), and the improvements in public health they bring about (draining the swamps in southern Italy, and in the Tennessee Valley in the United States, for example). To account for the expenses involved against the results achieved is not easy. The Tennessee Valley Authority devised a "yardstick" for costs in this connection, but one may wonder if it is possible to devise an accounting system for the human labor involved, especially in a situation of underemployment. Egbert de Vries and O. Zaglita presented a paper to the World Population Congress in Rome which will permit us to touch again upon the matter of Böhm-Bawerk's theory of "the capitalist economic detour."

They calculated the number of man-hours spent taking care of a water buffalo in Indonesia, including the labor involved in producing feed for the animal. Then they compared this figure with the number of man-hours saved in a year by using the water buffalo. The result is at first glance deceptive: the two figures are so close we may as well consider them equal.

Now, a specialist in agricultural production might conclude from the above that from the economic point of view it is of no consequence whether water buffaloes are used in Indonesian agriculture or not. It seems a highly unprogressive practice. But of course there is more to it than meets the eye. Use of the buffalo makes possible a better distribution of human labor over the course of the year. The buffalo is a kind of storage battery of human labor, thanks to whom seasonal underemployment can be cut down. The same labor force produces more food than it otherwise would. Though the end product cost the same number of man-hours per unit of production, the end product was greater per unit of human labor when spread over the year. Just as the fisherman doesn't make a net to avoid going fishing, so taking care of the water buffalo doesn't steal man-hours of work from the rice paddy. The animal is looked after at other times, and thanks to it more man-hours are available for the rice paddy (the man's labor plus the animal's). One man can work a bigger rice paddy than he would be able to do without the water buffalo: this is progress. In most primitive agricultural societies, the seasonal character of the work is a principal obstacle to economic development and doubtless the one it is most profitable to attack, but should we look upon seasonal unemployment of this type as equivalent to unemployment in industry? Investment, whether of capital or of man-hours (of labor that might or might not be otherwise expended), is in agriculture a means of increasing fertility, of enhancing nature's productive capacities. A number of key events in human history cannot be understood unless this is taken into account.

In ancient Greece, the first peasant settlements were on the mountain slopes, for the plains were unhealthy. Not until great landowners arose, warlords with plenty of slaves gained as the prize of battle, did the plains begin to be worked. It was of little importance how quickly they "used up" this particular form of wealth, at first, but gradually they became "agriculturists" in the proper sense of the term, which is not to be confused with "peasants." They were growers of human livestock for use as farm labor. As the plain became more salubrious and was brought under cultivation, thanks to the ample supply of slave-labor, it proved far more fertile than the mountain slopes. Economic competition brought antagonism between the rich aristocratic landowners of the plain and the increasingly poorer democratic peasants of the hills. Whenever new land is settled, something of the sort occurs. The medieval monasteries that branched out from the older centers (like Cîteaux, for example) and began to work insalubrious sites nobody else would touch, invariably turned out to be more fertile (in the sense of agriculturally productive) than the parent establishments. What is today the richest farming region in Illinois (around Champaign) was less than a hundred years ago peopled by a very few farm families who waged an uphill battle against malaria. Whenever they could choose, the pioneers picked fairly barren hillsides for their first settlements (New Salem), rather than the more fertile lowlands. They were healthier sites, with running water and woods nearby, and besides were easier to defend in case of attack. Not until the population had grown and modern methods of drainage were learned, did the more low-lying regions come under cultivation and their greater fertility become apparent.

Similarly, before Peter the Great made it safe to do so, nobody in the Ukraine ventured very far out of the woods, or attempted to farm save in forest clearings. How paradoxical the situation was has been brought out by P. Milioukov: for fear of Tartar raids, the rich black soil of the Ukraine lay untouched for centuries while right on the edge of it men struggled for a living working the vastly inferior loess. Land concessions have occasionally been granted in colonial countries, and with the help of heavy investment regions which the natives were incapable of clearing or cultivating have been turned into the most productive in the country. However, such improvements get "forgotten" in modern colonial states and by the independent regimes that succeed them. As in ancient Greece, the peasants see only that theirs is the poorest land, and they consider that they have been "robbed," that they are, at the very least, victims of injustice.

It should be clear that within an agricultural economy there is no such thing (as there is in a food-gathering or a pastoral economy) as a limit of natural productivity which, as it is gradually approached, makes the cost of subsistence ever greater. Actually, mankind can keep pushing back any such limit by making "basic improvements" that have the effect of increasing the quantity and quality of the plant life. Probably there is a maximum limit of increase, a figure beyond which no further quantitative development, at least, can be expected to go in a given case, and yet we must admit that nearly 3 billion human beings today and tomorrow can enjoy a far higher standard of living than any of those 1 million (at the most) human beings in the Neanderthal and middle Paleolithic epochs. Though most of the planet's inhabitants are still ill-fed, it is not overpopulated when we consider all the still untapped possibilities for continuous production. Whereas it *was* overpopulated before *homo sapiens* appeared. With the rise of agriculture and herding, the human population grew from 1 to 10 million and then, between 3,000 and 2,000 B.C., from 10 million to 100 million. (Gaul at this period is supposed to have grown from 500,000 to 5 million.) There was another tenfold increase over the next four millenia, though there were many ups and downs, but all this was before modern capitalism had much more than embarked on its great industrial expansion, based on the consumption of irreplaceable sources of energy (coal and petroleum), and before mankind had "mechanical slaves" at its beck and call.

Moreover, there are those who think of this population expansion as the superimposition of new layers of people who live in terms of the new economy, upon older layers who still live as their ancestors did. According to Prat, there are nearly as many human beings in the world today living a Paleolithic mode of existence (Eskimos, pygmies, Australian aborigines, Indians of the Amazon, tribes in northern Siberia) as there were in the middle Paleolithic epoch. That is, a few hundreds of thousands. And there are actually more human beings today living a Neolithic mode of existence than there were at the height of the epoch of that name: a few tens of thousands. (These would be found almost everywhere, even in the most advanced countries.) Race, or inherited traits, have nothing to do with it. We will not repeat here the oft-repeated story of Paul Rivet's about the child who had been abandoned by an especially backward tribe of the Gran Chaco, who was adopted by an ethnologist trying to find the tribe, and who went on to a brilliant academic career. But we may observe that

The cultural distance is not always so great as it seems. There are Eskimos driving tractors to clear landing strips in the Far North, whose families are still hunting seals in the best Stone Age traditions. There are Arizona Indians working in garages, whose closest relatives cling to every one of their age-old ways of life.[12]

James Mooney has estimated that the Indian population north of Mexico City at the time of the white man's arrival was about 1,153,000, of whom 850,000 lived in what is today the United States.[13] This is one of the larger estimates. We may speculate that at the time, the population had reached a saturation point such as might be expected in an economy without beasts of burden, whose agriculture revolved around the same three products: corn, beans, squash. However, today some 190 million Americans enjoy a standard of living incomparably higher than that of the Indians in 1630, and the country is still far from being overpopulated.

Prior to World War II, population growth in the United States was considered the classic illustration of Verhulst's logistic law. In 1921 Pearl and Reed, on this assumption, estimated that the maximum U.S. population would be around 200 million and that it would be reached sometime around the year 2020. The question is how they arrived at this "maximum." On the basis of the available means of subsistence, or on the basis of "living space"? It could hardly have been the latter, for the figure corresponds to a density of 26 inhabitants per square km. (67 per sq. mile), and in 1845 Verhulst had figured out the maximum density of Belgium, apparently on the same basis, as 213 inhabitants per square km. (552 per sq. mile), that of France as 73 per square km. (183 per sq. mile). Now, these figures have been exceeded in both these countries. In 1958, Belgium had a population density of 294 inhabitants per square km. (761 per sq. mile), and in 1959 France had one of 82 per square km. (213 per sq. mile). Indeed, Belgium had gone well over its predicted "maximum" by 1930, some years before World War II, the atomic age, and the baby boom.

Obviously, these countries had made progress, whether in production of the means of subsistence or in the development of natural resources attendant to such production. Sufficient progress, at least, to be able to support a population much larger than had not long before seemed possible. However you care to measure it, the standard of living went up along with the population figures. We may well recall here what Kostitzin wrote in 1937, comparing the population densities of Belgium and the United States:

These figures show that America is still dominated by economic and psychological factors of the pioneer settlement days, whereas in Belgium every tiniest bit of land is put to use. . . . A time will come there, too, when fuller utilization of the land will be as inevitable in America as it was in Europe. Then we will see a prolongation of the population curve which will depart from the pattern of growth between 1790 and 1930.[14]

Even though the projected limit of 200 million has not yet been reached in the United States, these lines strike us as prophetic today. Probably that figure will be reached before 2020. At a national conference on the population crisis in Dallas, May 19, 1960, Philip H. Hauser reported on "The Population Explosion, U.S.A."[15] Noting that the total figure had gone from 132 million in 1940 to 180 million in 1960, he estimated that it would reach 215 million in 1970, 260 million in 1980, and that it could go beyond 380 by the year 2000 and reach the 1 billion point by 2050.

Hauser believes that eventually such an expansion must pose problems relative to subsistence and the standard of living. He cites Ordway's theory of the "limit of growth,"[16] which is based on two premises. First, that "levels of human living are constantly rising with the mounting use of natural resources," and second, that "Despite technological progress, we are spending each year more resource capital than is created." If these trends were to continue long enough, basic natural resources would before long be in such short supply that growing costs must make additional production less and less feasible economically. The limit of growth will have been reached. Hauser thinks that the limit will have been reached by 2050, with the one billion figure. And yet, even that figure would give the United States a population density of only 130 inhabitants per square km. (336 per sq. mile). That is not including Alaska.

With Alaska, the figures would drop to 107 per square km. (277 per sq. mile).

The short-term problems that preoccupy Hauser are not problems of subsistence, but the urbanization crisis, the changing age-structure of the population, internal migration (especially the flight from the farms), and the more rapid increase of the non-white population relative to that of the white population. On this last point, we might observe that the figure Hauser cites with alarm— a non-white population of 200 million out of a 1 billion total population, or 20 per cent—is the same percentage of blacks to whites that existed at the time of the American Revolution.

Anxieties like these, and even Hauser's more long-term concerns for the standard of living and (especially) for the rate of economic growth, are simply not shared in many countries of Europe or Asia. The situations these American pessimists predict for the year 2050 just don't strike them as grave, let alone frightening. They might even welcome such a future as a set of goals for their own development programs! In this, they would merely be giving full weight to the views of Richard Cantillon and Arsène Dumont. It really ought to be asked whether, over and above legitimate concern for the exhaustion of natural resources, pessimism of this order does not constitute a psycho-social limiting factor on the growth of the American population?

This is quite possible, because even before the remarkable stepping-up of American agricultural production in World War II —which involved a profound change in American methods of cultivation and permitted a rate of population growth incompatible with that which had obtained from 1790 to 1930 (as Kostitzin had predicted)—even then the observed trend no longer fitted the pattern laid down by Verhulst's law.

O. E. Baker noted a sag in the curve of population growth and estimated that instead of a maximum 200 million inhabitants around 2020, and then a stabilization (as Verhulst's logistic law would demand), there would be a maximum of between 135 and 150 million Americans between 1945 and 1960, followed by a rather rapid drop if the prevailing rates held. It was Baker's opinion, he told us at the International Population Congress in Paris in 1937, that estimates based on the lowest assumptions have the best chance of being realized. Trying to account for these phenomena, we wrote in 1940:

It must be recognized that the curve of population growth reflects the stage of development of the biological environment. We agree with Kostitzin that the low population density in North America corresponds to a period of clearing and settling the land. However, we are less sanguine about the chances there of replacing the destruction of natural resources with a more intensive system of agricultural production —*unless, that is, the government steps in and takes an active part.*[17]

Of course, such a development occurs spontaneously when a country realizes that its future depends on changing its whole approach to its natural resources. Such has occurred long since in countries which have been settled for centuries. However, in the United States until now there have always been some new lands to move in on and despoil, just a bit farther on. This has kept the population on the move. It is what has prevented farmers in the older, more long-settled regions from learning and practicing a conservationist type of agriculture. Unable to compete with the production of the newly opened-up areas, farmers in the East have turned to different types of production, still in the spirit of draining the last drop of wealth out of the soil. Though agriculture in the East is more intensive* than elsewhere, it is no less a primitive, pioneering agriculture, as ruthlessly "extractive" in spirit as the mining industry.

That new limiting factors have appeared is the logical consequence of the destruction of basic capital. Not only does the very soil itself vanish, but the amount of labor that must be expended in struggling against the new factors reaches such proportions that the yield seems scarcely worth it. It becomes a question of whether it is possible to make a living from the land.

In a market economy, there is no way to replace extractive agri-

* As opposed to extensive. See above, p. 260. *Transl. note.*

culture with conservationist agriculture. The only end in sight is that of agriculture itself, and hence of the population which depends upon it. The situation is somewhat analogous to that of business firms who get caught up in price wars. As business falls off because they are being undersold, they slash their own prices, and so on until they have gone into debt, used up their capital, and find themselves bankrupt. Agriculturists in the United States have reached the first phase, at least, at the present time.

Further, *unless* the American population curve makes a recovery such as seems highly unlikely, what is going to happen will not be the logistic climb to a stable maximum, but a dropping off such as we observed for a microbe population in a closed culture.*

The population disappears when the environment has become incompatible with life.

The above lines were written just as America was undergoing a profound economic metamorphosis. The war had necessitated some spectacular decisions, in part prepared for by the New Deal and in part inspired by awareness of the enormous human needs which the war had left in its wake. Thus, twice in a generation, the United States' curve of population growth has given the lie to the predictions of demographers. What is the lesson to be learned? Before we can answer that question we must make a deeper analysis of the process whereby wealth comes about, and of how the means of subsistence are produced. For isn't it gradually becoming apparent: where production is concerned, there is true production and false production . . . ?

PRODUCTION: TRUE OR FALSE?

To view production from the point of view of money values, we have seen, poses some very difficult problems. The broader the geographical area to be covered, and the longer the period of time under study, the less useful is this particular form of measurement.

* See above, pp. 73–77.

To compare the production of foodstuffs with alimentary needs, we have to use other units of measurement.

Contrary to the opinion held by the classical economists, the prices arrived at in a market economy fail to supply a basis for taking the measure of the phenomena humanity confronts in its quest for means of subsistence.

To show just how inadequate the criteria of the market economy are in this connection, it should be enough to cite "the King effect." At the beginning of the eighteenth century, Gregory King had already observed that a drop of 10 per cent in the stocks of wheat for sale on the grain market, made the price double. In the depression of the 1930's we could observe for ourselves that every time 10 per cent more wheat was thrown on the market, the price fell to half of what it had been. Thus, the "King effect" applies to a situation of "plenty" as well as to a situation of "scarcity."

Now, if we take 100 as the index number to indicate the initial state of affairs on a supposedly balanced market, we can draw up the following table to show what happens when changes occur in three categories: volume of production (G), unit price on the market (P), and total value of production (V):

		G	P	V
	b	121	25	30.25
	a	110	50	55
At opening		100	100	100
	x	90	200	180
	y	81	400	324

Paradoxically enough, when the market opens and more of the product is put up for sale (movement upwards to a and b)—a quantitative *increase* in production—there is a parallel drop in prices which means *decreased* production in terms of money value. And conversely, when the volume of production available becomes scarcer (movement downwards to x and y)—a quantitative *decrease* in production—there is a rise in prices which means *increased* production in terms of money value. Thus, in the market economy the satisfaction of needs is not reflected in money values; scarcity makes it necessary to place a value on the satisfaction of a partially unsatisfied need. Where humanity is concerned, the problem is one of subsistence, ie., of the satisfaction of needs, not one of setting a market price on a product in full knowledge that the supply can satisfy the needs only of those who are solvent and with sufficient purchasing power. And turning from prices to quantitative measures of production, we must recognize that when we use the term "production" to designate the mere appropriating or harvesting of natural wealth, we are in danger of overlooking an essential feature of the phenomenon.

Indeed, the Physiocrats put their finger on it when they drew a careful distinction between "net product" and "gross product." The fact that other writers (Sismondi, for example) have used the same terms in altogether different senses, does not make the distinction a less important one. To the Physiocrats, a "net product" is one the consumption of which leaves the economic books balanced. A "gross product" implies wealth placed at our disposition, irrespective of whether a "net product" may also be involved. Let us say that "gross product" implies *appropriation* in some form or another, whereas "net product" applies only to that form of appropriation which can go on indefinitely because there is *production* behind it. To these founders of modern economics, only agriculture in the broadest sense could supply "net product," because it alone gives a continuous return, thanks to nature's reproductive powers. They referred to the other forms of economic activity as "sterile."

Nicolas Beaudeau argued the matter with Adam Smith. The latter held that you could not call sterile a class that "every year reproduces the *value* of what it consumes, any more than you can call sterile a couple who reproduce themselves in two children, without going on to have more and more." Beaudeau, however, kept coming back to a biological concept of reproduction:

When we gather in a crop of a single species, we do not just say "It produced, it was productive," we also say "It reproduced, it is reproductive." A seed planted, a fruit tree started, reproduce themselves in a long line of many descendants of their species, by virtue of the fertility of nature and the infinite benevolence of the Creator towards the human race. Besides what it needs for its own seed each year, the wheat that is sown reproduces the daily bread of all mankind, and besides the new lamb each year the sheep reproduces its fleece.

This was what so struck the Physiocrats: how something new is put at man's disposal, in such quantity that he can take what he needs of it without breaking the continuity of production. It was in this spirit, reflecting on such examples as these, that they envisaged a "net product."

It comes out again in Turgot's paper on mines and quarries:

Though a field may bear fruit year after year, it is not so with a mine of metals. It bears no fruit ever, *but is itself the fruit to be plucked.* So truly speaking it gives no "net product." It furnishes man a "gross product."

Their conception had little success in the history of economic theory. Adam Smith and, even more Ricardo, combatted it effectively enough so that what was sound in the Physiocrats' notion was practically ignored for more than a century. The one exception, perhaps, was Karl Marx, to the slight extent that his theory of capitalist surplus-value incorporates something of the net-product idea. To economists solely concerned with explaining the mechanical operation of markets and prices independently of human actions, it was just not fashionable to be concerned with anything but "the production of value." However, just as Quesnay's *Tableau économique* has been given a new lease on life by developments in national and world economy, so that it seems pertinent to the accounting problems met in inter-industrial relations (Leontieff's Input-Output Table, for example), in the same way we find ourselves coming back to the Physiocrats' long-decried notions of "net product" and "gross product." They seem pertinent to the problem of production viewed in terms of human needs.

It is no mere historical accident that Malthus, in his famous treatise, had to recognize the validity of the Physiocrats' thinking. The problem he addressed himself to demanded it, and it, too, was a problem economic theory has until quite recently been loath to come to grips with:

But the surplus, which a given quantity of land yields in the shape of rent, is totally different. Instead of being a measure of the increase of labour, which is necessary altogether to produce the quantity of corn which the land can yield, it is finally an exact measure of the relief from labour in the production of food granted to him by a kind Providence. If this final surplus be small, the labour of a large portion of the society must be constantly employed in procuring, by the sweat of their brows, the mere necessaries of life, and society must be most scantily provided with conveniences, luxuries, and leisure; while, if this surplus be large, manufactures, foreign luxuries, arts, letters, and leisure, may abound.[18]

If the earth had been so miserly as to make all her inhabitants work to get her products, there would have been no idlers and no manufacturers, either. To the contrary, however, there are no strings to her generosity, though there are limits to her prodigality. What she supplies mankind with is a sufficient capital in the way of means of subsistence, so that we can get started and by our own efforts increase that capital. The earth has the property of being able to produce more in the way of food, shelter, and clothing than is needed by those who cultivate her with these aims in view. This remarkable property accounts for what distinguishes agriculture in the broad sense from all other forms of human labor: it produces surpluses. The more hard work and intelligence go into it, the more surpluses pile up and the greater the technological progress realized. And with each such advance, more and more farmers' sons and daughters find themselves in a position to move to the cities, there to take employment in industry or in the liberal and service professions, The increase in numbers which has taken place within all of the urban occupational categories over the past few generations, would never have been possible had not farmers steadily become more efficient, while at the same time they kept up a higher birth rate than the rest of the population, Indeed, it is in the farmers' own interest that there should be more hands in the factories and fewer in the cotton fields:

Still more people in industry, including lumbering, will in a way mean more market gardening, more dairy farms, and more livestock raising to meet the needs of the people so engaged in those areas.[19]

These latter, of course, will thereby find their own standard of living raised. These optimistic words by Henry A. Wallace follow from his conviction that "Human genius will find a way to make use of our abundance so as to enhance the well-being of the race." Though the tone is very different from Malthus', these words hark back to the same guiding principles which the Physiocrats were harshly judged for giving voice to.

We must recognize that the nineteenth century's economic expansion—which represents on the part of the science of economics a breaking away from nebulous theorizing, whether in defense of the status quo or with a better world in view—has not seemed primarily due to the increase in agricultural production, but rather to the contrary.

What really launched the modern industrial development was the substitution of mineral products like coal and petroleum for agricultural products like wood, *as sources of energy*. As each successive advance led to another, iron, steel, concrete in turn—mineral products, processed with the aid of mineral sources of energy—served to take the place of a single agricultural product, wood, in the construction of buildings and machinery. At the present time plastics, which are chemical byproducts of the coal and petroleum industries, are taking the place of a number of agricultural products.

To try to maintain that such industries involve no "net product," that they do not contribute to "production" in the proper sense of the term, is an argument that simply will not stand up. It is not hard to show that, although capitalism in its early stages thrived almost solely on a fuller, more rational employment of human labor —in conjunction with primitive machinery and the division of labor it encouraged—still the real spurt forward and the triumph over the preceding family economy came only with the invention of thermal power, of machinery which, no longer propelled by hand, runs on the consumption of capital wealth, indeed, "uses up" the latter in a destructive sense.

The Florentine and Flemish industries of the Middle Ages were, indeed, capitalist enterprises, but what made them so was the more systematic exploitation of human labor they entailed. Commerce, and especially maritime commerce, was capitalist in character because through the pooling of capital ever more ambitious expeditions could be sent out to exploit the labor of less evolved countries, in rivalry with that of the rich countries, thereby to make the latter still richer.

No doubt the earliest machinery, such as that utilized by the English textile industry in the eighteenth century, was powered by water. However, it was with the nineteenth-century development of the steam engine that we saw capitalism coming into its own, triumphing everywhere, producing ever greater wealth—ever greater capital. That is, if we are prepared to allow that the mineral riches of the earth, such as coal and petroleum, represent capital wealth— part of nature's bounty to be harvested and made use of by man.

In 1800 world production of coal was something like 10 million tons annually. By 1900 the figure was 700 million tons, by 1925 it was 1,300 million tons, and by 1950 the figure of 2,000 million tons had been reached. And yet, geologists today estimate world coal reserves at several million billions of tons, with more deposits being discovered every year.

Coal is becoming less important as a source of energy than it was. This is because other sources have come to the fore, also because in some parts of the world coal production is becoming more expensive than it was. Mining at great depths or working seams of low yield raises the price over that of rival fields where these conditions do not obtain (an instance of Ricardian rent). As the following tabulation shows,[20] France is no longer one of the big five producers of coal, and China is. Production in China and in the U.S.S.R. has greatly increased, while there has been a falling-off in the United States, Great Britain, and West Germany.

Production
(in millions of tons)

1925		*1958*	
1. United States	500	1. United States	500
2. England	250	2. England	230
3. West Germany	200	3. West Germany	150
4. U.S.S.R.	70	4. U.S.S.R.	350
5. France	50	5. China	250

Another mineral source of energy, petroleum, today rivals coal. Professor de Launay used to tell his classes at the School of Mines in Paris (around 1930–31), "It seems likely that petroleum will be the first mineral all supplies of which will have been used up by our civilization." At that time, petroleum production had already for many years been mounting dizzily:

1860	70,000 tons	1920	89,000,000 tons
1880	4,000,000	1924	130,000,000
1890	10,000,000	1925	140,000,000
1900	24,500,000	1928	170,000,000
1910	45,750,000	1929	190,000,000

Of that last figure, no less than 150,000,000 tons came from the United States. It was then estimated that the petroleum reserves of that country had dropped from 3,750 million tons to 1,680 million tons, i.e., were already 55 per cent consumed. Although about 75 million tons of new deposits were being discovered every year, American consumption had reached a figure close to 10 million tons per month.

And what has happened since? Nearly everywhere production has continued to mount, in the United States as elsewhere: 270

million tons in 1950, 350 million tons in 1957 and 1959. In Venezuela production went from 20 million tons in 1929 to 80 million in 1950, 150 million in 1957 and 1959. Increase in the U.S.S.R. was from 13 million in 1929 to 40 million in 1850, and from 100 million in 1957 to 130 million in 1959. In the six main petroleum-producing countries, total production was 520 million tons in 1950, 880 million tons in 1957, 1,000 million (i.e., one billion) tons in 1959.[21] Of course discovery of new deposits has gone on apace and is still going on:

Svante Arrhenius wrote in *La Revue Scientifique* (May, 1923), "At the senseless rate of present production, there will probably be no more petroleum by 1940, certainly no more by 1950." Since he wrote that, consumption has increased tenfold and never before have reserves been so high in relation to it.[22]

The point to be underlined is man's changing attitude with respect to such natural wealth. Afraid that rival sources of energy may soon reduce the value of petroleum as such, and that in consequence oil investments will cease to yield a good return, the operators are going all out to exploit as fast as possible every new field as soon as it is discovered. Not so long ago, the same operators were doing all they could to spread fear of depletion in the world's reserves, by this means keeping prices high. The intervention of governments today in petroleum research and marketing is not in view of conserving deposits for future human needs, but in view of immediate profits.

Economy of consumption ought to enter into any rationally organized appropriation of those natural resources which do not yield a "net product" (in the sense of the Physiocrats), but only a "gross product." Wastage and loss ought to be guarded against, and the most efficient possible utilization made of non-renewable natural resources. Of course, theoretically at least, all natural resources fall in this category.

Solar energy itself will fade out in a few billion years. Even before that happens—supposing nothing occurs to disturb the predictions of our leading twentieth-century scientists—the planet will have become uninhabitable already, either too hot or too cold to support life (depending on the theory you prefer). Actually, however, predictions of this type impinge on the realm of the infinite. Exhaustion of a source of energy long after the species has itself disappeared under the same conditions and on the same hypotheses, scarcely need disturb our sleep. Can we feel the same confidence, however, where a natural resource like petroleum is concerned? We cannot, not even allowing for recent discoveries of untapped reserves. Nor does it seem that exhaustion of coal deposits is beyond the bounds of possibility. As for atomic energy, it seems more promising, especially if technical advances are made so as to utilize other substances besides uranium. But only where the sun's energy is concerned can we be perfectly at ease on this score. . . .

Instead of distinguishing between natural resources as renewable or non-renewable, it would be more to the point to single out those resources which are capable of being conserved, that is, those which can be made use of in the future as well as in the present. This is very much the case with the so-called non-renewable resources.

Healthy exploitation of them would not just avoid wastage, but would so organize consumption that their material substance is not dissipated, that is, so that the energy consumed by their use may be reincorporated in them—so that they may be used again. What this means is clear enough where the materials concerned are merely broken up or get rusty. In the natural state as ore, metals are anything but readily usable, and we might well reflect that less energy is involved in melting down and refashioning a piece of metal apparatus which has merely worn out or been broken, than in starting the entire industrial process all over again at the mine. This sort of recovery is not always practicable, but more and more industries make use of discarded materials, so-called junk. The copper-products industry, for example, has since 1930 relied more on scrap metal than on the mines.

Not that copper mining has not kept growing apace, and many deposits been exhausted. In the eighteenth century, England had something very like a monopoly on copper, thanks to her mines in Cornwall. By the beginning of the nineteenth century, production had reached the figure of 20,000 tons, of which England supplied no more than half. By 1850, England supplied only 27 per cent of the world total of 50,000 tons, though her production of copper had increased to nearly 15,000 tons. The record of the principal producers since then is seen in TABLE 61.[23]

TABLE 61

Mined Copper Production by Principal Producing Countries
(in percentages)

Year	World Total in Metal Form (tons)	England	Chile	U.S.S.R.	U.S.	Northern Rhodesia	Canada	Katanga
1850	50,000	27	23	12	1	—	—	—
1900	500,000	—	8	?	50	—	—	—
1913	1,000,000	—	—	?	50	—	3	—
1926	1,500,000	—	5	?	50	—	?	5
1939	2,000,000	—	14	5	30	12	13	8
1958	3,000,000	—	15	14	27	13	10	7.5

Other countries at various times have also engaged in copper mining: Germany and Sweden (5 per cent at the beginning of the nineteenth century), Austria (15 per cent in 1800, 6 per cent in 1850), Japan (5 per cent in 1900, 2.5 per cent in 1957), Mexico (4 per cent in 1913).

It is hard to see why more recourse is not had to the technique of recovering scrap metal, especially in the case of the rarer metals so much in demand by industry today. Actually, the technique is most often employed in the case of scrap iron. Steel, however, ranks first in metallurgical production: 300 million tons annually, followed by manganese (8 million tons) and aluminum (4 million tons). Copper ranks fourth. The explanation must be sought in the

capitalist market economy, which assigns value to goods solely on
the basis of the price they bring today, without thought of the mor-
row. It would be paying out money to take steps so that our children and our children's children might enjoy at least as much
natural wealth as we have enjoyed. "After us, the deluge," seems
to be the watchword of the present generation in its avidity for
consumption, quite capable of asking without a trace of Mark
Twain's humor: "What has posterity ever done for us?" It is as
though we owed nothing to anyone, save the one who bestowed
something on us, or rather, merely loaned it to us. . . . Whatever
the cause, such an attitude can only lead to wastage, whether in the
exploitation of resources or in the failure to recover what can be
recovered of them once they have been used. It is to squander
nature's bounty to practice a "gathering" economy without a
thought for the future.

The exploiter of natural resources gives no thought to whether
they are renewable or not, salvageable or not after use. All he cares
about is getting his hands on them and selling them for more than
they cost him. In this connection, we are frequently reminded that
the classic case of "exploitation" is the primitive savage, who finds
it easier to cut down a tree to get at the fruit. The trouble with this
classic case is that it was invented by civilized men. It is far from
certain that such a primitive savage ever existed. Certainly all we
have learned of tribes who still live by hunting and food-gathering,
goes rather to confirm the ancient scriptures, and to suggest that
their respect for trees is carried so far as to constitute a worship of
them. Sir James G. Frazer assembled a good deal of evidence to
this effect in *The Golden Bough*. It is at the next stage of human
economy, with the nomad shepherds and herdsmen, that trees cease
to inspire respect. And above all, it is with the appearance of
"civilized" men that all such "prejudices" fall away entirely. What
he does not have to pay for costs him nothing; nature's bounty is
free for the taking, in itself valueless. Only civilized men have perpetrated anything so appalling as the destruction of the American
forests since 1630. The area of the continental United States (ex-

clusive of Alaska) at that time included nearly 1 billion acres of forested land, more than 800 million acres of it dense virgin forest.

In 1930—three hundred years later—only a tenth of the original forest was left, of which 150 million acres were in the hands of the lumbering industry. Another 200 million acres which had been cut down were in process of reforestation, and 100 million acres similarly treated had been left to die out. Thus, out of what in 1630 might have been estimated at some 7 billion board feet of lumber, had by 1936 shrunk to 1.6 billion, approximately 23 per cent. Meanwhile, cutting was going on at four times the rate of new growth.

Consider what happened in Wisconsin, for example. Originally, it had been forested over six-sevenths of its territory. In the year 1899 the lumbering industry turned out 3.4 billion board feet, two-thirds of it pine. In 1932 what is called "production" had dropped by 13.2 million board feet. In the interval, the consumption of wood in Wisconsin had multiplied by thirty and the State was purchasing it from the Pacific coast. The most sought-after species were the first to go, without a thought for future growths: first the white pine, then the yellow pine, then the Douglas fir, and so on. . . . The less prized species were frequently destroyed by fire on the site, so as to make it easier for the loggers to get out the others. In 1928 the American Forest Service estimated that, for every 100 trees cut down, only 32 were eventually made use of. The 68 others were variously lost or destroyed: 25 at the logging site, 12 in the sawmills, 20 while stockpiled or in transit, and 11 for miscellaneous causes. Out of all this wastage, a quarter of it could *easily* have been avoided.

Petroleum resources may possibly have been squandered to a no less shocking extent, for one byproduct after another was simply thrown away for lack of any idea of the uses to which it could be put. All effort went to extracting the product most in demand, as quickly and as cheaply as possible. So long as kerosene was the product in principal demand, benzine and the other more volatile byproducts were thrown away. Later, when the main concern was the chemical transformation of petroleum into one or another light fuel, the gases were allowed to escape—all they seemed to be good for was assistance with the extraction process. As late as 1934, the U.S. Board of National Resources estimated that more than 30 million cubic meters of natural gas were being allowed to escape every day, "Enough," according to the General Report for December 1, 1934, "to meet the consumption needs of the United Kingdom twice over. That is forty times as much gas as all the Scandinavian countries together use. It is almost enough to meet the needs of every inhabitant of the United States presently consuming either natural or artificial gas." As for the crude oil itself, it was estimated in 1935 that for every barrel used, five were wasted.[24] Today natural gas is consumed at the rate of 400 billion cubic meters annually, which is more than 1 billion per day and equivalent to 500 million tons of coal. Petroleum chemistry has lately found important uses for the heavier byproducts, too, but some producers (in the Sahara, for example) are still eliminating them in the manner of a century ago.

Wood is one form of natural resource that in principle is renewable. Both as fuel and as a raw material it can compete with the non-renewable resources. Indeed, as we have already seen, the growth of modern capitalism over the past two hundred years was due to the replacement of wood by mineral resources, both as a raw material and a source of power. This makes it possible for "wood units" to serve as a standard by which to express the needs of civilization. Egon Glesinger, whose suggestion this was, goes still further toward justifying the title of his book, *The Coming Age of Wood,* when he writes:

The modern science of nutrition has developed standards for measuring human want. By translating food requirements into calories, proteins, and vitamins, it has found a common denominator applicable to beef or potatoes, lettuce or ice cream. But what unit can function as a common denominator for the consumption of such disparate necessities as automobiles, books, underwear, and houses? The answer is wood, for these and all other commodities involved in a complete standard of living can be made in whole or in major part from the forest.[25]

He shows what the effects of a wise world forestry policy would be, in the way of steady yield over the years. Despite the "competition" of mineral and petroleum products, which, however, is principally confined to the most highly developed countries, the actual per capita consumption of wood still served fifteen years ago as a measure of a country's standard of living, parallel to the nutritional level. It averaged 1,100 pounds per person per year for the world, but ranged from 5,280 pounds in Sweden to 3,300 in the United States, and from 1,320 pounds in continental Europe to 440 pounds for Asia (110 pounds in China).

No very high value attaches to wood in Asia, despite the cost of fuel in deforested countries like China. There it averages $1 a ton, whereas in a country like Sweden which makes a far more refined use of wood, it brings $20 a ton. Figuring now, not in terms of actual consumption of wood, but converting into "wood units" the consumption of textiles, buildings, furniture, the various forms of energy, automobiles, plastics, rubber, and so on—on this basis Glesinger drew up the following scale of living standards to correspond to nutritional levels. He expressed these nutritional levels in final calories, but for reasons the reader of this chapter will appreciate, we have added a column expressing them in original or vegetable calories.

	Living Standard (in tons of wood per year)	Nutritional Level (final calories)	(veg. calories)
Critical	0.5	2,000	3,000
Adequate	1.5	2,500	6.500
Optimum	3.5	3,000	9,000

If it is true that 3.5 tons of wood are enough to assure the highest standard of living, this means that were the consumption of wood to be substituted for *all* the other raw materials, fuels, and sources

300   THE MEANS OF SUBSISTENCE

of energy presently consumed, then the 5 billion human beings demographers tell us constitute a "threat" to us in the near future
could all enjoy an *optimum* standard of living. The only condition
would be that every acre of forest land in the world should give an
annual yield of less than 1.2 tons. This is far from an excessive
demand, for even a quite ordinary bit of woods can supply 140
cubic feet per acre under year-round care of no very strenuous or
refined character. At the same time, of course, nobody envisages
the abandonment of our other natural resources, the cessation of
textile production, etc.

In his *Mémoire sur les forêts,* Vauban long since remarked that
forests which are cared for are much more productive than those
which are exploited blindly. At the same time, forestry is a long-
term undertaking. It is no occupation for reckless men, and there
are whole peoples who give so little thought to the future of the
race that they are incapable of initiating a system of scientific
forestry and sticking to it regardless of changing circumstances.
The whole system can be compromised by just one descendant of
the original owner, whose need or whose extravagance drives him
to lay about with the ax more than the plan calls for. As Vauban
wrote:

Too many things happen in families over a period of 120 years, for
any of them to fail having their ups and downs. For one that finds itself
in just the same status, many others will have succumbed to impatience, and the public will have been frustrated in its expectations,
short of some miracle.[26]

Forests, however, are not just important from the point of view
of what they produce. They play an essential part in conservation
of the soil, in controlling the water table and enriching the ground.
Thoughtless destruction of forests, as well as the pollution of
present water supplies, could bring about a water shortage even
before humanity suffered from any real shortage of food or raw
materials. Such an eventuality would constitute a new limiting

factor upon population growth. Again, the problem is not one of the planet's total resources, but of how we may affect by our actions the cycles of life (and of industry as well) which depend upon water.

Forests are our best protection against soil erosion, for the same reason that forests are found in nature in humid climes. Plant life regresses where there has been deforestation. The land passes to barren heath, then to steppe or savannah, unless erosion goes so deep as to lay bare the rock. In arid country, the streams tend to go underground. With deforestation, the very climate is altered; instead of the natural, steady, slow progression to a seasonal climax, the forces of nature rush headlong to the anticlimax of barrenness.

Pastoral economy can also lead to the destruction of natural wealth. The shepherd or herdsman can be ruthless in pursuit of grazing land, in his concern for protecting his animals from the denizens of the forest. He can be as destructive as the worst type of lumber magnate. A nomad, of those peoples who live "in space" rather than "in time" (as it has been said), it seems to him that the land stretches ever onward, and that whenever the grazing land has been used up in one spot he need only push on with his herds. In 1630, some 38 per cent of the land surface in the new world was grassland. The prairie proper was so lush that when Castenada moved up from Mexico in the sixteenth century, he said that the vegetation closed immediately over all traces left by his band of a thousand mounted soldiers, 500 cattle, and more than 5,000 Indians and servants. In 1868 General Bradley wrote that, as it seemed to him, there was plenty of pasture for "all the sheep and cattle and horses in the world," so much of the Great Plains and the foothills of the Rockies was still uninhabited.

In general, cattle do little damage to the plant life where they pasture, for they keep moving about in search of watering places, and they do not crop the grasses so close as to destroy them. They leave the carpet of vegetation intact so that it can renew itself. Nonetheless, by 1885, prairie lands capable of supporting 1 head of cattle per 10 hectares (24.7 acres) were being expected to support 3 or 4. In 1882, when the price of meat was soaring, big outfits (some with 150,000 head) began to spread out over the plains of eastern Colorado and down into Texas and New Mexico. Now began the real destruction of the American grasslands. The particularly severe winter of 1886 killed off half the livestock in this area, however, and the destruction of the land might yet have been arrested, but now to the depredations of the cattle was added a much deadlier enemy: the sheep. Sheep require less water than cattle, and they crop the vegetation close enough to kill it. Wyoming and Utah, at this time, were the scene of fierce and bloody battles between the cowboys and the sheepmen.

The next blow was the gradual establishment of farming in the Plains states. The methods of cultivation practiced were "modern" enough, but no thought of conserving the natural fertility of the soil entered in. So-called "dry farming," especially, spelled a threat to cattlemen and sheepmen alike in the more arid regions. It constitutes a real "mining" or "extraction" of the riches of the soil. The first Homestead Act of 1862, which allotted 160 acres to a settler, was gradually increased by local and national legislation— to 640 acres in Nebraska in 1904, to 320 acres country-wide in 1909, and finally to the 640 figure for the country as a whole in 1926. It was plainly becoming profitable to farm the Great Plains. Within one 20-year period the population of the Dakotas rose from 14,000 to 510,000, and between 1910 and 1920 alone 10 million acres were put under cultivation in the state of North Dakota.

Not many years had to pass before the topsoil was gone, and windstorms turned the Plains states into one enormous "dust bowl." In 1935 American government statistics stated that in the years immediately preceding, some 100 million acres of former farm land had been destroyed entirely, that a good part of the soil was gone from some 310 million more acres, and erosion was beginning to threaten another 250 million acres.

Of course, we may think of what happened in the United States as an utterly untypical, isolated instance, such as could only have happened when a young people spread rapidly over a new continent, overconfident of its unlimited natural wealth. Actually, however, the case is not unique, for vast areas of the world have been subjected to similar devastation at different times and places in the history of the world, also by human agency. In 1905 A. Woiekoff observed that more than half the world's population lived in the northern hemisphere between the 20° and 30° parallels, a zone which excludes all of Europe and the industrial areas of North America, but includes the principal deserts of our hemisphere.[27] It is hard not to conclude from such an observation, both that this zone is biologically most favorable to the development of the human species, and that the deserts in it are a consequence of the multiplying of the species there.[28] From the most ancient times, it is clear that a sort of curse has been visited upon the especially splendid sites of human habitation.

The deserts of the northern hemisphere, at least, all seem to have at one time or another provided the setting for a brilliant civilization which only disappeared once it had become corrupt. It is a sad truism that our planet has been plundered time and again, and the fact that there are 1,000 more human beings in Algeria every day gives probably less grounds for anxiety than the fact that there are also 250 fewer acres of arable land. Knowing all this as we do of past mistakes, we have only to act so as to avoid them in the future. What most seems to favor the least forward-looking exploitation of nature's resources is the competition of the marketplace.

At a given moment, it may appear that the costs of production are about the same in the extensive and "extractive" type of agriculture, as in the intensive type which is or ought to be, if not actually conservationist, at least improvement-minded. As soon as the slightest economic depression occurs, however, the former type may find itself—seemingly, at least—in the stronger position. In that type of farming, the greatest part of the cost of production goes to pay off the capital investment, to repay loans, and to underwrite new investment in buildings and equipment. Actual annual expenses, including labor costs, are slight. In the intensive type of farming, it is the other way round. Though the cost of soil conservation—the enhancement of the basic capital—may be greater per acre, it represents a smaller percentage of the unit cost of production, the bulk of which consists of annual expenses (seed, fertilizer, fuel, and labor—this last the biggest item).

To make our reasoning easier to grasp, let us construct the following comparative example of what happens cost-wise in the production of any given unit (x bushels of wheat, for example) according to the two different types of farming: E for extensive, I for intensive. This theoretical example is not at all remote from reality, though we set 1,000 as the arbitrary figure for the unit cost of production:

	E	I
Return per acre	8	40
Cost per acre	8,000	40,000
Expenses (average, long-term)	6,400	8,000
Expenses (annual)	1,600	32,000
Cost per unit	1,000	1,000
Expenses (average, long-term)	800	200
Expenses (annual)	200	800

This is a good point to recall that in the Roman Empire the *colonus* (serf or tenant farmer) was allowed to keep one-fifth of the fruits of his labor, a proportion basic also in the agricultural system of ancient Egypt. Even today, when contracts allow the tenant farmer to keep two-thirds, the owner of the land has still to pay some annual expenses out of his one-third of the gross product.

What happens when the market price drops to half the return needed to pay off the unit cost of production of 1,000? The farmer who practices E can still meet his annual expenses and pay off three-eights of his long-term investment obligations. Of course, he will be unable to meet his loans and will have to try to get a moratorium or a postponement from his creditors. With a certain sacrifice of capital, he can stay in business, however. The farmer who practices I is in a more difficult position, for 500 is not even enough to meet his annual expenses—though he may just possibly, by circumventing the "free" market, be able to sell his crop at an unusually high price. If he cannot, he is out of business. The depression of the thirties, as it affected agriculture, is more comprehensible in the light of such an analysis. As we shall see, there is not much chance that agriculture will go the same way after World War II as it did after World War I—with the world grain market a case in point.

The following table permits us to compare the actual situation before and after the two world wars, as the four leading exporters of cereal grains (Argentina, Canada, Australia, and the United States) experienced it. For the purposes of comparison it is unnecessary to convert the metric measures:

Years	Area under Cultivation (millions of hectares)	(index)	Return per Hectare under Cultivation (quintals)	(index)	Total Production (millions of tons)	(index)
1909–13	34.6	100	8.8	100	30.4	100
1921–22	46.6	135	8.5	96.5	39.5	130
1926–30	50.9	147	9.1	103.5	46.5	153
1934–38	52.8	100	7.1	100	37.5	100
1945–48	50.1	95	10.6	144.9	53.2	142

With the outbreak of World War I, European production dropped considerably and the price of grain on the international market went up. The exporting countries then stepped up production by putting new lands under cultivation. As European production recovered, prices began to go down again and this had an effect on producers. The countries practicing the extensive type of farming continued to produce, but were obliged by circumstances to take measures for reducing repayment of capital investment. Countries practicing the intensive type of farming, the countries which had been importing grain, now had recourse to protective tariffs or (more often) restrictions on quantities imported. Unless, through considerations more political than economic, the exporting countries obtained preferential markets abroad, their producers were ruined and had to cut back areas under cultivation. Within each country, the situation was very nearly the same. Those farmers who practiced the extensive type of cultivation could, by reducing labor and other costs, and by acquiring more land so as to make the system ever more "extensive"—such could survive. Those, however, who were condemned to the intensive type of cultivation, whether by the smallness of their acreage or by their dependence upon family labor, were along with the wage-earners the first to fall victim to threats of economic slump. To make enough to keep going, such had to work still harder so as to be able to supply more for the market.

Despite all the programs for cutting back and plowing under, which we all watched during the Depression years, what happened in agriculture was that farmers sold more and more for less and less. Industry, meanwhile, laid off workers wholesale, and cut down production, so as to keep prices up. Only in a truly industrialized agriculture where, as in industry, production is in the hands not of the worker but of a "shepherd of workers," can production effectually be cut down by cutting down employment. Peasant agriculture is by its very nature condemned to go on increasing its production.

What happened during World War II was similar, and for the same reasons—grain prices climbed and production was stepped up in the exporting countries about as sharply as before. This time, however, increased production was due to better yields, rather than to bringing more acres under cultivation. Farming became somewhat more intensive. The result was, that when European production was back to normal again, and prices on the world market began to drop, the country chiefly responsible for the intensification of production—the United States—could not allow grain prices to drop at home below the minimum price it had guaranteed its producers. Rather than flood the market, a system of stockpiling "surpluses" was instituted, which the United States offers for sale at very low prices. In this manner the United States has gone right on exporting year after year since the war, more grain than it exported during the previous peak period of 1919–21. Were prices allowed to drop, just when a country's agriculture is becoming intensive, the result would be a very serious drop in production and well-nigh intolerable social discontent.

Competition, too, can encourage agriculture of the "mining" or "extractive" variety under a market economy. One of the most frequent reasons why agricultural products can be offered at very low prices on the export market is because they represent a cheap and hasty exploitation of the soil.[29]

The foregoing digressions should have helped us to grasp that there are modes of so-called "production" which come to no more than the consumption of capital seemingly there for the taking, but which is not renewable at the rate we consume it and therefore takes on value as supplies dwindle. We have seen that mankind is perfectly capable of damaging nature's productive capacities, of harming the environment without which life cannot prosper and grow. We have also seen that agriculture can be practiced as a technique of obtaining from nature's bounty a steady return greater than that to be had in a food-gathering economy or in a pastoral economy—and without endangering nature's productive capacities. This is not the place to go into further analysis of particular cases, nor to discuss the theory of production in detail.[30] For present purposes, we need here say only that there is no net production unless appropriating the product leaves nature's powers of reproduction intact and unless the appropriable capital remains quantitatively what it was before. In this sense nature, properly guided, is the sole "producer," as, by this very fact, the Creator alone, ultimately, is the source of life. (It will be recalled that even the sun will one day go out.)

Like mining itself, agriculture of the purely extractive type substantially reduces the capital of natural wealth; its product is a "gross product," which merely adds to the quantity of materials susceptible of our doing or making something with, as consumers rather than producers. On this score, a full accounting of profits and losses has still to be drawn up. Only those human actions which supply a net product serve to increase consumer wealth without at the same time making inroads on our basic capital. Or, to borrow Baudeau's term for this over-all net product—"the entire stores of the world-wide, universal harvest"—we recognize with him that

The whole species obviously and without exception has an everlasting interest in assuring the steady, continual increase of this lately gathered harvest—which comprises every substance and all the raw materials that go to make mankind's more durable works . . . in securing the indefinite conservation of all of it in its present state. This is *justice*. . . . To be the means of bringing about its continual, ever-mounting increase, is *charity*. . . . To damage or squander it is a *crime*, at the very least a *misdemeanor*.[31]

If we recognize that the world population and man's standards of living are limited by "the entire stores of the world-wide, universal harvest," we can understand how the latter is being threatened by "the plundering of the planet," and how only in the seasonal food-gathering and pastoral economies is it checked sufficiently to assure steady returns. At the same time, it is inherent in the agricultural economy to struggle against the factors that limit nature's own production.

Today we know that it is not agriculture alone which can produce a net product. The Physiocrats can scarcely be blamed for not having realized this, as they knew little of how natural forms of energy contribute to such production. In the eighteenth century, the power of wind and water still seemed of minor importance compared to what could be achieved by tilling the soil. Nor was the role of solar energy in the development of plant life precisely grasped as yet: how the sun contributes 9,000 horsepower to every hectare of land (in temperate climes), of which plants use up 7,200 horsepower to attain full growth. Of this last only as little as 50 horsepower is consumed in the key process of photosynthesis. Emphasis on machines ("mechanical slaves") powered by energy wrenched from the depths of the earth has, in recent generations, led us to forget about the plants ("natural slaves"), some 72,000 of which quietly go on working for us in every hectare of cultivated land.

They were on earth before we were, and the farmer today has his choice, as he goes about modifying the natural carpet of vegetation, of making them work for us or of destroying them. Properly used, they can by their reproductive powers supply us indefinitely with the food, the wood, and the other natural products we require. Improperly used, the land can pass entirely to the species which are useless or harmful to us, and those 9,000 horsepower of solar energy (per hectare) can transform the land into a stony wasteland incapable of sustaining human life.

It is perfectly true, today, that in water power, in the tides, and in the differences of temperature to be found in nature, we have new sources of natural energy which can be tapped without reference to the process of photosynthesis in plant life. There are even some who tell us that solar energy can be directly tapped, with a yield of something like 10 per cent. That is an impressive figure, when we recall that plant production requires no more than about 0.6 to 0.8 per cent for its most essential activity (photosynthesis). These are very recent developments, of course, merely the latest of the continuing transformations going on in the conditions of our life in time.

THE PARADOX OF SURPLUSES

LOOKING AROUND THE WORLD

In the countries today in process of development, a rather high percentage of the working population—and sometimes a very high percentage—is engaged in agriculture. In most of these countries, it runs higher than 70 per cent though the figure is almost everywhere getting smaller. At the same time, agrarian production is in general low grade and not enough. Already inadequate to the needs of the inhabitants before World War II, it has become more so since. As is well known, some two-thirds of the world population does not get enough to eat.

On the other hand, the all but defining characteristic of the most highly developed countries is that they are industrialized and only a small percentage of the population is engaged in agriculture. Some of these countries, indeed, do not only enjoy a rich and copious diet, they are unable to consume all that the country produces in the way of foodstuffs. Production is in excess of need. Thus, they are potential exporters of food to the rest of the world. The United States, Canada, Argentina, and—most especially— Australia are all in this category, and they have all offered their products to countries in need of them. Of countries in this second category, a certain number can by this means make up for their own shortcomings and provide their populations with a no less rich and copious diet. The United Kingdom, West Germany, Italy, Belgium, and the Netherlands import some part of their foodstuffs from the countries of overproduction.

The predominately agricultural underdeveloped countries, however, are unable to import the surpluses of the exporting countries, because they are not financially in a position to do so. This is how we find ourselves in the situation which obtains today, where two-thirds of the world does not get enough to eat from the cradle to the grave, and one-third is not only well-nourished but obliged to stockpile its surpluses for lack of buyers. This is the paradoxical situation at present, when predominately agricultural peoples are literally dying of hunger, especially in Asia where the population increase is the highest in the world.

The Well Nourished and the Underfed. The inadequacy of agricultural production in many of the underdeveloped countries, combined with the financial inability to import foodstuffs in sufficient quantity, results in widespread and unrelieved hunger as well as in frequent famines.

FAO has devoted a number of studies to the problem, in an effort to encompass it. In its *Second World Food Survey* (1952), it published some figures that speak for themselves, contrasting calorie needs with calories available—per day and per capita—to the inhabitants of the following countries:

	Available Calories	Calories Needed	Availability as % of Need
India	1,700	2,250	75.6
Peru	1,920	2,540	75.6
North Africa	1,920	2,430	79.1
Tanganyika	1,980	2,420	81.8
Mexico	2,050	2,490	82.4
Ceylon	1,970	2,270	86.8
Japan	2,150	2,330	92.3
Mauritius	2,240	2,410	92.9
Brazil	2,350	2,450	95.9

In the highly developed countries, however, including those which are not self-sufficient in respect to food production, the average consumption runs higher than nutritionists consider strictly necessary:

	Available Calories	Calories Needed	Availability as % of Need
Italy	2,580	2,440	105.7
U.S.S.R.	3,020	2,710	111.4
France	2,850	2,550	111.8
Canada	3,130	2,710	115.5
Switzerland	3,150	2,720	115.8
United Kingdom	3,100	2,650	116.9
U.S.A.	3,130	2,640	118.5
Australia	3,160	2,620	120.6
New Zealand	3,250	2,670	121.7
Argentina	3,190	2,600	122.7

These figures underline one of the most striking aspects of the very notion of "underdevelopment." It is not because of climate, or population density, or politics, or religion, or culture, that these peoples are underdeveloped, though each of these factors may play a certain role. The paradox of food surpluses in a world where people go hungry is due to the fact that one-third of the world is sufficiently developed to be able to meet its needs, whereas two-thirds of the world cannot provide the subsistence its own population requires. The countries in this latter category are not just underfed, they are caught up in a vicious circle. Undernourishment reinforces underproduction and underproduction assures undernourishment.

The Overproducers and the Underproducers. Food production in various countries has been sufficiently studied now, so that we can make a close correlation between the level of production and the nutritional level. It is in the countries where the latter is low that the former is inadequate. Could India, for example, only manage to bring its rice yield up to the level of Italy's, the worst of its subsistence problems would be solved. The data of TABLE 62 are from FAO's *Yearbook of Food and Agricultural Statistics* for 1952.

TABLE 62

Estimated Harvests of Certain Food Commodities
in Some Countries
(averages for 1949–51 in 100 kilogram/hectares)

Country	Wheat	Corn	Rice	Potatoes
Denmark	35.0	—	—	—
Holland	—	—	—	250
United Kingdom	27.3	—	—	188
France	17.9	—	—	—
Canada	11.8	30.4	—	—
Australia	11.0	—	48.7	—
U.S.A.	10.6	23.6	25.9	163
Italy	—	18.3	47.8	—
Argentina	10.1	12.8	—	65
Japan	—	—	39.6	—
Burma	—	—	13.9	—
Pakistan	—	—	13.6	—
Thailand	—	—	13.0	—
Java & Madura	—	8.2	—	—
India	6.5	6.0	10.8	67
Algeria	5.8	—	—	—

Since the war nearly all the as yet underdeveloped countries have managed some increase in agricultural production. In all the countries of Asia and the Far East, except for South Korea and Burma, production levels are higher than before the war. Taking the 1934–

38 levels as the base year (= 100), we get the following indices for 1956–57: Indonesia, 119; Japan, 126; South Korea, 100; Burma, 97; Ceylon, 157; Taiwan, 133; India, 122; Malaysian Federation, 143; Pakistan, 115; Philippine Islands, 148; Thailand, 192.

However, when we compare these higher levels of agricultural production with the rates at which the population has increased in these countries, we must acknowledge that these countries are worse off than they were before the war. The food situation has become more, not less grave. The only countries which are exceptions to the rule are Thailand and the Philippines, and in some degree Japan and Ceylon. Once again taking the 1934–38 figures for the base year, the production indices per inhabitant for 1956 and 1957 (food products and cereal grains) were as follows:

	1956	*1957*
Philippines	106	109
Thailand	119	132
Japan	103	88
Ceylon	98	103

In all the other countries of this part of the world, the indices are lower than before the war. In Indonesia, South Korea, Taiwan, and India, they are falling still lower.[32]

TABLE 63

Index of Agricultural Production

(1934–38 = 100)

	Food Commodities per capita	*Cereal Grains per capita*
South Korea		
(1930, 1934 and 1936 = 100)		
1953–54	75	81
1954–55	76	76
1955–56	75	72
1956–57	66	63

Indonesia

1953–54	90	87
1954–55	93	96
1955–56	89	87
1956–57	88	86

Burma

1953–54	71	66
1954–55	71	67
1955–56	71	67
1956–57	74	72

China (Taiwan)

1953–54	78	81
1954–55	77	81
1955–56	74	75
1956–57	76	80

India
(1936–38 = 100)

1953–54	97	101
1954–55	96	94
1955–56	96	95
1956–57	95	97

Federation of Malaysia

1953–54	71	88
1954–55	76	86
1955–56	74	85
1956–57	77	95

Pakistan

1953–54	94	92
1954–55	96	92
1955–56	89	79
1956–57	94	92

The Food Surplus. Four of the highly developed countries have so increased their food production, and especially their grain production, that for some years now they have been obliged to stockpile huge quantities as unsaleable on the world market. In its 1960 report on international problems relating to basic commodities[33] the special committee of the UN's Department of Economic and Social Affairs made the observation that, according to the FAO Group on Grains, the production and consumption of grain had reached extremely high levels in 1958–59, along with the amount of surplus grain, although international trade had not yet developed to a degree commensurate with the amount of surplus grain that could be exported. According to this Group, the existence of a surplus amount of grain could now be considered as a more or less permanent feature of the world grain economy.

In the same report, we find some interesting statistics on how stockpiles have been accumulating, both of the secondary grains in the United States and Canada, and of wheat in Australia and Argentina as well as in the United States and Canada.[34] Where barley, oats, corn, and sorghum are concerned, much higher yields are being recorded in a number of countries, as well as increased production. Surpluses in several countries have grown up because production has outdistanced consumption, a situation that is likely to become worse in the near future as further technical progress affects production. Here are some figures for the United States and Canada (in millions of metric tons):

	1956	1957	1958	1959	1960 (*Est.*)
Barley	4.9	5.9	6.4	7.0	6.3
Oats	6.8	7.0	7.1	7.3	4.4
Corn	29.6	36.1	37.3	38.8	52.1
Sorghum	2.1	2.0	7.8	12.7	14.0
Total	43.4	51.0	58.6	65.8	76.8

As for wheat, the four countries mentioned above have been building up tremendous surplus reserves these past few years. Although, as the following figures show (in thousands of metric tons), there was a slight drop in 1957–58, it was more than made up for in 1958–59, especially in the United States:

	1955–56	1956–57	1957–58	1958–59
Argentina	1,279	1,617	1,609	1,728
Australia	2,291	1,129	449	1,774
Canada	15,774	19,854	17,104	14,859
United States	28,124	24,733	23,977	34,746
Total	47,468	47,333	43,139	53,107

The Paradox of Food Surpluses. As it has developed over the past twenty years, the world situation in wheat has been characterized by three main sets of circumstances:

1. The growing importance of government intervention, effects of which have been especially felt in production and marketing.
2. Rapid technological advances and application of the results of scientific research to the methods of production.
3. Diverging trends in world consumption: increased consumption in the underdeveloped countries, stagnation or decline in the highly developed countries.[35]

The most urgent question is what is to be done with the stockpiled surpluses of the secondary cereal grains. Are they to be destroyed, or are they to be exported to the underfed peoples at no cost to them? World public opinion is strongly opposed to the destruction of foodstuffs. However, gratuitous distribution poses serious problems—it could cause a drop in prices on the world market, with grave consequences not only for the wealthy countries, but also for those of the less developed countries which rely on exports of basic commodities and agricultural products. Even inside these latter countries, the free import of cereal grains could easily bring economic chaos, such that the governments might find themselves obliged to begin stockpiling native products. A policy of outright gifts would in the end come to no more than a geographical displacement of food surpluses. In a recent article, J. Stassart suggests a sane criterion for implementing any such policy:

What must happen, is that food consumption in the beneficiary countries increases quantitatively to the same extent as the tonnage of the food surpluses received.[36]

In any case, over any long-term period the free export of food surpluses cannot be made a substitute for assisting the underdeveloped countries to modernize their economic structure. As this gradually comes about, such countries will become normal partners in world trade—and the countries of the West will find their strictly economic position all the stronger, no longer that of rich relatives obliged to help support the rest of the human family.

WHAT WAS LEARNED IN
THE DEPRESSION YEARS

The experiences of the thirties were such as to revise a good deal of our thinking in economic matters. It was those years that brought to light the paradox of food "surpluses" co-existing with widespread hunger and malnutrition. As we have seen, the Depression seems to have been caused by the gradual return of European agriculture to normal in the course of the twenties. Both during the First World War and for some time thereafter, the exporting countries outside Europe had been building up their agriculture by putting hitherto unused land under cultivation. Economists have maintained, not without some appearance of justification, that the worldwide economic crisis was caused by agricultural "overproduction," notably of food products.

In the same spirit, the solution to the problem seemed to lie in the practice of an "economic Malthusianism," that is, in restoring a so-called "balance" between supply and demand. There is nothing abstruse about the thinking involved. As we have seen, on the basis of King's law, when production goes up 10 over the initially balanced market, prices drop from 100 to 50. It would seem to follow, then, that by *not* producing that extra 10 units, or by destroying them as soon as they are produced, then the value of the production actually up for sale must rise again to the 100 of the initially balanced market, and thereby the purchasing power of the producers.

This kind of thinking ascribed an absolute value to the market's "initial balance." It assumed that essential needs must necessarily be taken care of under such circumstances, and that any increase of production must represent some mere "secondary" need, in as much as it could not fetch a normal price. What was lost sight of, was that King's law does not just illustrate a so-called "overproduction," but also the case of extreme shortage. From the point of view of the value of production, 100 is not nearly as good an index of balance as—say—90, which brings a price of 200 and represents a production value of 180. Of course, beyond a certain point, price rises of this type are not tolerated. However, we can only conclude that by this line of thinking producers would do well to take advantage of the free market by organizing scarcity so as to raise prices and keep them just as high as the traffic will allow.

In actual practice, agricultural producers cannot control the quantities of products offered for sale, and their own tendency, by and large, is to keep increasing production so as to improve their own position. For the most part they have little to say as to how the market fluctuations are to be taken advantage of. That role falls to the "professional" speculators, who try to fix the asking price at a level of relative shortage, taking into consideration current economic conditions and giving particular weight to those bids that reflect financial solvency—that is, real purchasing power. The over-all effect, despite all the fluctuations that go on in this "balanced" market, no matter how much or how little is produced and no matter where asking prices are set, is the steady reduction of income from agricultural production. King's law no longer applies except in a falling market, when commercialized production has overreached the demand it seeks to satisfy. When it happens, in the modern world, that public demand is not met, then recourse is had to imports from abroad—save in times of world-wide shortage. And even in such times, government rationing steps in to keep demand in line with supply and thereby to prevent any sharp rise in prices. In a major depression, however, it is not a question of organizing scarcity. The trend is downward. Where the market is balanced at depends on purchasing power.

Policies of "economic Malthusianism" are rarely effective on agricultural production in the hands of large numbers of independent owners, working for the most part family holdings. It is doubtful that such policies enhance their purchasing power. In capitalist agriculture, as in capitalist industry, efforts to counteract economic depression have the effect of reducing production and of increasing unemployment. The purchasing power of the poorest strata of the population diminishes, and attempts to "hold the line" on prices, by curtailing supply to the proportions of a diminishing demand, further accentuates the downward spiral.

At the same time that economists were imputing the cause of the Depression to agricultural "overproduction," and especially to the "overproduction of food supplies, nutritionists were discovering everywhere they looked, even in the economically most advanced countries, that the poorest reaches of the population were not getting enough to eat to remain healthy. It was perfectly true that such gentlemen as the Messrs. Krupp, Rockefeller, and Deterding had but one stomach apiece, and that therefore the "overproduction" the economists were bemoaning could hardly have been for their benefit, but what the economists did not recognize was that plain ordinary Michael, John, and Peter, their wives, their children, and their friends among the other unemployed, were simply not getting enough to fill *their* stomachs, not even when the economists were successful at "holding the line."

At this time the nucleus of the future World Health Organization was being formed in Geneva, within the League of Nations, around such men as André Mayer, E. J. Bigwood, W. R. Aykroyd, Burnet, J. Boyd-Orr, and Rajchman. It was thanks to their efforts that the International Labor Organization found a scientific basis for the claims of its member affiliates that what was needed was increased purchasing power. Their efforts also attracted the attention of figures such as Frank McDougall and the present Viscount Bruce of Melbourne, who were encouraged in their own conviction that the duty of the agricultural producer, above all, is to put food into the mouths of men. Thus was brought about what has since been called "the marriage of food and agriculture," subject of the first UN meetings in May, 1943, at Hot Springs, Virginia, out of which came the creation of FAO.

The first comprehensive study of the economy of nutrition appeared in 1936. Written by John Boyd-Orr and titled *Food, Health, and Income,* it was to be followed by an ever-growing literature on the subject.

In 1946 FAO published the *World Food Survey* which the League of Nations group had got under way in 1934–38. It showed that, at a time when everyone was concerned over the overproduction of food, two-thirds of the world population was not getting enough to eat, either quantitatively or qualitatively. Given the importance in this connection of products of animal origin, which we have already noted, the problem thus comes down to matters of fact which can be expressed in terms of agricultural production. What the Depression years had taught us was that the economists' fixed ideas about the "balance" between supply and demand did not, as they supposed, imply ideal or optimal conditions. As Keynes had occasion to remark, "balance" is to be had at varying levels of underemployment, and specialists in food economy recognize that balanced markets are possible under conditions where the most elementary human needs are not being satisfied. Just as after World War I it was proclaimed that "human labor is not a commodity to be bought and sold," so after the Depression years of the thirties it has come to be recognized that food production can no longer be treated as just another marketable commodity. The Depression period taught us also that, in the case of the basic agricultural commodities, the free market does not of itself or automatically regain the "balance" it has lost, once supply is coordinated again with demand—not with respect to prices.

The effect of the "time lag," discovered at about the same time by H. Schultz, J. Tinbergen, and U. Ricci, has been given its neatest formulation by M. Ezekiel. A certain time elapses between the day it becomes clear that the market is "off balance," and the day the grower can effectively take steps to remedy the condition. This lapse of time (or time lag) derives from the fact that the process of production is a lengthy one, often one year, sometimes less (poultry and pig breeding, for example), sometimes much longer (fruit growing, for example). Let us say it is one year, and that this particular year (quite by chance) the product is in abundant supply. In this case, prices will depend solely on demand, and they will be low (P_1 in table below). Let us say, further, that the grower is the classic "economic man." Under the circumstances, he will prepare to grow less next year, so as to bring supply down to the demand level represented by the low price (P_1) he got this year.

What happens the second year? Well, just as soon as a small quantity (Q_2) of the product is put on the market, the price is going to rise appreciably in response to demand, to the level P_2. Encouraged by this development, our "economic man" now plans to increase production the following year to the quantitative level Q_3. He does this in response to the increased demand represented by the better price he got the second year. What happens the third year? Why, now the best price he can get for what he has grown is a discouraging P_3. And so it goes on, year after year. This was the effect N. Kaldor suggested calling "the cobweb theorem," in view of how it looks when expressed graphically. W. Leontieff has shown that the fluctuations may tend either to diverge ever more widely (see graph no. 1) or to converge (see graph no. 2), becoming smaller and smaller as they approach a balanced market, depending on the directions taken by the curves of supply and demand. Were the curves of supply and demand to move in the same direction (see graph no. 3), or—it goes without saying—in exactly opposite directions (see graph no. 4), then the fluctuations would repeat themselves exactly every other year or hold to a steady pattern.

There is not just a delay between the grower's decision for the following year and the delivery of his crop to market that year; he also runs a constant risk throughout that time. Farmers can never be perfectly sure of the results of their labors. The quantity actually produced at the end of that time may not correspond exactly to the quantity planned for that year. Besides the market fluctuations expressed by the cobweb theorem, there are the uncertainties of wind and weather. A difference of ±20 per cent is not at all unusual at the end of the season. Other elements enter in as well. Some growers will just not "respond" as economic theory says they must, either because they plan without reference to market developments, or because their decisions taken with reference to market developments contradict expectations of "economic men."[37] However, it is of great value to have shown that even with the theoretical terms of how the system works, fluctuations from the norm may occur, even to a startling degree.

The cobweb theorem could also be used to explain, in a purely economic context, the different ways in which different forms of agriculture—extensive and intensive, gathering and planting—react to market trends. What these differences could be shown to come down to, is a different "time lag" in each instance. There is a longer

TABLE 64

Theoretical Development of Supply and Demand in Agricultural
Products in View of Quantities and Prices

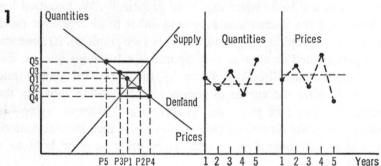

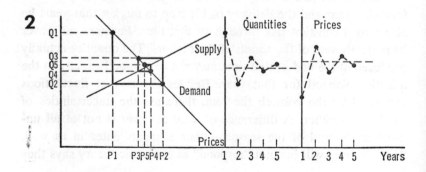

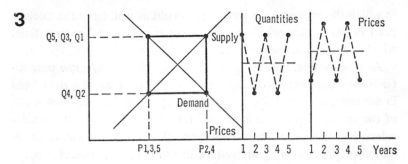

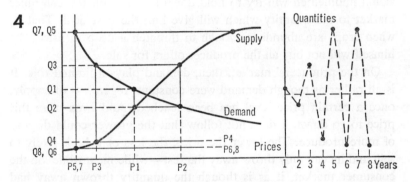

lapse of time between the decision to put new land under cultivation and the first harvest, than there is between the sowing, fertilizing, or later stages of cultivation, and the harvest. The least time lag occurs where only gathering is involved. However, such an explanation would only be worth making if it were, indeed, the case that properly economic motivations (as economists understand them) are dominant influences upon man in his aspect as *Wildbeuter*. This, however, is not generally the case.

On the other hand, were we to analyze the different responses of producers' markets and consumers' markets to the various economic situations, we could show that supply strictly dominates in the former, demand in the latter. When these are located some considerable distance from each other, the professional speculator or middleman who already profits from being spared the "time lag" to which the grower is subjected, can profit as well from the fluctuations in the market which occur—a lag in space, rather than time, which works to his advantage.

As an example, take the grower who specializes in some particular form of market gardening. He has to deliver as of a date fixed in advance, and the price he gets will depend strictly on how much of the specialty produce is offered for sale that day to the wholesalers. Meanwhile, on the consumer market a no less strict determination of price is being arrived at, in terms of "the actual supply" on the consumer market. Under these circumstances, the professional middleman will try to hold down supplies on the consumer market to the quantity which will give him the best deal. That is, when crops are abundant enough to threaten a drop in prices, he himself will not buy all the producer offers for sale.

On the producers' market, then, demand plays a limited role. It is all rather as though demand were constant, regardless of supply, once a certain price level has been reached. And even were this price to go down, it does not follow that the grower could dispose of more produce. The lower the price, the less of it he is likely to sell, and he can only throw away the rest—while meanwhile, on the consumer market, it as is though the quantity thrown away had never been produced, for it never came on the consumer market.

When producers and consumers are separated by great (economic) distances, especially in international commodity trading, such phenomena occur rather frequently.

All these lessons of the Depression years have helped to make clear that the free play of supply and demand in a market economy does not necessarily culminate in the maximal satisfaction of human needs, but that rather it may culminate in economic depression while a majority of human beings are not getting enough to eat. When the point is reached where we cannot any longer pretend that all is for the best in this best of all economic worlds, within which economic theory finds simple explanations for so-called "economic heresies," then it becomes possible to strike out at economic structures which one had long felt morally necessary but which one feared must prove ineffectual, at best likely to produce (in Paul Reynaud's phrase) "the economy of prosperity." Just as mass unemployment could no longer be accounted for as a refusal to let wages fall to the market price (Rueff's law), so one began to wonder whether something could not be done to combat underconsumption and the depression at the same time. Policies of "economic Malthusianism" were plainly of no avail in coping with the depression, and they were morally intolerable besides. Not being successful at reducing agricultural production, the only recourse in the way of reducing supply was to destroy the natural wealth produced—at a time when men were dying for want of food.

The Depression years also brought some lessons of a more positive character. First the nutritionists, and then more especially John Boyd-Orr, set out to demonstrate that it is a "paying proposition" to see that mankind gets properly fed. Milk distribution in the schools of Scotland demonstrated, not just that the lucky children attained a better growth than the others, but that, because they were healthier, the saving in doctor bills and medicine more than met the cost of the free milk. Similar experiments in France, in Luxembourg, in the Scandinavian countries, in Indochina, in the United States, and elsewhere, brought out further advantages to be gained from dietary supplements. Every country has poor people, or people poor enough, who do not get enough to eat, and especially in a situation of market surpluses it is to the common interest that consumption should increase. And yet, for lack of purchasing power, such unsatisfied needs do not show up on the market in the form of "real demand." Under the circumstances, why not try ways of "getting rid" of the surpluses such as can only spur development of more and (eventually) more prosperous consumers?

The economists, meanwhile, were thinking of ways to make use of the "surpluses" so as to counteract the harmful effects of a fluctuating economy. As we have seen, agriculture seeks economic stability, whereas the natural variations in production make for instability. It would be, then, in the common interest to organize some means of stabilizing supply, rather than allowing the market to be run primarily for the maximum profit of the middlemen, the professional speculators. For producers are also consumers: their income constitutes an important part of the over-all population's purchasing power. Many an economic depression can be traced to a cutting down of the "real demand" that purchasing power represents. Business and industry being always capable of retrenching, of operating on a more modest scale, what follows from the lowering of agricultural incomes is working-class unemployment, loss of purchasing power by the poorest part of the non-agricultural population. At the same time, it would be desirable to prevent the rise of food prices, whose effects will be felt most painfully by the same section of the population.

While a drop in agricultural prices is often at the origin of a depression, a rise in food prices can set off the well-known vicious cycle of inflation.

The most practical procedure, whenever it can be used, of controlling the market is what Keynes called "buffer stocks," a method known in the international organizations as "Operation Joseph." This is a reference to Joseph's advice to Pharaoh, about putting aside during the "years of plenty" the wherewithal to feed the people in the "years of famine." The idea, then, is not a new one, and has survived even the periods of mercantilism at its most uncontrolled.

Though the system of buffer stocks was not put into practice until later, the depression years did give men the courage to experiment by putting in question the inevitability and the adequacy to human needs of the so-called "laws" of classical economics. Many of the experiments were unsuccessful, but lessons were learned from them, and when, for example, the system of the "ever-normal granary" was put in effect by the Agricultural Adjustment Act of 1938, it was something nobody could even have suggested ten years earlier.

The Office Interprofessionnel du Blé did not go quite so far in France. It was created to supply French agriculture with the price guarantees and the assurances of selling its products which it must have to keep going, and to hold food prices firm. Stabilization through stockpiling was never achieved from harvest to harvest, because attempts along this line had in the years preceding aroused the opposition of such financial powers as the Bank of France, which forbade any policy of financing the market by carrying forward the reserves of the previous year. However, it has been possible to eliminate violent price fluctuations where the consumption of such an annual crop as wheat is concerned, by spreading it out over the course of the year. When the market is uncontrolled, supplies are great at the beginning of the season, and growers without sufficient funds to hold off start selling right after the harvest. This works naturally to the profit of the businessmen, who can afford to buy up immediately and store the product while prices are low, while at the same time, almost the sole supplier to the consumer, they can make the latter pay as dearly as possible. It is to the interest of producers and consumers alike that there should be control of the market, to minimize the risks to both, and to hold costs of storage and financing to a just price, whether these services are supplied by private business or by growers' co-operatives.

In the mid-nineteenth century, American agronomists were already alarmed about the effects of wasteful exploitation of the soil, and in 1870 the geologists of the American Association for the Advancement of Science issued a warning. At the beginning of this century, such voices as those of Theodore Roosevelt, Charles Van Hise (president of the University of Wisconsin), and Gifford Pinchot (founder of the American Forestry Service) were also raised in pleas for greater public concern over the problem of soil conservation. However, the forces of "rugged individualism" were so strengthened by the economic boom which accompanied World War I, that little was accomplished. Only the depression made it possible for Franklin D. Roosevelt to put through a series of measures relating to the conservation of natural resources, and a Soil Conservation Service was established. Looked upon more often at the time as an indirect means of slowing down production than as a changeover in American farming methods,[38] nonetheless the measures of the depression years helped prepare for the transformation in American agriculture which World War II was to bring. What came about now was that instead of ploughing up ever new, hitherto untilled land, a more intensive agriculture began to be practiced, naturally more conservationist and improvement-minded than before. Farm production, with the aid of technological advances, increased enormously, but no longer through eating into the capital of natural wealth. The increase was due to a truly supplementary production, not to "extractive" or "mining" procedures. There is no reason why measures of incentive to the producer, of market control, and of improved distribution should not encourage still further increase, especially if the measures single out for favor those farmers who give up ruinous old practices for practices that look to the future of the soil and the needs of ever-growing numbers of consumers. Should it occur that the prices of farm production become abnormally low due to unfair exploitation of farm labor, then it is possible to demand fair wages and the establishment of social assistance programs to profit from the guarantees laid down by the system which controls distribution and assures fair market prices.

When Roosevelt began his experiment in the United States there were already sizable "surpluses," and the policy adopted was not, as some believed, directly "Malthusian." The stockpiles have, ever since, tended to maintain themselves at the same level, or to be increased. It seems the "ever-normal granary" was destined to be kept full. It was in this situation that the advice of the nutritionists coincided with that of the economists, and it began to be proposed that, once the stockpiled reserves of food had reached their maximum possible volume, the "surpluses" might be used in programs to improve consumption—"outside" the "business framework." The idea was that they might be distributed "at special prices," even for nothing, to those sections of the population without sufficient purchasing power to represent any "real" demand on the commercial market.

Obviously, it is necessary to establish priorities once such various "outlets" have been created. But from the economic point of view, all that matters is that such products go to consumers who would never have purchased them—the effect then would be as stabilizing as those policies of "economic Malthusianism" which had destroyed agricultural products so they could be of benefit to no one. First a program of school lunches was put in effect, then a broader Food Stamp Plan in May, 1939, at Rochester, N.Y. The latter was improved and broadened further as the Food Allotment Plan. With the taking of such measures, it was at last possible to envisage "the problem of abundance" as not necessarily bringing poverty to the agricultural producer. For the first time, a limiting factor on production far more serious than any natural factor was being effectively coped with by mankind. Prospects were opening up for achieving economic equilibrium at a higher level of the satisfaction of needs, involving the satisfaction of more people's needs.

The foundations of an economic policy were being laid as the lessons of the depression years sank in. Empirically, organizationally, what Roosevelt did was to put into practice measures for which the Geneva studies had supplied the theoretical basis. Instead of setting off a new boom to encourage anew all the more destructive tendencies of capitalism, World War II was instead to bring about a mutation of economic life, with new perspectives and prospects for the future very much influenced by recent memories of the terrible depression years. One thing World War II brought about was the carrying over to the international plane, of such a purely American and Rooseveltian policy as the Agricultural Adjustment Act of 1938. Thus, for example, it was right after the Atlantic Charter had been signed, that such Geneva "old hands" as Frank McDougall and André Mayer presented the results of their labors: that "marriage of agriculture and food" which was to lead to the founding of FAO.

Just as, during the thirties, the "ever-normal granary" policy led to the Food Stamp Plan in the United States, so at the international level "Operation Joseph" looks ahead to measures which will make possible the utilizing of food "surpluses" for the well-being of all mankind. With famines occurring every year somewhere in the world, must there not be some way of getting this food to starving peoples who never, at such times, present any sort of "real demand" on the world market? Especially when such "surpluses" threaten the purchasing power of the producers and tempt them to destroy the wealth they have built up, or at least to slow down production? Surely the positive policy must be to store up reserves against famine.

Were mankind better fed than it is—and especially children, pregnant and nursing mothers, men doing hard physical labor— what we would see is an enormous expansion of economic horizons, and of standards of living. Agricultural production, which everyone admits is indispensable to life, would be itself encouraged, for it would have more remunerative outlets than it has at present. The great lesson of the Depression years of the thirties is that the world does not suffer from any physical incapacity for feeding mankind, and feeding it well, but from outmoded economic systems that cannot assure producers a just reward for their labors. At present, what they grow floods the market with more of everything than those "happy few" who *have* the purchasing power to buy it, care to pay for it. Attempts to readjust the classical balance through cutting down production leads to ever more serious food shortages, the effect of which nonetheless shows up as a market "surplus." Life must keep growing and expanding. To give away what cannot be sold, on the condition that it be given away to those whose lack of purchasing power prevents them from buying it because their needs are not economically "real," is at once good business and a good deed.

We must observe, however, that the problem is not solely one of distribution, of unloading the "surpluses" on the starving. There are advantages to be gained by doing this, but precautions must be taken against hurting the development of the local economies. And however burdensome may seem to us the pressure of these "surpluses" on the market, it must be noted that they represent a mere drop in the bucket, weighed against existing human needs. The 130 million tons of cereal grains which go unsold at the present time, principally in North America, represent no more than one month's supply of the world's caloric needs. This quantity would be enough to correct the chronic shortage in the countries of the Far East—estimated at 200 calories per capita per day—for a bit more than three years. At the rate stockpiling has been going on over the past few years, approximately 10 million tons per year, these "surpluses" could satisfy the caloric needs of no more than 39 million people, while over the same period the world's population has been growing by 45 million each year. The inadequacy of present "surpluses" to satisfy mankind's alimentary necessities is yet another illustration of the effects of King's law, and obliges us to recognize that for mankind to be properly fed we must find some way of producing more food. To distribute the "surpluses" will not be enough; we must also find ways of encouraging the producers to grow still more.

Understanding the lesson of the Depression years, producers ought to have gotten over their fears of abundance, for if they have not there will be no abundance. Too often, like the drunken porter in *Macbeth,* we have been obliged to say, "Here's a farmer that hanged himself on th'expectation of plenty." It remains to be seen whether, as such fears fade away, enough food can be produced to keep mankind fed adequately in its present numbers, let alone in the years to come. Certain achievements in the United States during World War II and in France since the Liberation, suggest that an affirmative answer may yet be given.

EXAMPLES OF
INCREASED FOOD PRODUCTION

THE UNITED STATES

After a round-table conference of the best-qualified experts then in the United States, President Roosevelt in 1941 announced the production goals which would have to be met if the war was to be

won for the Allies and if the peoples of the war-torn nations were
to be fed when hostilities ceased. The production increase was to
come to 40 per cent over the annual agricultural output of the
United States during the years 1935–39, and it would have to be
reached in two years. Many doubted it could be done.

And yet, taking the 1935–39 figures for base (= 100), the
agricultural index had already reached 128 in 1942, and climbed to
140 in 1948. This in a country where, it might have been feared,
many producers still thought in terms of a frontier economy, and
where only a few years earlier millions of acres of good land had
"gone with the wind" or been washed away with the rains. Actually,
the United States came close to meeting the needs of the Allies
singlehandedly, and it did not do so by putting new land under
cultivation as had been done during the First World War. Rather,
it embarked on more intensive methods of cultivation that made
greater and greater use of mechanization. Agricultural output increased even faster than the gross agricultural product—output in
this case being gross product less that part of the product consumed
by agriculture itself (seed-grain, feed for animals, etc.) in the production process.

It is clear that just about every part of the United States pitched
in, though it goes without saying that the greatest expansion occurred in the already predominately agricultural regions, rather
than in the older, more settled regions. The indices for 1948 indicate that the North Central and Northwest (169) and the Rocky
Mountain states (147) broke all records, but there were gains elsewhere too: the Middle Atlantic states (123), the Southwest and
South Central states (124), the New England states (128).

All that held back production, under these more intensive methods of cultivation, was the amount of acreage utilized. Wheat
affords the typical example: by 1942 the number of acres under
cultivation had dropped to 67 per cent of the 1938 figure, but
yield had been so improved as to give an index of 106 (1938 =
100).

More acres were put under cultivation from 1942 on, but even at the peak in 1947–49, only 98 per cent of the 1938 acreage was utilized. Taking into account the fact that 1943 was a poor year, and that less fertile land was now beginning to be farmed again, the output for that year was 137 per cent of the 1938 output. It was 164 per cent in 1947 and 153 per cent in 1948. Clearly, intensive methods were being more and more widely employed.

Much remains to be done, or rather, further progress is yet possible along these lines. The yields obtained, in wheat for example, are no longer those to be expected of the extensive type of farming (1938 = 11.6 bushels per acre, 1939 = 10.7 bu./a.), but neither are they yet quite up to the yields we expect from a fully intensified type of farming (1942 and 1948 = 18 bu./a., 1947 = 19.04 bu./a.). All indications point to an as yet heterogeneous rural economy, in part practicing intensive methods of cultivation, in part extensive methods. American agriculture would seem to be in transition.

For present purposes, the lesson to be drawn is that production increased to meet the wartime goals, and did so without meeting any physical obstacles to its increase, though many had deemed it impossible to achieve.

Some may be tempted to reflect that in this case increased food production cannot have been so hard to bring about, circumstances providing an occasion merely to make the transition from one economy to another, neither involving any very high degree of intensiveness. It might be to the point, then, to turn to a very different example of increased food production within recent years in a country where the practice of supposedly intensive methods of agriculture had long resulted in all but stationary production levels.

FRANCE

By 1948 France had very nearly come back to the pre-war level of agricultural production. In 1945 the output index had fallen off 64 per cent from the 1938 level. It was the opinion of some that now French agriculture had once again found its normal level of production, and would hold it. A very few optimists suggested timidly that perhaps the increased productivity of human labor might now compensate for the factors which had hitherto held it back. From time immemorial in France, the complaint had been that the farms are "short of hands," and in recent generations it has frequently been alleged that "the flight to the cities" of the rural population has "hurt" French agriculture.

The farmers themselves were sincerely convinced that they were doing the best they could, and that in any case to increase production would be economically unsound, both for them and for the country.

In point of fact, French agriculture was then and still is extremely heterogeneous. The wheat yield, for example, which was 19.4 bushels per acre in the years 1909–13, had only increased to 23 bu./a. by 1934–38. And yet, though the over-all picture is of slow but steady progress, there are very striking differences when we compare average yields in different parts of the country. In the same year the département du Nord reports 52 bu./a., whereas Lot and Corsica report 7.4 bu./a. Taking the average yield for the years 1930–39, the Nord registers 46 bu./a. and Lot 14 bu./a. In passing, we might mention that this is higher than the national average for Greece, Spain, and Rumania in Europe, and that for the United States, over the same years.[39]

It seemed obvious that technical advances could offset the disadvantages of a diminished labor force and some reduction in the acreage under cultivation, but it was considered unlikely that over-all production could be increased purely by enhanced productivity. Moreover, it was thought dangerous to try. Only the Malthusian economic lessons of the Depression years were still remembered by French farmers, who were carefully protected and alert to the tiniest crack in the status quo through which the old virus might come seeping back.

And yet, what happened between 1948 and 1958, and is still going on? What has changed the face of French agriculture, hitherto so carefully protected from foreign competition, into an agriculture eager for foreign outlets, and whose products are priced so low on the home market—in some instances, lower by far than in any other country of Western Europe?

Enormous efforts to increase productivity were not enough in themselves, both to improve producers' incomes and to bring about a corresponding drop in the price of their products. There had to be a sizable increase in production. This continues today, and in areas of France where the situation is still "critical," the poorest peasants know that they will have to increase their gross output to attain a satisfactory standard of living. Moreover, they know that scientific farming methods today bring it within their power to do this.

During the years 1951–56, the French farm worker's rate of increase in physical productivity reached 7.7 per cent per year. This was nearly as high as the corresponding figures for Italy (7.8 per cent) and for West Germany (8 per cent), well ahead of those for Belgium and Luxembourg (6.4 per cent) and the Netherlands (3.4 per cent).[40]

In an old country like France, there is no new land to be put under cultivation. In fact, the acreage under cultivation dropped from 125.9 million acres in 1938 to 124.8 million acres in 1956. This is accounted for by the spread of urban agglomerations into the surrounding countryside. There was some gain to agriculture, however, in that 3 million acres of uncultivated farmland were put to use over the same years: 123,000 in crops, 1.9 million in forestry production, the remainder in various tree and orchard plantings, fisheries, etc.

As for the acreage under cultivation the following changes took place: 3.7 million acres of tilled land were let go to pasture, 247,000 acres of vineyard passed from winegrowing to fruit-growing, and approximately 160,000 acres were added to the country's specialized market gardening.

France's increase in food production was brought about, then, through obtaining increased productivity, both from the land (yield, intensive farming) and from the human labor working it. What this goes to show is that, even in the old country, there are marginal opportunities for expansion, and that they can be realized without raising—indeed, in such a way as to cut down—the unit cost of production.

NOTES

1. André Mayer, pref. to the French edition of Josué de Castro, *The Geography of Hunger* (1949).

2. *Dissertation sur la manière d'amollir les os et de faire cuire toutes sortes de viandes en fort peu de temps et à peu de frais avec la description de la machine* (Paris, 1682).

3. Denis Papin, *Emploi de la vapeur comme moteur universel* (Leipzig: Acta Eruditorium, 1960).

4. Cépède and Lengellé, *Economie alimentaire du globe*.

5. *Ibid.*, pp. 87 ff.

6. *Proposals for a World Food Board and World Food Survey*, Food and Agriculture Organization of the United Nations (combined reprint), Washington, D.C., October 1, 1946, p. 19 & n.

7. Michel Cépède and Maurice Lengellé, *L'Economie de l'alimentation* (Paris: Presses Universitaires, 1954).

8. Quotation from Chardin's *Le coeur et la matière* (Paris, 1950) cited in F. A. Viallet, *L'univers personnel de Teilhard de Chardin* (Paris, 1955).

9. Prat, *Métamorphose explosive de l'humanité*.

10. Cépède, *Du prix de revient au produit net en agriculture*.

11. Eduard Hahn, *Von der Hacke zum Pflug* (Leipzig: Quelle & Meyer, 1914).

12. Prat, *op. cit.*

13. James Mooney, *The Aboriginal Population of America North of Mexico* (Washington, D.C., 1924).

14. Vladimir A. Kostitzyn, *Biologie mathématique* (Paris: Armand Colin, 1937).

15. *Population Bulletin*, XVI, 5 (Aug. 1960).

16. Samuel H. Ordway, Jr., "Possible Limits of Raw Material Consumption" in William L. Thomas, Jr. (ed.), *Man's Role in Changing the Face of the Earth* (U. of Chicago Press, 1956), pp. 990–92.

17. Cépède, *op. cit.*

18. T. R. Malthus, *Principles of Political Economy*, etc., 2d ed. (London: William Pickering, 1836), pp. 209–210.

19. Henry A. Wallace, "Outstanding Facts in American History," *The Southern Planter* (1940).

20. Raymond Furon, *La Géologie et l'économie moderne* (Paris, 1960).

21. *Ibid.*

22. Jean Majorelle, *Les perspectives énergétiques de l'Europe* (Nancy: Centre Européen universitaire, 1960–61).

23. Furon, *op. cit.*

24. Van Hise and Havemeyer, *Conservation of Natural Resources* (New York, 1935).

25. Egon Glesinger, *The Coming Age of Wood* (New York, 1947).

26. Vauban, *Oisivetés et correspondances rassemblées par le Colonel de Rochas* (Paris, 1910).

27. A. Woiekoff. *Verteilung der Bevölkerung auf der Erde unter dem Einfluss der Naturverhältnisse und der menschlichen Tätigkeit* (Gotha: Petermann's Mitteilungen, 1905).

28. L. Febvre and L. Bataillon, *La terre et l'evolution de l'humanité,* 2d ed. (Paris, 1924). W. C. Lowdermilk, *Man-Made Deserts,* Fac. Ar. VIII. P. B. Sears, *Deserts on the March* (U. of Oklahoma Press, 1935). Stuart Chase, *Rich Land, Poor Land* (New York: 1935).

29. Theodore W. Schultz, *Agriculture in an Unstable Economy* (New York, 1945).

30. Cf. Cépède, *op. cit.*

31. Nicholas Baudeau, *Première introduction à la philosophie économique ou Analyses des Etats policés* (Paris, 1957).

32. Table "Indice de la production agricole," *Etude sur la situation économique de l'Asie et de l'Extreme-Orient en 1957* (New York: United Nations, 1959).

33. New York, May 20, 1960, p. 31.

34. *Ibid.,* pp. 34, 64–65.

35. *Ibid.,* p. 62.

36. "Les surplus agricoles et l'avenir de l'Agriculture," *Annales de l'Economie collective,* XLIX, 1 (Jan./March, 1961), 21.

37. Michel Cépède, *Fatis,* no. 9 (1960).

38. Michel Cépède, "Agriculture américaine et agriculture européenne," *Sillons* (Brussels, 1939).

39. Michel Cépède, *Agriculture et alimentation en France durant la deuxième guerre mondiale* (Paris: 1961).

40. Michel Cépède, "L'evolution de la productivité," *Economie agricole française 1938–58* (Paris), nos. 39–40.

Chapter 7

The Process of Food Production

ECONOMIC AND TECHNICAL FACTORS

ADVANCES IN TECHNIQUE

SINCE 1945 most of the countries in process of development have set up long-term plans for increasing food production with the expert assistance of FAO and other UN agencies. In countries of Asia and Africa where such plans were first put into vigorous operation, there were some spectacular results by the early fifties.

A great many factors enter into all attempts at improving agricultural productivity, and it is very hard to say in a given case which of them was the crucial one. New techniques of soil improvement and re-organization of marketing practices can only be made operative once the social and cultural climate has been prepared for such innovations, and once the hostility of the population to such interference with their age-old habits and traditions has been neutralized. Problems arising from hostility to change cannot be solved within the narrow framework of production techniques, but only within the broader framework of plans for over-all economic development.[1] It is enough to recall such matters as the sacredness of monkeys and cattle in India, or the social prestige the Batutsi (in Ruanda-Urundi) attach to ownership of unrealistic numbers of domestic animals, to grasp that economic reform is a long-term project and will be successful at changing the more harmful heritages of the ancestral past only to the degree that it respects and safeguards as much as possible all the more valuable

338

elements in the cultures of the various underdeveloped peoples. First among the factors that make for bigger harvests and improve the quality of what is grown for food, we may single out new production techniques, more and better versions of which are being discovered every day. They represent the application of scientific methods to agriculture, forestry, and fishing.

There are a great many ways to improve upon how the various crops are grown and livestock is raised and bred. Agronomic techniques exist for enhancing the productivity of the various soils. Plant specialists have developed high-grade strains whose seeds assure greater yields, and specialists in stockbreeding have made improvements in all the animals which are raised for food.[2]

To cite some examples, there are now strains of wheat that require no more fertilizer than the ordinary strains, but which supply a higher number of vegetable calories. A superior breed of cow has been developed to give more milk with the same amount of feed. "Indica" rice, which grows in tropical countries, has been crossed with the higher-yield "japonica" rice of the temperate zone, to produce bigger harvests in the former. Hitherto the average rice yield in Asia had never been more than about 1800 lbs. per acre, whereas the "japonica" strain gave more than double that. Attempts to develop more productive strains of wheat have been very successful, both in the United States (Iowa) and in France (Etoile de Choisy). On the basis of these experiments, FAO will be introducing these higher-grade strains in other parts of the world, including southern Europe.

In England and in several countries of western Europe a shortage of the cereal grasses for livestock has led farmers to give more attention than heretofore to the improvement and conservation of pasture land.

In Russia some remarkable results have been obtained from efforts to breed plants specially resistant to cold weather. It has been possible to put more and more areas of the U.S.S.R. under cultivation, stretching up into northern Siberia. In Canada, too, experts have developed quick-ripening wheat which has similarly permitted the extension of this kind of farming hundreds of miles into the north country.

Scientific stockbreeding, combined with improved control of animal diseases and better understanding of their nutritional needs, has greatly increased the productivity of the domestic animals. In the United States today, there are fewer cows than formerly, but milk production has never been higher. In Denmark between 1870 and 1934 the number of milk cows somewhat more than doubled, but over the same period milk production increased from 1.08 million long tons to 5.3 million long tons.

Another factor in increased agricultural productivity has been the motorizing of equipment and the rise of the mechanical harvester. Various countries have gone about this in different ways; the revolutionary zeal of the Russians on this score is well known. Before World War II, England imported approximately 60 per cent of its food. With mechanization, however, its own farmers (who practice the world's most intensive agriculture) now supply 60 per cent of the nation's needs. TABLE 65 gives an idea of how the use of tractors has increased since 1939 in the agriculture of Europe.[3]

A recent study of a village in Gambia shows how seasonal wheat production varies according to the methods employed, from 5.8 bushels per agricultural worker to 12.4 bushels.[4]

With motorization and mechanization, new prospects for the future are opened up to agriculture, in the developed countries no less than in the underdeveloped ones. In the former, where the farm population has been shrinking steadily, both in crude figures and proportionately to the rest of the population, mechanization has become indispensable. In the less developed countries, however, where there are great numbers of agricultural workers, where the majority of the population is so engaged, too sudden or too insistent an introduction of mechanization tends to upset the occupational structure. This is the more likely, as in these countries population excess requires an economic structure heavily weighted with unskilled labor.

TABLE 65

Number of Tractors in Use in Agriculture (per 1,000 hectares)
of European Countries, 1939–1955

| County | No. of Tractors per Thousand Hectares of Agricultural Land | | | | | Number of Men Employed per Tractor in Agricultural Work in 1954 or 1955 |
	1939	1950	1953	1954	1955	
United Kingdom	1.6	10	13	14	—	2
Western Germany	1.6	4	8.5	1.06	—	6
Norway	1.2	4.4	7	9.7	11.6	7
Sweden	1.6	4.9	6.8	9	9.7	4
Switzerland	2.8	6	7.3	8	9.3	12
Denmark	.25	2.4	5.3	6.4	7.2	6
Netherlands	.8	3.2	5.2	6.4	7.2	10
Belgium	.25	2.4	4	4.8	5.6	13
Finland	.25	1.6	3.2	4	5.2	11
Austria	.2	1.2	3.2	3.6	—	13
France	.25	1.6	2.8	3.2	3.6	11
Italy	.8	1.2	2	2.4	—	45
Ireland	.2	1.2	2	—	—	19
Greece	.08	.2	.32	.32	.36	160
Turkey	—	.12	.28	.28	.32	100
Yugoslavia	.08	.16	.24	.24	.24	340
Spain	.08	.08	.16	.2	—	230

Technical advances have also been made in fishery production, such that

Average production, per year and per man, varies from around 1 ton in a number of the still undeveloped countries to more than 80 tons in countries which have perfected techniques of the catch.[5]

Further increases in fishery production are quite within the bounds of possibility. As yet something less than 1 per cent of world food production has come from the seas, lakes, and rivers. Moreover, 90 per cent of the annual catch of about 25 million tons is limited to the northern hemisphere, mainly to the shallower waters of the North Atlantic and the Pacific. These fishing grounds are in danger of being overexploited. Experts at the sixth FAO Congress in 1962 estimated that world production could easily be doubled by development of greater fisheries in the southern hemisphere and by fishing deeper waters in the northern hemisphere, with no danger of exhausting resources. The two coasts off Latin America and the Atlantic coast off South Africa are at present being fished more extensively than formerly.

A still more important potential source of food supply is plankton, which exists in enormous quantities in all the world's oceans. Cultivation of the algae in artificial ponds and tropical lakes is another great potential source of food for mankind. It has been estimated that 50 million acres given over to this latter activity would at least double the world food supply as of the present time.[6] To realize such a project, however, would as yet be prohibitively expensive.

Similar difficulties of a financial order face the efforts so far made toward any large-scale production of synthetic foodstuffs and raw materials. Remarkable results have been achieved already, however, notably in the manufacture of margarine, in the production of sugar from coal and sawdust, in the extraction of protein from grass, and in the chemical transformation of the nitrogen in the air into fertilizer.

Among other technical possibilities which bear upon increased world food production, are research findings applicable to the struggle against plant and animal diseases, against the depredations of insects, parasites, and weeds, and applicable also to the protection of food stocks against damage in storage and in transit.

Vast areas of Africa, Afghanistan, China, India, and Pakistan are subject to the cattle plague known as rinderpest.

In 1947 a committee of FAO experts estimated storage losses due to insects, rodents, and other damaging factors at 10 per cent of the world production of grain, legumes, and oil seeds. This would amount to some 65.5 million metric tons and equals the annual volume of sales on the world commodity markets.[7] It would be enough to feed 250 million people for one year.

Damage from insects is especially great in the parts of the world subject to swarms of migratory locusts: North Africa, the area from the Near East to Pakistan, and northern India. Wherever they multiply they leave the land waste, and it is to be hoped that the modern method of spraying insecticides from the air will eventually stamp out this plague.

Further scientific aids to increasing world food production relate to the processing and preservation of the basic foodstuffs. In cold countries like Canada, the climate protects certain products, while in tropical countries such products as fish, for example, spoil almost immediately. Here, too, FAO has found scope for its energies.

SOILS

The most plausible estimates of the total land surface capable of being cultivated give a figure of 7 billion hectares (17.3 billion acres). Of this, half is actually put to some use. To get an agricultural product out of the rest, enormous efforts, both of human labor and of investment, would be required. Vast forests would have to be cleared in some parts of the world, enormous areas of brush in others, and with precautions against soil erosion. Elsewhere, the problem would be to reforest lands presently threatened with erosion. Great desert areas would have to be irrigated, a difficult as well as a costly operation. In other parts of the world age-old epidemic diseases, such as malaria and sleeping sickness, would have to be stamped out before the work of cultivation could begin.

It is a fact that to reclaim these lands not presently in use, would have little relation to the world population as it is presently distributed and growing. Only a third of them are in Asia, where the annual rate of population growth is 55 per cent higher than for the world as a whole. What is needed, over and above the reclamation of unused land, is to increase the yield from land already under cultivation, especially in the just developing countries where yields are low. Earlier, in connection with discussing food surpluses, we supplied some figures which are pertinent here.*

* See above, pp. 312–314.

There are various ways of getting a better return from the soil:

1. Scientific utilization of soil and water supply on arable land, grazing land, and forested areas; more rational organization of inadequately developed forestry resources; application of improved methods for exploiting common lands and pasturage, including a more intensive approach to the latter.[8]

Deterioration of soils through erosion has been observed everywhere, but the form it takes varies from country to country as do the causes and effects. Lessened fertility, poorer and poorer crops, are very often the first symptoms. Wind and water are the natural agents, but poor management is most often at the bottom of the process. It has been shown how in the United States, as of 1934, only one acre out of every four had been untouched by one or another form of soil erosion. One-eighth of all the cultivated land was ruined, another one-eighth very nearly so, and one-fourth had been seriously impoverished. Much the same sort of thing is going on in other parts of the world, especially in Asia and Africa. Northwestern Europe is the single exception. There are other problems of soil exhaustion, as in the case of the New Zealand phosphates. The United States government has created agencies for soil conservation which supervise use of nearly half the arable land, divided into "soil conservation districts."

Another abuse is deforestation, which increases the danger of soil erosion, and still another the growing of crops ill-adapted to a particular soil. The pampas of South America which serve as grazing lands were made much more productive by occasionally ploughing them up and planting specially selected forage grasses, especially lucerne. In Canada crop yields were sizably increased, wherever in the central prairie provinces farmers could be persuaded to plant an occasional crop of something besides wheat.

2. In a number of parts of the world, better returns from the soil could be had by more careful use and control of the water used for irrigation.

Besides the great irrigation systems created by building dams, there are no less important smaller systems in parts of the world where by enhancement of the already existing water supply bigger crop yields can be obtained or a more diversified agriculture be encouraged.

The increasing development of irrigation in the western United States will very substantially increase agricultural production there. In tropical and sub-tropical Latin America the problem is rather to expand existing systems of irrigation, to obtain similar results, for example, in the San Francisco valley in southern Brazil. Most of the countries of the Near East are arid or semi-arid. Increased production in Iran, Iraq, and Syria depends upon making better use of water from the Tigris and the Euphrates. Certain parts of Turkey could also benefit from the expansion and improvement of existing resources.

Ceylon has a number of irrigation projects underway at the present time. The goal is to put nearly 100,000 more acres of land under cultivation, to help meet the needs of the rapidly growing population. Similar projects are underway in India, Pakistan, Mexico, and Australia.

3. Diversity in agricultural production and the use of fodder and fertilizers should be encouraged, since they bring about a varied type of cultivation that brings profit to the farmer and maintains fertility in the soil.[9]

Until quite recently it was believed that the only mineral deficiencies in the soil were due to lack of nitrogen, phosphate, potash, or lime. Some surprising discoveries have recently been made as to the importance of other elements normally present in the soil. Cobalt, for example—or rather, the lack of it—was found to be causing a mysterious disease among the sheep and cattle in southeastern and coastal Australia. Elsewhere in Australia, it has been found necessary to add tiny quantities of molybdenum to the soil before certain species of legume will grow properly. There are regions in California where the soil lacks zinc. In a great many more cases, the legumes themselves suffice to enrich soils with the elements for lack of which crop yield is poor.

Here we need scarcely emphasize the basic importance of fertilizers for the increase and improvement of food crops all over the world. The steady progress in European agriculture, with respect both to quantity and to quality, is largely due to a systematic, ever more efficient use of both organic and synthetic fertilizers. In the most advanced European countries at the present time, grain yields have reached levels as high as from 37 to 45 bushels per acre, and have sometimes run higher. On other continents, where soil-enrichment methods are more seldom practiced, grain yields are still where they were in Europe circa 1850, that is, around 15 bushels per acre. And in some of the most underdeveloped countries, just at the beginning of their economic modernization, grain yields are where they were in Europe at the time of the Roman Empire: between 4.5 and 9 bushels per acre.

One of the enormous differences between that one-third of the world which is highly developed and the two-thirds which have as yet to catch up with it, is shown in the fact that some 18 million tons of chemical fertilizer are used every year by the former, scarcely 4 million by the latter.

LABOR

Mankind does not just represent so many mouths to feed, but a sum of human energies available among other things for producing the food it eats. Not all human beings are or can be producers in this sense, nor to the same extent. Some remain for whole periods of their lifetimes mere mouths to feed, with varying needs in this as in other respects.

Precisely as a factor in production, and often as a limiting factor, human labor should be approached historically, in terms of different stages of the developmental process.

In the classical world, concern for limiting the numbers of people applied solely to the citizen class, not to the slaves. From the point of view of consumption, slaves were on a par with livestock. They did not work to feed themselves, but to create more wealth for their master than it cost the latter to keep and feed them. Statesmen were not concerned with their numbers, for their reproduction was as much under the control of their master as was the reproduction of his domestic animals.

Concern over the growing numbers of human beings today is expressed very differently than it was in the ancient city-state, very differently even than in the society Malthus studied and addressed. Mastery over their fellowmen, not the mastery of nature, was their leading concern. In Malthus' case, his concern over the increasing numbers of the poor was, of course, different from that of slave-owners in the ancient world—but only in the sense, perhaps, that slavery had been superseded as an institution by the system of wage labor. Today the bulk of all workers, including those on the farms, are not slaves but consumers who work to provide themselves and their dependents with a certain standard of living. Unless we are to dissociate the worker from the consumer, it behooves us to grasp the connection between labor power and the needs of consumption.

The Working Population. It may seem as though an easy way to grasp the connection would be to compare the working population with the total population, but actually the connection is much weaker in the so-called underdeveloped countries than in the others:

% of Population Working	Underdeveloped Countries		Advanced Countries
32	Puerto Rico		
34	Indonesia		
35	Chile		
38	Egypt		
39	Ceylon		
40	—		U.S.A., Netherlands
41	—		Canada
42	India		Australia
44	—	Italy	
46	—	Japan	
50	—		France
51	—		Finland
52	Colombia		Austria
57	—	U.S.S.R.	

When we analyze the phenomenon, we find that it is the result of two elements acting at cross-purposes: the sex and age structure of the population, and the rate of economic activity in the various categories.

The percentage of population of working age (15–60, for example) is highest in the more advanced countries. In the other countries, a disproportionate number of children (under 15 years) more than makes up for a much smaller percentage of older people (over 60 years). TABLE 66 illustrates the situation.

TABLE 66

World Population Broken Down by Age Groups, c. 1950

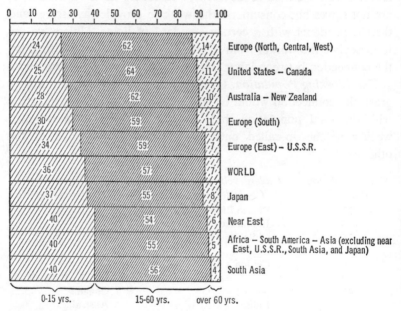

24	62	14	Europe (North, Central, West)
25	64	11	United States – Canada
28	62	10	Australia – New Zealand
30	59	11	Europe (South)
34	59	7	Europe (East) – U.S.S.R.
36	57	7	WORLD
37	55	8	Japan
40	54	6	Near East
40	55	5	Africa – South America – Asia (excluding near East, U.S.S.R., South Asia, and Japan)
40	56	4	South Asia

0-15 yrs.   15-60 yrs.   over 60 yrs.

At the same time, rates of economic activity seem to be highest in the underdeveloped countries. Getting an accurate measure of the economic activity of women is often an insoluble problem, but we do have some age-specific rates for the male population in various parts of the world. These are shown in the following tabulation, for three stages of economic development:

A: Advanced countries, i.e., where less than 35 per cent of the active male population is engaged in agriculture.

A^1: Intermediate countries, where from 35 per cent to 60 per cent of the active male population is engaged in agriculture.

B: Underdeveloped countries, where more than 60 per cent of the active male population is engaged in agriculture.

	10–14	15–19	20–24	25–34	35–44	45–54	55–64	65
A	4.9	68.9	90.7	96.2	97.2	94.9	83.5	40.6
A^1	8.6	70.9	91.8	96.1	97.1	96.1	90.0	62.5
B	30.8	81.8	93.1	96.2	97.2	96.2	90.7	78.5

Labor Productivity. It is appropriate to stress here that very young people and very old people, of course, do not have the same capacity for work as adults of the ages in between. In the case where an underdeveloped country shows as high a percentage of its population economically active as a more advanced country does, we must recognize that the latter represents a more sizable labor force (in terms of available energies) than the former. There is the further consideration, with regard to the less highly developed countries, that "Undernourishment and malnutrition, like natural selection, cripple more than they kill" (René Sand). A man over sixty in a country with high standards of public health and sanitation, and with a high nutritional level, has the productivity of a man ten years younger in a less fortunate environment.

On the basis of these and other experimental data, we have constructed the following table and graph,[10] for three types of population: advanced or industrialized (A), underdeveloped but stable (B^1), and underdeveloped but growing (B^2). TABLE 67 describes the three types of population.

	Expectation of Life at Birth	Birth Rate (per 1,000)	Gross Reproduction Rate (per 1,000)	Age Groups under 15	15–60	over 60
A	68	15.5	317	23	62	15
B¹	35	25.5	510	30	59	11
B²	35	50.0	900	40	55	5

TABLE 67

Life Expectancy at Ages 0–60 in an Advanced Country (type A)
and in an Underdeveloped Country (type B)

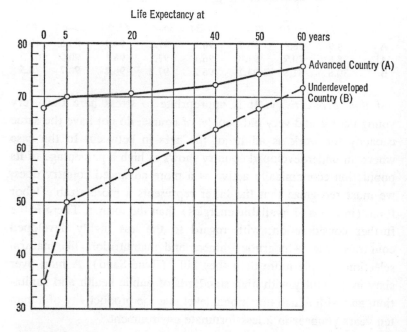

Applying the activity rates defined above and the coefficients of
productivity obtained for three populations, viz. Intermediate
Country A¹, Underdeveloped but Stable Country B¹, Underdeveloped but Growing Country B², we get the following index numbers (taking as base A = 100):

	A^1	B^1	B^2
Pop. of working age	100	94.5	89
Working population	103	101	90
Available Labor Units	97	74	68

In as much as the foregoing figures reveal very slight differences (less than 2 per cent) between the alimentary requirements of these very different types of population, some light has perhaps been thrown on the problem under discussion.

On the basis of the foregoing, it has seemed necessary to ask what would be the situation if, as a result of undertaking a program of economic development, children born once it had got under way were to reach the ages given below under physical conditions identical with those of the more advanced, industrialized countries. We have assumed that the activity rate of this new labor force and its coefficient of productivity would then no longer follow the model (A) for an advanced country, but rather constitute one for a country intermediate between A and B, that is A^1.

Taking the situation in the type-A countries as base ($= 100$), we get the following figures for the first 40 years that the program of economic development is underway:

	0	5	10	15	20	25	30	35	40
Pop. of working age	94.5	94	90.5	89.5	91	94	97.5	100	101
Working population	101	100	98	92	91	93	95	97	99
Available Labor Units	74	71	70.5	68	70	75	81	84.5	88

The above figures are for a country of the type-B (stable). These are for a type-B^1 country (with growing population):

	0	5	10	15	20	25	30	35	40
Pop. of working age	89	87	76	68	77	85	92	98	101
Working population	90	87	77	69	70	77	84	88	93
Available Labor Units	68	65	57	49	56	66	73	83	88

TABLE 68

What Happens When a Program of Development Is Undertaken
in an Underdeveloped Country (type B) of Stable Population

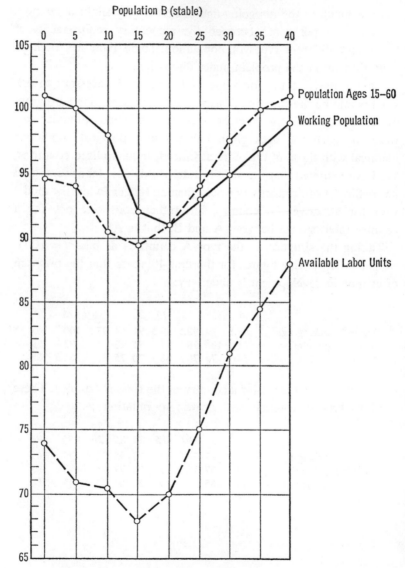

Population B (stable)

TABLE 68A

What Happens When a Program of Development Is Undertaken
in an Underdeveloped Country (type B[1]) of Growing Population

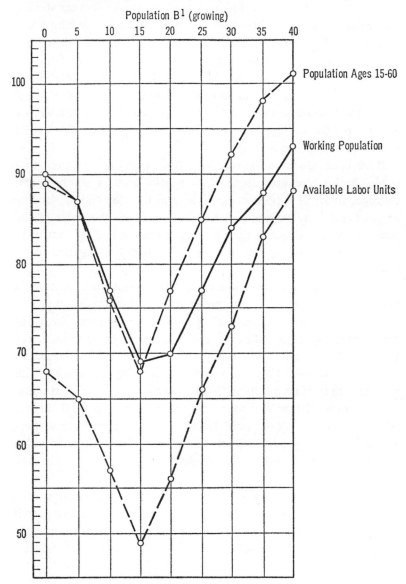

In each of these cases, we can see that it is not a straight-line development from underdeveloped to developed status but that, under the terms of our guiding assumption, the process involves a *negative* phase. During it, the number of available workers shrinks with relation to the total number of mouths to feed, reaching a low point somewhere around the 15th year, after which the disproportion begins to be made up, especially from the 25th year on. At the 40th, however, it has still not been fully made up: *growth* has not as yet permitted the attainment of employment levels or labor productivity equal to those of the more advanced countries. As we might expect, the B^2 type of underdeveloped population dips lowest in the negative phase of its growth.

If we conclude from the foregoing figures and observations that public health measures alone, with special care of mothers and children, make development possible, and that the task of feeding all mankind is by no means a hopeless one—on the order of the punishment meted out to the Danaïdes—then it is clear that ways must be found to overcome the obstacle which the negative phase poses.

The gradual transformation of an undernourished population with low standards of health and productivity into a healthy, efficient one is its own solution to the problem of producing enough to satisfy needs. Outside aid can of course be enormously valuable for initiating the process and carrying it through the negative phase, but is it indispensable? Can the negative phase be shortened? With reference to the first question (but without bearing on the second), we must observe that in the foregoing discussion of simplified types of population, we left deliberately out of consideration such matters as the increased production and better use of labor power which might come about during the gradual improvement of workers' health and diet.

Agricultural Underemployment. There have been many studies of this topic, but our understanding is still too incomplete to permit conclusions that would not be hasty and therefore dangerous.

Merely to observe that a farm worker in countries which practice age-old forms of agriculture works no more than 80–100 days a year, is not a sound enough basis for claiming that he and his fellows represent a reserve of labor power such as industry might tap. To transfer half the agricultural workers in this kind of country to other sectors of economic activity would not be to double employment while maintaining production levels. It is perfectly true that a worker does not find 160–200 days a year beyond his powers, but this kind of thinking does not allow for the seasonal character of agricultural labor. The Indian peasant who sits there day after day, looking out over his rice paddy from his raised platform, is not being lazy. Quite apart from the fact that there is literally nothing else for him to do while the rice ripens, he is storing up strength for the frenzied harvest to come. If he should fall ill at that moment, there is not a soul to take his place, for the entire village will be out in the fields working to the very limit of its endurance day after day from dawn to dusk. At *that* moment, the available labor power is the limiting factor on production.

In this connection, we might recall the lesson drawn earlier* by E. de Vries and O. Zaglita from their study of the role of the water buffalo in Indonesian agriculture. Cared for in the farmers' spare time, we may be sure that the animal is pushed to the limits of its endurance, no less than the rice farmers themselves, at the busy planting and harvest seasons. Then it is that his "storage battery" function is called upon, and in terms of production proves much more valuable than any industrial economist, thinking in terms of units of production per man-hours of labor expended, can readily grasp.

Suppose that one man devotes 100 days labor to the water buffalo every year—labor that comes back to him when he most needs it to supplement his own. Now the 80 days of human labor become 180 days of man plus beast, and it is possible for the two of them to work a paddy proportionately ($\times$ 2.25) larger, and thereby to increase production proportionately. As an example of how a process of growth is initiated, this one can hardly be bet-

* See above, pp. 277–278.

tered. P. Coutin's study of harvesting in Limagne[11] tells how, before the consolidation of small holdings, using hand tools and horse-drawn implements, two men could from planting to harvest work 30–32 acres, three men twice that. With tractor and mechanical harvester, after the consolidation of small holdings, three men could work 85 to 120 acres, or double the acreage. Nonetheless, the principal bottleneck in agricultural production is still the harvest.

The seasonal character of the labor is a problem all rural economies have. It explains why certain underdeveloped and seemingly overpopulated countries nevertheless have arable land lying untouched. Paradoxical though the situation may seem, these countries lack the manpower—at the crucial seasons—to exploit these additional lands. Moreover, the situation is further aggravated by the inability of existing agricultural production to provide adequate subsistence for the farm workers and their families.

Only by such technical progress as the "storage battery" buffalo represents, or by the introduction of farm machinery, can the seemingly overpopulated countries break the bottleneck that holds them back.

Productivity of the Agricultural Worker. The productivity of the agricultural worker does not just depend on the age and average quality of the human mechanism. (We examined the connection a few pages back before arriving at figures for a population's available labor power.) It depends also on how much and how well the worker is eating. A great many studies have brought out the influence of food on the productivity of labor.[12] Besides Prof. Dill's study of the Polish miners in the Ruhr, comparing caloric intake with work performed, there is Dr. Canet's on the rubber plantations of Indochina, Marc Bullio's on a steel mill in eastern France, and one on building the Costa Rican portion of the Pan-American Highway. All of them reveal a qualitative side no less important than the quantitative one. With an impressive array of evidence, they show that there may be as much as a 40 per cent difference in productivity between a poorly fed worker and a well-fed one. Obviously, the same must apply to agricultural production.

THIS PAGE ONE LINE LONG

What can be done to increase productivity and better utilize the available labor power, by improving workers' health and by progressive farming methods, must at the same time ease and shorten that negative phase in an underdeveloped country's economic modernization.

SOCIAL, CULTURAL, AND POLITICAL FACTORS

Although some experts believe that the world supply of food may triple in quantity during the second half of the twentieth century, this does not mean, according to Woytinsky,[13] that each continent will be able to supply its people with a sufficient amount of proper food. Nor does it mean that each country will be able to produce enough food for its people or compensate for this by importing surplus food from other countries. In Woytinsky's view, poverty continues to exist because existing political institutions prevent mankind from making full use of the techniques and methods of the advanced nations.

So it would seem that, even though technical obstacles to the increase and improvement of subsistence may be overcome, and though agricultural production can be doubled by simple readjustments in the production factors, there are still economic, cultural, social, and political obstacles. The undeveloped countries lack capital to buy the equipment they need, or have their capital tied up in more immediately profitable enterprises. Optimum agricultural development is a long-term venture and riskier than investment in building construction, land speculation, or underwriting industrial development.

The socio-cultural and political obstacles which mankind sets across the road to progress are harder to overcome. According to a UN study, ignorance, the desire for profit, discord, superstition, and the uncritical attachment to tradition prevent man from enjoying the full effects of human technology.[14]

We can hardly avoid analyzing these peculiarly human factors, and to the degree they stand in the way of improved agricultural production, we should try to render their efforts nugatory. Better yet, though it cannot always be done, we should try to convert them into stimulants to progress. To rid the world of hunger is not solely an economic problem. For all its physical, material character it involves also patterns of behavior and of attitude which, though linked, are by no means solidified in one monolithic obstacle.

We may distinguish three sorts of obstacle, those of an international order first. Within the framework of their discussion, we may gain a certain objectivity which will be useful in what follows. After all, it is a world problem that we are addressing ourselves to. The rich countries, no less than the poor, are deeply involved. No effective plan of action will come to anything unless it is clearly and correctly grasped from the start that the nations of the earth are interdependent. Once the premises have been clearly set down, it will be easier to go into such matters as to how the various social and cultural factors help or hinder economic and technological progress, how it is up to each nation to arrive at a suitable practical policy which avoids side-issues in contradiction with the ends in view.

Before embarking on our discussion, we should like to dwell on two points. The hunger in the world today demands a prompt solution, yet every suggestion toward solution must be envisaged within broader, long-term perspectives: that of the harmonious development of the world's different peoples, that of a more just acquisition and distribution of the world's wealth. No problem is more urgent. What do we find when we examine the national incomes of the underdeveloped countries over the past twenty-five years? A few countries do seem to have done a little better each year: Brazil, Venezuela, parts of Malaysia, Taiwan, some countries of eastern Europe. But most of the African, Asian, and South American nations have not even reached the starting-line of the race they have to run, and the bulk of their inhabitants do not get enough to eat.

Mankind no longer is as willing as it was to go along with the inequitable distribution of wealth. Resignation has given way to resentment, and a major problem for the governments where this condition obtains is to keep their people satisfied with the immediate enjoyment of the well-being that science and technology seem able to bring them.

However, every assistance program, every practical plan for battling poverty, must be part of a long-term program: involving all the nation's economic and human potentialities, its growing autonomy, its progressive participation in the world economy. Development will not have ceased once hunger has been banished from the earth; it goes beyond the objective of increasing agricultural production.

Technological progress is a means of attaining "better-being," not just well-being, though all too often the advanced countries omit to mention this, in their ideologies-for-export.

Moreover, it would be a dangerous illusion to suppose that the problem of hunger will be solved by increasing the means of subsistence alone, to suppose that the underdeveloped countries should drop all else and concentrate on that objective, or that outside aid can be limited to distribution of food surpluses by the exporting countries.

We shall be saying it again and again in the pages that follow: increased returns from agriculture will be had, among other conditions, on that of drawing agricultural laborers into other sectors of the economy: into the mines, industry, the crafts, the service professions. Part of the present difficulty in increasing production is due to the great number of farm holdings too small to be worked profitably. Moreover, higher peasant incomes imply an increased demand for agricultural products on the part of people who own no land but enjoy other sources of income.

There can be no economic development within a country unless goods circulate inside it, and this circulation comes about only when agriculture produces surpluses it can exchange for other goods with the non-agricultural population. Countries like Denmark and Australia, which are big exporters of agricultural commodities, show how few "hands" are required to make their farms extremely productive, so that 65 per cent of their populations earn their living in other ways.

INTERNATIONAL OBSTACLES TO SOLVING
THE PROBLEM OF HUNGER

No one today questions that underdevelopment is a world problem, one that can be solved only through cooperation between the industrially advanced countries and the others. Ever since the Hot Springs conference in 1943, the purpose of which was to arrive at a policy bringing agriculture and nutrition closer together, the United Nations and their specialized agencies have given more and more attention to the need for narrowing the gap between standards of living in the different countries. International solidarity ought, then, to be wholeheartedly caught up in the problem—this is the positive way of looking at it.

Yet how are we to conceive of such solidarity? What practical basis does it have to stand on? As soon as we look past the speeches and the programs, we find a good many differing, even contradictory points of view as to how the goal of cooperation is to be translated into acts.

Cooperation implies recognition of a certain equality of all peoples. Can we really deny that imperialist or at least self-seeking considerations *ever* enter into the American and European programs of technical assistance? Wasn't Dr. Aujoulat right when he pointed out that in Africa today, political colonialization is merely giving way to economic colonialization?[15] At the same time, aren't the industrialized countries right to make their aid conditional upon internal reform within the government of the countries seeking aid? We should like to pause now to analyze a few of the economic and political obstacles at the international level, which hinder true solidarity among the nations, but we shall at the same time insist upon the need for changing attitudes that prevail among both the industrialized and the underdeveloped countries. If real cooperation is to be achieved, there must be an end to resentment, aggression, and the will to dominate.

Lack of Coordination. First among the factors unfavorable to any really massive and world-wide program of assistance is the existence of the two power-blocs, East and West. Arms and military equipment make up a good deal of American and Russian aid. Their assistance is more often granted out of strategical considerations, than in view of any program for the rational development of the nations involved.

The former colonial powers, meanwhile, vie with one another for the dubious honor of setting up the most grandiose industrial combines, with the barest minimum in the way of coordinated effort. It is as though each of the small African countries were to be endowed with an economic potential it is unlikely ever to be able to utilize to the full. We have in mind such examples as the Inga and Kouilou projects in central Africa. At the same time, the way some governments in need of aid pit one potential source against another, waiting for the highest bidder, is hardly calculated to build trust between the assisting and the assisted.

The only solution, as we see it, for such competition and scattering of effort, is to organize assistance programs multilaterally and administer them through international organizations.

The Commodity Market. One factor which has a good deal to do with keeping the poorly developed countries continually off balance, is the way the prices of the basic agricultural and industrial commodities keep fluctuating on the international market.[16]

When, for example, the price of copper goes up or down one cent on the international market, it makes a difference of four million dollars to the national income of Chile.[17] Quite apart from the fact that exchange rates tend to work to the profit of the industrialized countries, the less developed countries with some basic commodity to export are most often at a disadvantage due to the fact that this is their only product for export. The whole health of the economy depends on the condition of the commodity market each year. When, as also happens, the actual mining, growing, or processing of the product is—moreover—under the control of the importing country, there is no denying the existence of a real economic bullying such as no principle of the international division of labor can justify. The countries affected have long pleaded for some stabilization of the international commodity market, always to no avail. Some such control is an indispensable condition for any lasting long-term program of economic development on the part of the underdeveloped countries themselves. Only international solidarity can master this problem, which neither the more industrialized countries nor the underdeveloped ones (for all that they urge control) are willing to solve between themselves—the market prices at any given moment are too immediately profitable to the one or the other.

Economic Enclaves. Let us look at the part played by foreign enterprise within the underdeveloped countries. Undoubtedly, by their payment of "royalties" to the local governments, such businesses and industries contribute to the economic development of the countries where they are located. They give employment to native labor, and such systems as they set up for processing and transporting the basic commodity (often for transporting it to the home country) constitute some sort of model of economic organization for the country itself. On the other hand, there are in some countries foreign enterprises which are totally cut off from the life around them and of no social utility whatever to the host country. Self-financed to begin with, they take out of the country the greatest part of their profits, take no interest in the training and advancement of their native workers, and fill all the responsible posts with citizens from the home country. Should not such companies, instead of being instruments of economic and political domination, and of social upheaval, rather become agencies for the advancement of the parts of the world they exploit? Should they not invest something in it, not just in view of further profits, but in view of economic and social progress? Such a policy would, of course, require guarantees from the underdeveloped country against expropriation, against racial and political discrimination on both sides, and against confiscatory extremes of taxation. The industrially advanced country, at the same time, could spur development by encouraging investment (there is little interest in investing in the underdeveloped countries today, even in consumer-goods enterprises), for example by tax advantages, by guarantees of the sort mentioned above, and by assurances to the investor of the home country that his earnings will be convertible into hard currency.[18]

International Migration.

Movements of people from country to country constitute an important safety valve to demographic presures, and have long helped to keep the balance between population and resources. Since the beginning of this century, there have been fewer and fewer such movements. The world's population seems to have settled down where it finds itself, and to be leaving it to natality and mortality to bring about a new distribution of the population.[19]

Problems of migration currently preoccupy such organizations as the International Labor Organization and the International Catholic Conference on Migration. Can we look to the movements of people today and in the near future to help relieve pressure on the means of subsistence?

The economic advantages of migration are obvious enough: to the country of departure, if it is overpopulated, or when the emigrant sends back some portion of his income; to the country of arrival, if the immigrant is skilled, enterprising, and his foreign experience of value to his new fellow citizens. Chinese emigration throughout Southeast Asia has long had a stimulating effect upon commerce and agriculture there. New arrivals in a country, moreover, tend to save their money.

When we look around the different continents today, however, in search of a practical solution to population pressures through migration, we find a number of obstacles. There are no longer, as there still were in the last century, vast stretches of land as yet unsettled.[20] It costs more to travel and to establish oneself in a new country; such land as is available requires special knowledge and technical skills to be worked profitably. Besides these economic obstacles, there are social and political ones. Any sizable influx of foreigners, especially if they are of another race, creates tensions and defense reactions—the more so when there is serious unemployment in the country. "The more diverse the religion, customs, and social structure of the newcomers, the less easily will they adapt."[21]

Actually, only Europe and the two Americas are today in a position to receive any considerable number of immigrants from the other continents. In the case of North America and Europe, "Modern industrial civilization imposes a certain uniformity of conditions and behavior favorable to reasonably prompt assimilation."[22]

Certain countries of Latin America could also absorb more immigrants than they do, "as the facilities for communication are made available and new lands opened to settlement. Their own mixed populations make them more inclined than others to be racially tolerant."[23] In this instance, the governments of the host countries must concern themselves with the reception and settling of the newcomers and, moreover, must practice a carefully selective immigration policy. Better adaptation of the world's resources to the needs of its population implies as well a greater degree of freedom in moving from country to country within the same continent. Even highly populated Southeast Asia has vast areas which could be exploited, were population better distributed: northern Borneo, for example, Burma, and Indonesia.

However, there are other considerations that oblige us not to expect too much from this approach to the problem. The population of India, for example, is increasing by some 3 million annually, and how could intercontinental transportation be organized for even a third of this number? Nor is India the only such instance. The countries presently capable of absorbing some sizable number of new settlers find their own populations growing by geometric progression, a fact which greatly complicates and makes more difficult their own development. Moreover, no country wants to lose the healthiest, most productive segment of its own population: the young men who have been raised and trained to the point where they are just beginning to prove valuable additions to the labor force. Lastly, there is a political obstacle. It would be extremely hard to get repealed the variously strict immigration policies which *all* countries have in force today, in line with their own interests. We can only conclude that migration is but a very secondary sort of solution to population pressures under present circumstances, scarcely capable of making more than a dent in the problem. Moreover, to put a great deal of time or money into improving the situation, would be to deflect energies from other approaches to the problem where they could be put to better use.

Cultural Interchange. There is a curious paradox to be discerned in the attitude of the industrialized countries toward the economically more backward ones. Nobody questions that development in the latter has to be spurred on by very sizable programs of financial and technical assistance. There is willingness to sink capital with little hope of any return, and to lend money at purely nominal rates of interest. What nobody is willing to do, however, is to put first things first and correct what is wrong with the existing structure of international exchange. Whenever it is suggested that greater equality in the relationships between nations would be desirable, the more advanced countries have recourse to the economic theory of an international division of labor. Though the theory is not incompatible with the principle of integrated development, it involves a prior assumption of the existing economies as being identical in scale. More and more, solidarity between peoples takes the form of a technical assistance carefully spelled out in advance as to goals and to the means whereby each party is to attain them. Time and again, however, the recipients of such assistance have expressed fears lest such foreign aid prove an imperialism in disguise. Among many instances that could be cited, there have been Leopold Senghor's speeches at the UN and Mamadou Dia's *Réflexions sur l'économie de l'Afrique Noire.*

Meanwhile, the technically developed nations think in terms of their own historical experience and with perfect sincerity urge solutions based on the methods they followed to get where they are today. As already pointed out, the problem of underdevelopment is not purely economic.

No assistance program can expect to succeed, with mutual trust and respect for the rights of all parties, unless certain obstacles of a cultural, rather than a political, order have been overcome. Prerequisite to success is a genuine facing of the facts of cultural dissimilarity and individuality.[24]

Underdeveloped and developed countries alike agree that economic progress depends on importing Western technology into the former. Where opinions begin to differ, is over the question of whether technological readaptation must necessarily involve taking over the whole of Western civilization, the comprehensive scale of values which in the West mostly antedates the industrial revolution. To this question Toynbee replied in the affirmative, in *The West and the World,* citing Japan as the strongest case in point. It is probably too early to go along with so clear-cut a conclusion. Certainly the educated classes of the underdeveloped countries have no intention of letting Western culture be thrust upon them wholesale, where it cannot be reconciled with their own historic values and sense of vocation. D. P. Mukerji goes so far as to criticize the term "underdeveloped":

This expression for inadequacy of economic expansion is improper, for it covers up the fact that two different, co-existing value systems are at stake. It makes them appear two phases or stages in a single historical process, the sole criterion of which is economic development as immediately measurable in terms of technological progress.[25]

More and more, the West is being accused of ethnocentrism, and the charge is not always unfair. The educated classes of the underdeveloped countries are quite properly concerned with the delicate problem of how to integrate Western technology with an economy organized very differently, in terms of traditions and value systems native to their own countries. The West is wrong to suppose that development from a subsistence economy to a modern economy must necessarily follow the pattern of the industrial revolution in Europe. Even without bringing up the lengthy period of slow development towards political and social maturity that followed the

Renaissance, the European industrial revolution of the nineteenth century was preceded by an agricultural revolution in the eighteenth century and by the mercantilist expansion of markets. As Georges Balandier has pointed out, the so-called "underdeveloped" countries today have nothing like so favorable an immediate past behind them, as preparation for the adventure they are embarking on today. Moreover, they have problems such as the West never knew 150 years ago:

Rapid population growth, more and more social and economic disequilibrium consequent upon external influences, sharp "break with the past" on the score of traditional production methods and the social relationships these implied.[26]

Under the circumstances, nothing is more important than to evolve original techniques of economic development.

Of course, there is disequilibrium in the West, too. The appeals of Bergson, Carpel, Camus, and others for a more humane organization of technological resources are of continuing pertinence. We might ask, as Gandhi did, whether the Western world ought not cultivate the Hindu values of detachment and unconcern for material possessions, and pursue an economy of needs rather than a chrematistic one.

Democracy is not the be-all and end-all. Westerners will grasp this eventually, as they watch a number of the young peoples being drawn almost irresistibly to the Marxist scheme of things and to the Chinese experiment. Can it any longer be doubted that, "Ideology, dictatorship, and the rest, the Russian system makes for a more rapid development, for all that it may be a less desirable one?"[27] Japan's extraordinarily rapid modernization was brought about in much the same way. Part of the same trend is manifest in concern over building new systems of education. At the Addis Ababa conference in May, 1961, all the African countries laid stress on the need for creating training programs which, while giving priority to technical education, should at the same time inculcate respect for the properly African values of each nation. They implored the aid of the rich countries in drawing up long-term plans to meet their specific needs. Does all this suggest the need for Western self-criticism? Yes, but there will be no true "cultural interchange" until the educated classes of the less highly developed nations, economically speaking, have formulated precise objectives and acknowledged that within the existing framework there can be no advance without some fundamental structural reforms. Gandhi's reaction to technology and the disintegration of the village as communal cell in India will no longer do. Basic changes are urgently needed.

It is not just fear of foreign influence that must be avoided by the younger nations, but also the compulsion to imitate. There must be resistance to the present-day trend towards what Paul K. T. Shih calls "revolutionary utopianism."

All the present-day revolutionary movements originate in a conviction that the West possesses the magic power for transforming the world into a real earthly paradise. And if the transformation is not soon realized, the delay is going to be attributed to the inefficiency or the wickedness of the governments actually in power which, for this very reason, will have to be overthrown by force if necessary. The regimes in question, if not condemned by the ordinary human standards of justice and effectiveness, find themselves being judged by utopian standards in the light of which nothing can escape condemnation.[28]

The author is not content to point out the danger, he also suggests the remedy:

One of the most important contributions the present generation of intellectuals can make to Asia's development both at the national and the international levels, is to encourage their peoples to pitch in and accomplish the very hard tasks that face them, urging ideals of a better life in store for them, but carefully refraining from arousing useless resentments or a spirit of rebellion founded on utopian idealism rather than on a fundamental realism.

SOCIO-CULTURAL FACTORS

A substantial increase in agricultural productivity would be a real victory in the race between population expansion and the existing means of subsistence. The most modern agricultural methods need to be applied on a score of fronts: soil-improvement and conservation, contour ploughing, reduction of pasture land, reforestation, measures against plant disease and insect pests, fertilization, use of scientific seed selection, crop rotation, etc. All such measures will come to nothing, however, if there is no demand for the products or if the demand cannot be recognized as a "real" one, because of protectionist market conditions or control by the middlemen. Increased production requires capital to invest in it and the ability to borrow more. Lastly, the peasants have to be persuaded to change many of their age-old ways of doing things. and have to understand why the changes are necessary.

Every agricultural expert has noted the obstacles which are presented to programs of technical and economic reforms by the very populations supposed to implement them and benefit from them. Moreover, even where the programs seem to have a fair chance of succeeding, various social and cultural processes are set in motion that tend to counteract the very benefits which might reasonably be expected to follow. In some instances, the existing institutions effectually stymie all change in their own structure.

Why should progress be so difficult? Isn't it possible to change one or another constituent element in a community without throwing it off balance or precipitating collapse? Are such collisions between old ways and new inevitable, or are there ways to minimize them? To restore balance once the initial shock has worn off? In this connection, two remarks would seem to be pertinent. We shall try to come to grips with these problems, dispensing both with the anthropologists' exaggerated view of individual resistance to all change, and also with the economists' optimistic faith in the self-regulating character of economic institutions. Such faith rather tends to gloss over the social cost of change. Though doubtless all progress involves sacrificing something, still the human intelligence and sense of justice are obligated to keep such sacrifice at a minimum.

In the second place, our discussion bears upon the main social and cultural obstacles as they are met with in the majority of the technically underdeveloped countries. We must generalize from the particulars, if we are not merely to write footnotes to folklore. A factor which is of overwhelming weight in one country or one community will not be found at all, or will be of slight importance, in another. Every society has its own culture, made up of a great many component elements: geography, history, institutions, external influences, etc. The solution to the problems of underdevelopment in one place will not be valid in another place. Especially where agricultural reforms are concerned, no program will come to anything unless it is based on on-the-spot study of existing practices and existing institutional structures.

How Cultural Factors Are Related to Social and Economic Development. We may as well take Taylor's now classic definition: "Culture is that complex whole which includes knowledge, belief, morality, law, custom, and every other habit or capacity acquired by man as member of the community."

Complex, but a whole: culture is structured, and the institutions that make it up represent a multiplicity of social relationships. Not only are the various institutions and the various social roles interdependent, they are stratified among themselves according to the relative importance the society assigns to a particular group, a particular relationship.

Every culture thus possesses a number of values that reflect, more or less unanimously, the agreement of individuals and groups as to approved patterns of behavior. The agreement is never unanimous, for values essential to one group will be rejected by another. This is the case, for example, in our Western societies, where a great many different scales of value co-exist, which are sometimes mutually incompatible. In primitive societies, the smaller size of the community tends to make for greater agreement and to suppress nonconformity. However, outside the clan irreconcilable value differences are all the more marked, and as between two clans are likely to be felt as an antagonism.

Actually, the values of the group are felt as the more binding upon the individual, to the degree that they appear indispensable to its life in common.

Thus, it is the value scale of the society that unifies culture and, in the last analysis, makes individual behavior in it comprehensible. It also helps us to understand how the various components of the society, or the society as a whole, will react when faced with a new situation.

So far we have been considering culture solely in its static aspect, as a structure. Situations change, however, and by their behavior men can adapt to new situations and even anticipate them. Culture is also dynamic. Over a period of time new structures are developed and the relative importance of one structure to another is modified. Some structures, some institutions, tend to change more rapidly than others; they have varying degrees of malleability. Family and religious structures are less susceptible to change than political and economic ones. With alteration in their mutual relationships, value conflicts and maladjustments arise within the society as a whole, and especially if the alteration is imposed from outside. Instead of readjusting their social structures when these appear to lag behind the forces of change, individuals and groups cling to their values all the more intensely and obstruct change. Thus is brought about the antagonism of Progress *vs.* Security. Every society is continuously experiencing this antagonism in some degree, and only occasionally does it become so intense as to throw the whole culture off balance. In the technologically underdeveloped countries, however, economic modernization does arouse intense resistance on the part of both individuals and groups, for it threatens a total transformation of those very patterns of thought and behavior which hitherto have served to integrate the culture. It is no longer a matter of slow but steady historical change, but one of cultural discontinuity, revolution, radical change-over.

The Socio-Cultural Structures of the Underdeveloped Countries. So long as they were cut off from a so-called "market economy," the presently underdeveloped countries had attained a certain cultural equilibrium within the framework of their subsistence economies. Though a good deal is lost in generalizations of this type, let us sketch rapidly the over-all characteristics of subsistence economies such as obtained nearly everywhere (save in the biggest cities) in Asia, Africa, Latin America, and Oceania, throughout the nineteenth century, and such as have not yet totally disappeared in southern Italy and in certain parts of Spain and Greece.

Geographical isolation in the mountains, the forest, or the bush encourages cultural isolation. All social functions turn on an agricultural production solely for immediate consumption. These functions are extremely varied and are not specialized. The dominant institution is the family, broadly conceived in all its ties of kinship and marriage, the symbolic value of which is often strengthened by religion. As for the economic structure, this is so narrowly conceived as to permit little change or development. So long as the earth supplies a relative abundance for the population, individuals find security in their social roles as members of the family. Tradition will be imbued with the greater value, the longer the community enjoys a stable existence. Unforeseen circumstances, should they arise, will be put up with by the community in the expectation that they will pass, rather than be treated as challenges to be met by readaptation.

Social stratification in such societies is limited to two, at most three classes, and the criteria of differentiation are the family, religious function, property. Although in Latin America an enormous gulf separates the rich from the poor, elsewhere the tribal chiefs do not live a great deal differently than their slaves. In most prescientific societies, wealth is measured less by the accumulation of possessions (which could only be strictly limited, at best) than by the numbers of human beings whose labor is at the service of a family or a tribe. "Social prestige is determined by the number of human beings one commands,"[29] whether this number is a result of the tribe's own prolificness or its enslavement of other tribes. Under these circumstances,

Individuals are in face-to-face relation with each other, a relationship relatively uncomplicated by the products of human labor coming between them. The social framework which links them all is organized on a small scale, and relationships are frequently regulated by the principle of repetition, which applies from the smallest unit to the biggest.[30]

In short, such societies have a fairly homogeneous character, and in them social processes are limited, within the family in the broadest sense, to cooperation, outside the kinship and marriage alliances, to conflict.

Features of a money economy, oriented to the export of products, early made their appearance within some of these subsistence economies. In Latin America the great landowners, and in Asia and Africa commercial producers of rubber and tea, brought these regions into contact with world markets and with such developments as credit and banking, distribution of goods via middlemen, transport facilities linking production sites with ports of embarkation, and the gradual building up of internal demand for imported goods and services. The two types of economy were never totally closed off from each other. The big landowners and the white or Chinese colonial settlers all "recruited" native labor, by one means or another, and sooner or later began to pay the workers at least partly in money. As the demand for "goods from the colonies" mounted steadily, the natives were encouraged themselves to raise cash crops for export. Meanwhile, public health measures and progress in the control of contagious diseases were steadily raising the rates of population growth. For the first time, subsistence economies were experiencing a land shortage. The countryside discovered hunger and hidden unemployment, neither of which was wholly offset by moving to the cities and by taking jobs in new mining enterprises.

Very often, the spread of agriculture for export in these countries has operated to the detriment of subsistence agriculture and brought about undernourishment. Moreover, population growth coinciding with the spread of commercial agriculture has led to soil exhaustion, erosion, and lower crop yields.

However, the co-existence of these two economic systems has had more than purely economic consequences. Little by little the age-old family and religious structures have been breaking up, precisely as economics has taken on new importance and an unfamiliar character. In the absence of education, individuals and groups find themselves torn between two antagonistic pressures. Should they "adapt," as a few do, and make a wholesale rejection of the "old" ways, or should they revert to their age-old patterns of life and combat the new through one or another reactionary movement? Meanwhile, the side-by-side existence of the two economic systems is giving rise to an extremely heterogeneous social stratification.

George Balandier has laid a great deal of stress on

The twofold impact of foreign economic pressures on traditional society: the effects of structures operating in the sense of a de-structuring, positive effects conducive to the growth of new structures and new modes of social integration.[31]

In his view, the two conflicting principles of structuring and organization are absolutely contradictory: on the one hand, broad blood and kinship ties and mythical justification for the established order of social relationships; on the other hand, the competitiveness and differentiations of the market economy, which oblige individuals and groups more and more to think in terms of "economic rationalism."[32] Rural communities can react to the challenge of an economic revolution imposed from outside with a variety of attitudes, depending on their degree of adaptability: opposition, inertia, controlled institutional change. Balandier gives the example of how the Bakongo of Central Africa have arrived at a workable compromise, the chiefs preserving the traditional institutions while permitting their substantial content to be fundamentally altered. Modernization is accomplished by a system of individual incomes, but it is the collectivity which invests them and profits from them—the traditional way.

The foregoing survey of the modalities of change within a traditional environment brings us to detailed study of the obstacles to be overcome when a governmental authority or a foreign expert sets out to introduce and popularize a technological, economic, or institutional improvement. First, we shall examine the social and cultural resistances, and then in a separate section the institutional obstacles, in the special case of agrarian reform.

One last remark is necessary. In the technologically underdeveloped countries still more than in the industrialized countries, agriculture is an especially depressed sector of the economy, in comparison with urban ways of life. Not infrequently, "The bulk of those who live in rural communities have a standard of living ten times lower, on the average, than the native civil servants."[33] And whereas in the developed countries this lag is of relatively little consequence (so small a portion of the total labor force being engaged in agriculture), the flight to the cities has become a major problem in a number of African and Latin American countries. "In some areas, two or three towns have drained off nearly half the total population."[34] For a long time to come, agriculture will be the principal resource in these countries, but how is production to be increased when the young people are fleeing the farms, "because living conditions in the country no longer suit them"? The most capable young men, once they have completed their education in the town, lose all interest in "the agrarian question." This is one of the principal obstacles to the success of India's Five-Year Plan: the lack of properly trained leaders in the rural communities. We shall be coming back to this thorny problem.

Socio-Cultural Obstacles. What we shall have to say on this score will turn on one or another of the following three ideas, which strike us as the key factors in any increase of agricultural productivity, at least when this is left in the hands of the native population. First, it must be to the peasant's own interest to increase production: this is the problem of his own motives, and of how to stimulate an economic sense in him. Second, there is no "wanting" or "willing" without the power or capacity for realizing it, and what Arthur Lewis has called "economic freedom." Third, the transformations in the economic structure must proceed through a redistribution of functions, a specialization of roles.

It should go without saying that all three objectives are closely linked, and that it is rather arbitrary to separate them at all, for they are at once causes and consequences of a complex situation in which economics overlaps custom and religion, as though to demonstrate that culture is always more or less integrated.

The Family System. Let us take the case of a peasant living in a subsistence economy, who would like to improve the bit of land he works, and succeeds in doing so to the extent of increasing his crop yield. What he has produced over and above his household needs can now be sold on the market, and constitutes a small cash income. With it, he ought to be able to buy fertilizer, to make improvements in his irrigation system, or to buy better-grade seed. He can't do any of these things, however, because the community stockpiles his surplus against its future needs. The money he earns must either be hoarded, or invested in luxury products that symbolize his or his family's wealth and prestige. His personal initiative is stifled under such a system, and there is only one thing he can do—leave his village, and either hire out as a worker on a commercial plantation or look for a job in a town. Of course, such a course of action scarcely helps to solve the problem of increasing the means of subsistence. Balandier gives a good description of the two choices open to the individual who has a little money saved up.

He may invest it in the properly economic sense, seeking profit and personal advantage, but to assume the "entrepreneur mentality" cuts him off from the social environment in which he was brought up. Actually, this rarely happens, and then only in and around urban centers. What is more likely is that he will invest it "sociologically," that is, will utilize the new economic conditions to enhance or strengthen his success along traditional lines. The size of his "clientele" and his capacity to be generous will serve as the measure of his success, his own profit being expressed in terms of prestige and authority.[35]

One objection ought to be immediately apparent. If ever a whole community grasped the nature of this choice, the problem would be solved. Here lies the key to the situation, which we shall have to look at in detail when we later discuss cooperative approaches to community guidance. The family system is founded solely on tradition, and is only held together by it; the sole function of education is to teach the children how to fulfill their assigned roles within it— that is, how their ancestors acted. Such a community would be meaningless except in a subsistence economy, and so the very notion of economic planning is alien and contradictory.

Under such circumstances, no incentive exists for additional expenditure of effort, whether on the part of the individual or the community. In some rural societies, however, the scale of values admitted within the framework of a subsistence economy has undergone some change from contact with the market economy. The example of the Bakongo, mentioned above, is very much to the point. Apparently, money wealth has come to seem important to them, since they are acquiring it, but it is not invested in economic enterprises, properly speaking, so as to multiply the income from agriculture. Disintegration of the family community, in consequence of the breaking up of the collectively held land, has allowed the chiefs of the tribe to take possession of the land, and now the criterion of wealth and prestige has become ownership of real property.

The family system does not favor the diversification of functions nor that "economic freedom" which is essential to economic development. Who does which task is strictly allotted by tradition, so that there are not a great many "jobs" and they are rigidly separated, though in fact they require little specialization and could just as well be done by one person as by another. Tasks overlap for the division of labor bears no relation to economic necessity, being founded on personal relationships frequently solidified by religious or symbolic considerations.

Increase of the agricultural population and, consequently, its progressive integration with a market economy, demand greater specialization and a new apportionment of functions. More and more, the tasks of production and those of marketing products become distinct. Large-scale farming involves active cooperation between the technical agricultural center and the farmers engaged in growing each particular crop. Combatting soil erosion requires the concerted action of all who are affected by it, as also does the consolidation of small holdings, reforestation, and contour ploughing. With mechanization, new jobs are created: truck and tractor drivers, mechanics, storekeepers, all more or less specialized tasks which cannot be allotted on the basis of kinship ties. The cooperation necessary between and among all these diversified workers also implies a totally different form of social organization.

In societies where education is not conceived of as a preparation for change and adaptability to progress, but as an initiation in age-old tribal ways, it is not surprising that advance is so slow and that "social bottlenecks" are by no means to be found only in the towns.

Development does not just imply a growing complexity of social roles, but also of social processes. As the functions of production and distribution become more clearly distinct, they will give rise to less elementary processes of interaction and competition. It is then that considerations of status and personal relationships must be set aside and the concept of economic planning in view of obtaining the greatest profit, firmly embraced.

In some communities woman's role is all-important in the subsistence economy. While the men perform the harder tasks of clearing the land, and so on, it is the women who do the sowing and the reaping, and who carry small loads of things from place to place, as well as prepare the food. This distribution of roles has made it possible for the men to hire out as seasonal workers in the mines or on commercial plantations, without detriment to the agricultural return. However, in certain parts of Africa where urban and industrial expansion has gone farthest, there are no longer enough women to feed the growing population, especially in the areas immediately adjacent to the cities. The problem is further aggravated by the lack of communication with parts of the country where there may be food surpluses.

This division of communal tasks according to sex reinforces what is already an inequality of status which works to woman's disadvantage. Although she is granted an important place in the home, since she feeds and takes care of the household, she plays no other role in society and is at the present time kept at home. With the rise of commercial agriculture and the appearance of some technical advances and manufactured products in the villages, she sometimes plays a less important part than formerly in a wholly subsistence economy. This has sometimes resulted in family disharmony, especially where religious belief or immemorial custom lays stress on female inferiority. In village communities where education or other institutional measures do not help to bridge this social inequality between the sexes, the inadequacy of the woman's role constitutes a check on development.

Religious Obstacles. Contrary to an opinion which is much too widespread, religion does not in itself constitute a barrier to technical progress. However, in many countries where for centuries there has been little social or economic change, it can become an especially overbearing institution heavily weighted on the side of stability.

Here we must not confuse the spiritual character of a religion with the historical contingencies that lead it, just like any other institution, to put up a certain resistance to economic and social progress. Moreover, religions differ greatly. Some are simply a model or stencil of the family community, the framework that holds it together. Others, more spiritually oriented, may be more or less fundamentally opposed to material progress depending on whether that particular value does or does not enter into their conception of the world, does or does not conflict with it.

There is, of course, an enormous difference between the polytheism of the African peoples south of the Sahara and the highly dematerialized spiritualism of India, but there is also a distinction to be drawn between how a religion is "lived" by its most devout religious or lay practitioners and its social expression in one or another ritual or superstition. There is a considerable difference between the cultivated Brahmin's experience of "nonpossession" and the formal rites performed by the bulk of the lower-caste Hindus.

From the point of view of economic development, it does not seem that most religions are opposed to progress as such, although actual adoption of one or another technical innovation may often run counter to some particular article of belief. We must remember that in rural communities agriculture is something more than just a way of earning a living, more even than just a way of life. How he tills his fields holds religious significance for the peasant, is bound up with rituals whereby he worships his gods.

The agricultural expert who would introduce changes in age-old practices had better know and understand the beliefs he may be outraging, if he is not just to arouse stubborn antagonism. Often enough, some slight change of procedure out of deference to those beliefs will help get his suggested reform adopted. Sometimes, however, a mode of agricultural production may be rejected by the population on religious grounds. Hindu attitudes toward their cows as "sacred" and worthy of veneration is an only too well known instance. In this case, nothing short of a fundamental revaluation of values within the Hindu society itself would seem capable of bringing about a rational economic solution of the problem. The fundamental attitudes of the various religions are probably more important where economic development is concerned than any of the particular ways in which their beliefs are given ritual expression. Obviously, Catholicism is much more favorable to material progress than Buddhism.

Paul K. T. Shih has stressed the Indian tendency "to turn everything into religion," and how hard it is for the Indians "to discover or recognize the fundamental validity of secular values."[36] The Muslim faith is much more practical-minded. The Koran specifies in everyday detail what the conduct of the faithful should be. Doubtless too sudden a technical changeover, which affected the pace of Muslim work habits, would present difficulties of adaptation. However, it is not beyond the bounds of possibility that the religious leaders of Buddhism and Hinduism will succeed in purging these religions of their archaic contingent values and, by recognizing material progress, give them new dynamic power. The future of the religions of Black Africa and Oceania is more problematical. In some cases they have collapsed entirely, and as the tribal community disappears, a religious vacuum comes into being. There would seem a priori to be three possible solutions: irreligion, reorientation of belief, adoption of other more universal faiths.

The religious factor is not always, however, an obstacle to development. Although in Latin America during the last century, the Catholic religion was far from championing economic progress— very often, from fear of social upheaval, openly compromising it —today the opposite situation obtains. Clergy and laity alike are in many places proponents of agrarian reform, their experiments with cooperatives and in educating farmers are supported by the governments, and some of these serve as guides for drawing up larger-scale projects.

Something of the same turnabout has occurred among the leaders of Hinduism. Gandhi's belief that material progress was hostile to religious rebirth is little by little giving way to a more synthetic point of view, which would make Buddhism the agency of human progress in the fullest sense.

In every religion we must distinguish between spiritual ideology and institutional habits: sometimes the latter allow the former to lie dormant. More frequently, when social upheaval breaks the institutional mold, the ideology reawakens to life and becomes the source of fresh developments.

Social Stratification and Lack of Mobility. We noted above that social stratification is slight in an economy founded on kinship ties and personal status. In country districts, there are two classes. The peasantry, made up of small landowners or tenant farmers, is often enfeoffed to a small number of wealthy landowners who keep control of education, social prestige, and political power. The middle class is very small: a few moneylenders, businessmen, local officials. It is very rare to find the specialized crafts. The term "class" scarcely seems to apply to either of these lower groups, the peasantry and the "middle class." The peasants are doubtless aware of their inferior status, but ignorance and resignation prevent them from united action in defense of their interests. The small middle class, meanwhile, is fundamentally different from that to be found in the developed countries: a better term for it would be "intermediate class." It has no very clear professional structure, remains close to the traditional agricultural structure, and its relations with the other classes are personal in nature.

What degree of social mobility is there within these classes, and from one to another? They are rigidly self-contained, membership most often being determined by birth, rather than by professional skills as in the industrialized countries. Movement from one class to another is not impossible, but highly unlikely in societies where the very nature of competition is unknown. There is at least one important exception to the statement about the rural middle class lacking professional stratification: India has an extremely complex caste-system, half religious, half economic, in character. Lack of social mobility, however, is a very widespread feature of subsistence economies.

As the technically underdeveloped countries move into a "dual" economy—in which subsistence economy and market economy exist side-by-side—there is a revolution in social stratification. Though naturally less marked in the rural regions, still the phenomenon of flight to the cities and towns has a bearing on agricultural production. In the cities, meanwhile, a proletarian class without professional skills begins to grow up, and a middle class of small-time dealers in goods and services appears as a sort of offspring of the European middle class. Mobility within this middle class is very great, due to the lack of qualifications. As for mobility from class to class, this is only just beginning to make its appearance. Though differences of individual income must be very great within these nonagricultural classes, they are as yet too unorganized to make themselves felt politically, having no sense of themselves as bound together within a structure of diversified occupational and social interests, what they do for a living as constituting a distinctive style of behavior.

A serious consequence of rapid urbanization in these countries, though truly an indirect one, is that the countryside is more and more disorganized. The most promising young men flee to the towns seeking jobs and a way of life free of parental or tribal constraints. Agriculture seems a dead end to them, and continuous unemployment reinforces the impression. Whereas agronomists ought to be able to call upon these young men to carry out reforms in both the quality and the quantity of agricultural production, actually all they have to work with are the women and the old men. Education, again, is the only remedy for such a situation. Instead of being organized solely to prepare for secondary instruction and government careers, elementary education should be adapted to the local needs of the countryside. Moreover, in view of the urgency of the problem, the most forward-looking of the young adult men should be given training in modern agricultural techniques, in the basic workings of the market economy, and in the attitudes both demand. Back in their own communities, and with the continuing aid of the specialized agricultural stations, these are the people to bring progress to their own country. Peasants are by nature suspicious of innovations that come from far away, and such a training program would do much to allay the suspicions. The effects would be social and political, as well as economic. Lastly, education of the peasantry seems to us the only natural way to go about achieving a long-term improvement in the status of the tiller of the soil.[39]

Resignation, Fatalism, Lack of Incentive. A few pages back we tried to point out how the familial structure blocks development toward specialization and adjustment to a market economy. Wages earned, a cash profit from crops could provide an incentive to agricultural production beyond the subsistence level, but spent for the enhancement of personal prestige it has no such effect.

Another obstacle to agricultural development is the failure of peasants to grasp *why* they should increase production so as to have a surplus to sell. They have no desires that require cash money for their satisfaction. When, as in South Africa, for example, the authorities oblige them to earn some money by taxing them sums payable only in money, what happens is that they work just as long as necessary to get together their tax money, and then stop. Before attributing such apathy to race, it might be well to recall that not a few Europeans in the "boss" category behave not so very differently. . . .

We must try to go into this matter more deeply, to diagnose the causes for it, and to suggest remedies. We have already touched on the main causes of social immobility: family restrictions, religious taboos, the impossibility of rising above the economic-social "condition" into which one has been born.

A fourth cause is the *breakdown* of the traditional structures. This produces individual disorientation. Before the appearance of the market economy, people's relationships rarely extended beyond their own village. The life they led was not too demanding; rather than try to master such conditions of nature as famine, disease, droughts, or floods, they were content to attribute them to evil powers. The features of the market economy, however, come to them from outside the familiar environment and present challenges without precedent; disorientation results from the fact that they must accept the changes before they have had time to adjust to them.

A consumer economy requires no long-term planning, merely looking ahead to the harvest or the time when the livestock will be ready for the slaughter. Now peasants are being asked to bring the volume of their production into line with a precise discrimination of prices and market conditions. Never before having had to bother with anything they could not judge for themselves, with their own eyes, now they are asked to raise new varieties of plants and animals to satisfy the demands of markets thousands of miles from their village, over which they have no immediate control and of whose complex workings they have not the faintest idea.

If only these large-scale alterations in the peasant's way of life and thought were realized in some orderly fashion, and with some continuity of ends and means, time alone would gradually show him how the improvement in his standard of living depends on them. But it doesn't happen like that! Distant threats of war, or a sudden flurry of financial speculation, suddenly sends the price of rubber soaring. Then the plantation manager doubles or triples the acreage under cultivation. Suddenly coffee is doing much better on the London market, and now governments urge their populations to cut down on rubber and plant more coffee. In as much as there is no international coordination of such efforts, and their effects are felt only some years after the decision is taken, the peasant who has found all this baffling, but believed what he was promised regarding rich profits, is further frustrated to learn that there is no longer a scarcity but a glut of his product on the market, and that consequently prices have fallen.

Probably an enlightened minority manages to adjust fairly quickly to the economic ups and downs, and to profit from them. In this way a rural bourgeoisie comes into existence. The bulk of the peasantry, however, is deceived in its expectations and ceases to trust the various governmental or agronomic experts who are so lavish with advice.

The same sort of thing can happen where purely technical measures for improving agricultural yields are in question. Two illustrations may suffice. In Central Africa, the native peasant farmers were discouraged by the fact that their experts were always being switched from place to place. A farmer got started on carrying out A's plan for improvements, then along came B with a different plan to meet his needs, and after him C showed up with a third plan

for reform. . . . Elsewhere in Africa, a group of peasants actually
went in a body to the governmental agency which was dispensing
technical advice to them, and begged to be allowed to do without
all those modern methods supposed to make them more prosperous!
In this particular area, some twelve separate offices were bombard-
ing them with information and advice, each bearing upon a different aspect of farming: crop control, cooperative organization, social
security, etc.[40]

There are also cases, it is true, where the trouble does not arise
from a time lag between the need for change and the lack of preparation for it, but from a community's impatience to speed up its
economic development.[41]

Thus, for example, such a community may buy and install a
generating plant and never realize it has been sold old-fashioned
equipment for which spare parts are no longer made, or the wrong
kind of plant for the community's needs, or a perfectly up-to-date
plant which nobody within a hundred miles knows how to repair
when it breaks down the first time. Failures like this plunge the
ambitious but still inexperienced community into worse apathy than
before. For years three Belgians tried to organize a cooperative
among Chilean fishermen without success. Why? Because a number
of years before somebody else had organized a cooperative, there
had turned out to be something shady going on with the finances,
and the experience was quite enough to condemn the cooperative
principle once and for all time in the eyes of the fishermen.

What practical conclusions may be drawn?

The resigned, fatalistic attitudes of many agricultural populations is in part due to a low standard of living with chronic undernourishment. Physical debility conduces to states of depression, and
the only remedy is higher incomes.

Experience has shown that the most potent incentive to the individual, when a subsistence economy is being turned into a money
economy, is the hope of increasing his own consumption. Similarly,
the individual adapts the more readily to a new technique or a new

kind of life, when it seems to him that he will thereby increase his material well-being. As Firth has put it:

Though ethical and psychological considerations may enter in, their influence is secondary when the change is permanent. What matters most in the long run is how income and consumption are affected.[42]

Imitation is a second incentive not to be overlooked. When individuals who enjoy a certain social prestige adopt an innovation, the bulk of the people however hostile or mistrustful hitherto must now absolutely have it themselves.

A permanent change in consumer habits, whether brought about through imitation or through creation of a new need, in the end modifies the community's scale of values. Consumption has cultural and social aspects as well as material ones. As some new consumer pattern in a rural community takes hold, it represents a higher degree of adaptation to modern economic conditions. One of the tasks of specialists in economic development in these countries is to create needs which so far as possible do not conflict with the traditional scales of value. They, too, have the task of persuading the peasants to make the proper technical changeovers, though as we have seen they must coordinate their programs if the population is not to be seriously disturbed. A single failure can compromise subsequent adaptation. Long and careful on-the-spot study, with preliminary experiments, will prove the best guarantees of a successful program of reform. It is preferable that a few be persuaded to try something new before any attempt is made to persuade a great many. People in rural societies only believe what they see, and no training program will ever amount to anything if it is not followed by a convincing demonstration.

Food. Industrialization and more diversified distribution of production are the indispensable conditions for any increase in agricultural production and any rise in peasant incomes. At the same time, however, to feed populations that are fleeing from the farms the increase desired must be understood in the sense of a more ample diet for themselves, not in the sense of more food for export. A certain minimum of organization at the national level is essential so that the surpluses in one part of the country can make up for shortages in another. An efficient, inexpensive marketing system, with transport facilities linking the centers of production with those of consumption, and with suitable storage facilities, is another basic need.

In the technically underdeveloped countries, undernourishment and malnutrition plague both the agricultural and the industrial sectors of the population, and these ills are growing worse with population pressure and exhaustion of the soil. They affect both crop yields and the quality of those yields. Malnutrition is caused by an insufficiently varied diet, with little or no meat, fats, fruit, and vegetables.

Hence the need for all-out effort on the score of the quality of agricultural production, a technical problem. Once this has been achieved there is the further problem of persuading people to change their diet. In all societies there is a cultural aspect to dietary habits. The way the food looks, or ought to look, and the most favored combinations of foods are aspects of tradition not always in accord with nutritional demands. In a family-centered community, meals take on a very great social value:

In most societies, food is the focus of emotional associations, a channel for inter-personal relations, for the communication of love or discrimination or disapproval; it usually has a symbolic reference.[43]

Moreover, the nutritive value of some of the basic foods consumed by peoples in the underdeveloped countries is still very imperfectly known. To try to supplant them arbitrarily might simply be due to prejudice on the part of Western experts in public health and nutrition. If one must in any way change the dietary habits of a given people, he should always keep in mind their basic likes and dislikes.[44]

Food is more than a consumer good in these countries. It has the value of an investment. Theodore W. Schultz is of the view that a population's state of health represents a "producer good." And in fact such capital wealth is very poorly utilized when workers are physically weak and ill fed. A number of industrial concerns in Africa have had to change the diets of their workers in the interest of productivity.

INSTITUTIONAL OBSTACLES: THE AGRARIAN QUESTION

The Problem. As we have already seen, some of the causes of economic stagnation have to be sought in the attitudes of individuals. However, institutions, too, are frequently ill-adapted to change. Agrarian reform has lain at the bottom of all the revolutionary movements in the underdeveloped countries. All of them, once in power, have promulgated complex legislative programs for their countries in an effort to remedy abuses and shortcomings in the traditional ways of doing things. We have seen this in India, China, Egypt, Bolivia, and Cuba.

Nearly always, results have been disappointing, though the causes for failure have been very various. Among these have been: unpreparedness and lack of realism, due to misunderstanding the actual on-the-spot situation; purely socio-political approaches; incompetence in the supervision of programs; resistance of landowners and money lenders whose incomes and political power are threatened by the reform measures; and, most important of all in our opinion, ignorance and lack of training in the peasantry who are supposed to be the most immediate beneficiaries of the reforms.

Before discussing the different types of agrarian reform and before pointing out what is wrong with the agricultural systems in the countries just embarking on their modernization programs, it is thus of the first importance to draw up the principles of a sound agrarian legislation—one that both goes to the root of the existing evil and supplies real stimuli to increased agricultural production.

There is no advantage in itself to be gained from altering an existing system of owning and working the land. The advantages to be gained from reform depend wholly on the wishes of the farmers and on their skill at putting new methods to work.[45]

Under the circumstances, both a certain freedom of choice and a certain institutional framework would appear called for.

What Are the Criteria? 1. The primary goal of any institutional overhaul must be the increase of agricultural production and its adaptation to the requirements of the market at home and abroad. No project for reform that does not meet this preliminary requirement can be considered, even if it has the incidental virtues of lessening social injustice and bringing about greater equality. There can only be one result from lower crop yields: delay in the country's economic modernization, due to the need to import foodstuffs —using up income that should go to buy modern equipment. Of course, there may be a short-term drop in productivity while the reform measures are being put into effect, but if this lasts more than one or two years the whole project may be endangered.

2. No agrarian reform will succeed unless it is integrated within a program of general reform, such that the institutional shakeups and readjustments all occur *simultaneously*. In many of the technically underdeveloped countries today, as a matter of fact, the cause of low crop yields is the scarcity of land in terms of the population to be fed. This situation leads to soil exhaustion, encourages archaic farming methods, and makes qualitative improvements impossible in as much as the diminishing returns have to be shared among a growing number of mouths to feed. Thus, parallel with (or even in anticipation of) the institution of new agrarian methods, there must be a transfer or shift of agricultural labor to other sectors of the economy. The case of Mexico might be cited in this connection. The first agrarian reforms there date from 1915, following the 1911 revolution. Land was redistributed, and the number of landowners increased, but few attempts were made to educate the peasantry or to set up facilities whereby they could

obtain cheap credit legally. What happened could have been predicted: 80 per cent of the cultivated land privately owned was by 1940 back in the hands of less than 1 per cent of the landowners with farms of 2,500 acres or more. A whole new process of agrarian reform had to be gotten under way, tending to restore the *ejidos*, and is still going on.

3. No one type of organizing and working the land is suitable to every country. How much land is available and how severe the climate are matters everywhere different. There are soils capable of producing two crops a year, but just how hard they should be worked varies from place to place, not only with the different crops but also with reference to the stage of technical progress attained. Thus, over-all institutional reform should allow as wide a scope as possible for future developments in the agricultural sector. People should be free to move into agricultural pursuits, and also to abandon them for others elsewhere in the economy. It can be assumed that with technological improvements in agriculture, and with the creation of new jobs in the secondary and tertiary sectors of the economy, there will be a gradual weeding out of the less competent, temperamentally unsuited population presently working the soil. For this reason, it would be unwise and dangerous to pass or to leave in force any law protecting tenants from eviction. No less disastrous are those feudal survivals which bind the peasant to the landowner (and his heirs), along with the land and the livestock, and for the same reason. The market in land should be based on the properly economic value of it, not on sociological considerations that inflate its value and encourage such abuses of "prestige" ownership as great landed estates (not always fully or efficiently worked), on the one hand, or fiercely contested smaller holdings which serve to block rational organization of the land in workable farm units. Another thing to be guarded against is that the clearing of new lands for cultivation does not give rise to speculation in values, with the result that future settlers will find themselves deeply in debt from the first.

4. Above all, agrarian institutions should supply peasants with

the maximum of incentives for getting ahead. The farmer should be able to be sure that his investment in the land is not just going to fill the landlord's pocket, the money lender's, or the tax collector's. He must be able to see how his labor is going to raise his and his family's standard of living. The tenant farmer, especially, and the new settler whose legal title is in doubt, require protection against unwarranted dispossession and arbitrary claims.

But it is the possibility of personal advancement that supplies the firmest incentive. The agricultural worker who can look forward to becoming a tenant farmer himself, the tenant farmer who can look forward to eventual ownership of the land he works, such men will save their money and really invest in the land they work. They have a real interest in adapting to the demands of the market, learning new methods of cultivation, and trying new crops.

5. We have already observed that the major cause for the failure of agrarian reforms in the past was the ignorance and unpreparedness of the peasant masses in the face of wholesale institutional change. The condition is not new and is widespread today, and it can be expected to continue just so long as research centers are not established in each part of the world for the study of local conditions: soil, methods of cultivation, climate, extent of erosion, etc. And just so long as the results of such experimental study are not followed up by agricultural inspections to show the peasants their necessity and how to profit from them. For it is worse than useless, it is dangerous, to show agricultural communities how (for example) to increase their crop yields through the use of fertilizers, if at the same time no fertilizers are available or the farmers cannot afford to buy them.

6. Lastly, a word of warning. There is a tendency to view the problems of land redistribution and the increase of production solely in terms of maximum efficiency and the fullest degree of mechanization. For a number of reasons, it is necessary to temper such optimism with a suspicion that technical efficiency does not always increase at the same rate as economic efficiency.

During World War II and after, a number of experiments were

made in several African countries to introduce highly mechanized one-crop agriculture. The only result was to speedily exhaust the soil. In Asia with the spread of the technique of "deep plowing," much the same result was reached. In both instances, scientific study of the various soils ought to have been made before the techniques were introduced.

There are two different approaches to the problem of increasing agricultural production: either through increasing the yield of each unit of land under cultivation, or through increasing the output of each farm worker. The second approach is inseparable from mechanization. However, in many parts of the economically underdeveloped countries, there is very little land to be worked by the available laborers. Peasants work only one-third of the year, and were mechanization to be introduced unemployment would increase, unless some better utilization of the available labor were to be worked out (on the model of the water-buffalo in Indonesia) to make use of the off-season months. In such countries, it seems to us that it would be more economically desirable to promote a more intensive variety of farming with the help of such technical devices as irrigation and tools not so much better made as better adapted to their purpose. Mechanization, in any case, demands more capital than most of these countries can presently afford, and takes a long time to pay back the investment.

However, in parts of the world where there is plenty of land— as in certain regions of Africa, Southeast Asia, and Latin America (at least the nonmountainous parts)—mechanization would be desirable. The problem would be one of increasing output per worker, through the practice of the extensive type of agriculture. Where the preliminary apportioning or redistribution of land has already been accomplished, it would be a good idea to set up agencies for the hiring out of farm machinery. Even so, it appears that there will have to be a certain breaking up of the biggest Latin American holdings for mechanized farming there to be fully successful.[46]

So far we have disregarded purely human, social considerations.

In countries where 80 per cent of the population is engaged in agriculture, the system of land holding and working does not just condition the economic position of the agricultural worker, but also determines his social and political status. It follows, then, that the legislator of agricultural reforms must take account of how the latter relationships are affected. Dispossessed landowners will constitute a particular problem, for unless they are properly indemnified they will throw the whole weight of their political power into making the new distribution of land fail. As for the actual tillers of the soil, they will at first enjoy a greater degree of equality and a more stable income, whether they fall in the category of wage-earner, tenant farmer, or small landowner. Unlike the very biggest land holdings (the latifundia), the plantations of Central America are characterized by high crop yields per acre and soil of great productivity. From the economic point of view, they are well managed, yet at the same time they are a source of continual social friction. To break them up would merely cut down production and, consequently, the output per worker, for the crop yield of the small farms may be as little as half that of the plantations. However, if at the same time the plantations were broken up, a system of technical and financial aid to the farmers were instituted, then it would be possible to obtain a better distribution of wealth along with superior economic results, for profits would stay in the country rather than be invested abroad.

What Is Wrong in the Underdeveloped Countries? There are several types of juridical obstacles to better exploitation of the land.[47] Some relate to the size of agricultural holdings, some to the system of tenantry in force, and some to credit and taxation. In the technically underdeveloped countries, poor use of the land may be due to the fact that farm holdings are either too small or too large. With the disappearance of communally held lands, these two opposite developments have occurred: small holdings get broken up into ever smaller holdings. and a privileged few (tribal chiefs or foreign settlers) acquire whole vast territories for themselves, much of which is never worked or is used for grazing only.

Small farms, meanwhile, are cultivated ever more and more intensively to the very limits of what the soil will bear, without bringing in sufficient income to feed the farmer and his family. Mounting population pressure produces this constant subdividing of already small holdings, as well as inheritance laws which permit it. The most enormous holdings in Latin America and in Southeast Asia do not just derive from original royal grants, and from usurpation of communal lands, but even more importantly from foreclosing the holdings of small farmers unable to extricate themselves from debt.

What juridical principles ought to govern the rental of farm land? The majority of farmers in these countries are tenants of one sort or another, who pay an annual rent in cash or in kind, the amount of which is often set once and for all time when the land is leased. As land has got scarcer in certain parts of Asia and Latin America, rents have risen to truly exorbitant levels—where, for example, the farmer turns over two-thirds of his crop to the landlord. The latter's only part in the relationship is to collect what his tenants have contracted to pay him, and so the farmer who would like to increase his production must make the investment himself. Moreover, all too often, law and custom decree that he can claim no greater share of his production for himself when collection time comes. The landowner collects his profit on the farmer's own investment, as well as on the land. Obviously, under such circumstances, farmers are scarcely encouraged to produce more. And when, as also happens, the landowner is also the local money lender, then it is clear that he does better to collect rent and interest from his tenants than he could do by ploughing back profits to improve or conserve the fertility of his land.

But there is a kind of tiller of the soil whose lot is even worse than that of the tenant farmer. This is the worker on big estates who is allowed to farm a small piece of ground for himself, in return for his labor in the fields of the estate-owner or *haciendero*. He has no title to the land he farms for himself, and no hope of ever acquiring it, and when he leaves—after however many years—

he has no claim to any indemnification. Such conditions of insecurity and exorbitant rents clearly reflect the lack of adequate legislation regarding land tenure.

Nor is the landowner himself always in so privileged a position. There are many countries where titles to land are not registered, where large areas have never been surveyed or are just beginning to be, and where the courts are clogged with lawsuits contesting individual and collective rights to land never hitherto clearly defined. In some places like the Middle East, there is a further source of insecurity in the anti-economic practice of recognizing rights "in" the land as distinct from over-all ownership: water rights, for example, or rights to the fruit of certain trees.

One of the most obvious indications of the poverty of tillers of the soil, is their eternal indebtedness, usually due to the fact that they can only borrow money at excessive rates of interest. There is not much left at the end of the year to plough back into the soil, when debts have been paid—and yet how is production to be increased unless money can be borrowed at a reasonable rate of interest? There are banking systems in these countries, but no system of agricultural credit. The bankers lend money only to industry, business, and the big landowners. In India, 90 per cent of peasant loans have been obtained from usurers, landowners, or businessmen. And what is the money borrowed for? Seventy per cent of it goes to pay off old debts, 10 per cent for new loans, 16 per cent for household expenses, and only 2 per cent for livestock, seed, etc.[48] Obviously, this indebtedness is caused by insufficient income, since the money goes for consumption, not for investment in the land. What makes the situation worse is the scarcity of money available to borrow, and interest rates of from 10 per cent to 50 per cent. Moreover, these are loans against assets of from 100 per cent to 300 per cent the value of the sum borrowed. As for taxation's effect upon agricultural incomes, two methods of collection are frequently employed in these countries at the present time: a land tax based on the value of the land or on current income from it, and a tax on production. The former would normally be a tax on ownership, but the increasing scarcity of land has led to the principal burden falling on the tenant farmer—in addition to his indebtedness and the high rent he must already pay. Moreover, as is not the case in the more advanced countries, there is rarely any adjustment of the tax to the personal situation of the farmer—the number of his dependents, whether he has had a good year or a bad year, etc.

The tax on production varies more widely, and affects incomes more or less depending on whether the amount is set arbitrarily or is based on the economic facts, whether it applies only to marketed produce or also to the household's own consumption, and so on. Proportionately to the total population, the agricultural sector of the population is much more harshly treated than the commercial and industrial sectors. In the latter sectors, it is much easier to falsify tax returns, even in countries where the system of collecting taxes is much more primitive than it is in Europe.

Types of Reform and Results to Date. Taking the term "agrarian reform" in its broadest sense, we include within it both measures of basic improvement in the system of land tenure and all that goes into raising the volume of production. The organization of agricultural credit and fiscal policy generally thus both fall within this broad definition. A number of reform measures have aimed at adapting the size of farm holdings to criteria of maximum economic efficiency. Wherever great land holdings (latifundia) are poorly farmed, legal redistribution of the land and of title to it could be effective if, at the same time, the government would put capital at the disposal of the new farmers, initiate them in modern agricultural techniques, group them in production cooperatives, and supervise to some extent what they plant and how they raise it.

In other parts of the world, the problem is the great number of tiny holdings, a situation which makes proper soil conservation impossible, entails a loss of arable land and poor use of invested capital, and resists all efforts to introduce progressive techniques. Two approaches can, a priori, remedy the situation. Whether voluntary or imposed from above, any redistribution of holdings invariably arouses first and foremost the hostility of the peasants, as we have seen even in the most developed countries. The land has for them sentimental value, and insoluble problems are raised in deciding who should get which holding and how much indemnity should be paid for the loss of a holding. The other approach to the situation is cooperation. It is not an easy system to establish, but governmental legislation can help enormously by extending every facility of purchase, credit, pooled farm equipment, scientific research, planning, etc. Some coercive legislation may be necessary, but education will in the long run work better. In most countries of this type, laws will be needed to prevent subdivision of holdings beyond a set limit through inheritance, sale, or mortgage. We need not repeat that such measures will come to nothing, unless at the same time a policy of industrialization is evolved to drain off the presently excessive number of persons engaged in agriculture.

Ownership is not the sole incentive to technical progress in agriculture. Tenant farming can have the same results if the lease makes a just division of responsibilities and guarantees the farmer security of tenure. Legislation can back this up in two ways: assuring the tenant he will be indemnified for improvements made by him, or sparing him the cost of changes he is not responsible for, and by instituting rent controls where high rents have been the problem. Cutting rents too drastically, on the other hand, would encourage landowners to stop carrying out their part of the bargain, which is to keep up the permanent capital of the holding. Where applicable, there should be some provision for compensating the "settler" who has cleared and works some previously uncultivated portion of a big estate. The big commercial plantations which are economically healthy could often be improved in social respects, with higher rates of pay and more humane working conditions geared to a program of increased worker productivity.

One of the most thorny problems for the underdeveloped states is that of agricultural credit, for there are the old debts to be paid off as well as a new system of encouraging investment to be put into effect. Moratoriums on old debts, partial reduction of them, or laws preventing foreclosure may be necessary. Putting a legal ceiling on interest rates would encourage investment, and hence production, but it is also likely to make money scarce. A better system is to increase the number of credit agencies under government backing and supervision, leaving it up to the farmers themselves to accumulate the capital. Local farmers' credit cooperatives will have to be backed up at the regional and national levels by semi-governmental institutions underwriting risks and losses, keeping costs within reason, and supervising the over-all operation. There will be the problem of making sure the funds do not get deflated from their primary purpose of encouraging production. The business and industrial concept of "credits for education" may be adapted to agricultural needs, with loans granted only for specific purposes: to raise a particular crop, to purchase fertilizer or insecticides, etc.

With respect to fiscal policy, taxes must not just take into account income, but also the burden of responsibilities being carried. Any system of agricultural taxation should be arrived at within the over-all framework of governmental goals and the programs it has set out to achieve. Likewise, citizens who are obstructing government policies should be penalized by being taxed more heavily than the rest.

Some measures of encouragement that might be tried: deductions for monies tied up in investment for production; temporary exemption for current expansion; bonuses for particular crops; deductions for dependents; total exemption below a certain minimum income. Suggested penalties: surtax on profits from speculation or other causes than planned improvements; steep inheritance taxes on great estates; special penalties for absentee landlords, land left unworked, etc.

In 1955 and 1957 the UN published special reports on the current state of agrarian reform, which described a great number of legislative programs. Few countries have failed to draw up some sort of program. The experts who review these programs, however, are not very optimistic with regard to the results so far obtained. Private political and economic interests still play too great a role, and in too many places the great landowners are still powerful enough to combat the programs effectively, though popular pressures may oblige them to pay lip-service to them. In other places, where the sole objective was a more equitable distribution of incomes, there were unforeseen economic consequences, and the results were short-lived or worse than before.

Keeping strictly to the problem of hunger, and how it is to be solved, we suggest that the following two sets of considerations ought to underlie any project for agrarian reform:

1. In those parts of the world where land is scarce (a situation becoming more and more widespread), redistribution should be in terms of arriving at a minimum legal holding. In these places there should be a reduction in the number of persons working the land, through the creation of jobs in other sectors of the economy.

2. Turning a system of tenantry into one of private ownership is no panacea. Production is likely to decrease, unless a system of peasant control and supervision is set up at the same time. And in countries where landed property is surrounded with the halo of social prestige, there is a danger that the peasants will put every penny aside solely for the purchase of land.

Nearly all the developing countries today face the agrarian question in one form or another. Agricultural reform has so many ramifications, economic, social, and political, that it must be very carefully planned and scrupulously carried out. It can be done, but every government must learn the lessons which are to be learned from past experience and not be afraid to compare its own results with those of neighboring countries.

Conclusion: Cooperative Action. Our rapid survey of the institutional and socio-cultural obstacles has produced a certain number of findings worth keeping in mind in view of harmonious agricultural development. It appears inescapable to us that it is not possible to alter the economic structure of a culture without producing side-effects sufficiently serious to compromise the over-all program for its modernization. The problem would seem to be that of, for example, doubling agricultural production within a very short time, without aggravating social tensions and bringing about a disequilibrium threatening to fundamental individual values throughout the society as a whole. What we are looking for is a middle-of-the-road solution, one that takes account of economic and technical needs, but at the same time tries to enlist the support of the people who are to benefit from the reforms envisaged.

One question that might be asked is whether the traditional structures of culture in the underdeveloped countries represent nothing more than obstacles to development? Granted that there are forces for inertia in the archaic tribal and clan communities, might they not yet serve as a rallying-point for changes in their own interest? Cannot their energies be enlisted in a "new ideal of feeling," as A. Gerschenkron phrases it? Are there no stimuli or incentives latent in the existing familial structures, which a daring, dynamic social policy could turn to the advantage of economic reform?

In his book *Le Monde en friche* (The Undeveloped World),[49] Gabriel Ardant asks whether it is really necessary to dislocate existing familial structures as a pre-condition to economic modernization. Is it absolutely certain today—as it was in the eighteenth century—that technological progress can only be carried out on an individualistic basis? As he observes,

The most progressive farmers, in Denmark and Holland for example, represent a system of small individual holdings grouped within a network of regional co-operatives. What is the point of breaking up the family system, when it is going to be necessary to regroup its members afterwards in any case, only now in ways that will cause them hardship?

One attempt to answer this sort of question is the "community development approach."[50] Rural reform in India is today going forward in the spirit of this guiding principle. We may cite as an

example of this approach the various types of agricultural co-operatives which have so far been organized, for production, sales, purchases, loans, savings, consumer goods, pooled agricultural machinery, etc. Such is the goal, for example, of the Centre Catholique
International de la Coopération. It is time now to decide how well
these various efforts have worked out by comparing results and
pointing out mistakes and utopian delusions.

There is no question but that some agricultural cooperatives
have proved ideal. Not only have they provided a framework for
improving farming methods, but they have educated their members.
We need not point to the Kibbutzim in Israel, for they have grown
up under rather special conditions, but Riobamba in Ecuador and
Fomeque in Columbia are very much cases in point.[51] Here resigned, apathetic populations have slowly been transformed into
enthusiastic, hard-working, forward-looking communities. It is true
that in these cases the promoters prepared the ground slowly, both
in the material and the psychological senses. More cooperatives of
this type have failed than have succeeded, but do the failures lie in
the nature of the institution or in the haste with which it has been
organized, very often without taking account of basic conditions?

It seems that a number of prior conditions have to be met, for
any cooperative movement to succeed.[52] In fact, experience shows
that there are three absolutely indispensable conditions: adaptation
to local needs, control and supervision of the population, and integration within a program for national development.

The population's human needs and resources, as well as its economic ones, have to be carefully explored to discover how to arouse
its interest and sympathies in a particular plan for reform. Individuals have to be persuaded that progress is really within their grasp.
Such sacrifices as may be demanded for long-term results to be
achieved, will not seem too much to ask if there are immediate
compensations as well for all to see, in terms of current hopes and
needs. There must be some stimulus for steady, continuing effort.

Leaders must be chosen from within the community, if collective
energies are to be engaged. Their training may be brief, but must be

sufficient to make clear both the immediate and the long-term goals, as well as the psychological and technical means for attaining them. It is by their enthusiasm and energy that the traditional mentality of the community is to be transformed.

Attempts along these lines have often failed simply for lack of support by the public authorities. This is fatal, because the very nature of agricultural reform is such as to require expert advice in many areas, in matters of finance as well as from agronomists and veterinarians. Allocation of areas to the various crops can be intelligently decided only with relation to existing roads and existing water supplies for irrigation, two considerations that require coordination with the public authorities involved, and possibly assistance from them. A certain minimum of central planning is implied in any very large-scale agricultural enterprise which means to take advantage of existing market conditions.

Some mistakes, however, are hard to avoid. It is possible to be too afraid of shaking up individual habits, and to fall over backwards in exaggerated respect for cultural traditions—with minimal results both from the point of view of progress and from that of the effort expended. To solve the problem of hunger and pull the economy out of its rut, there has to be a radical break with the old farming methods. The age-old ways of doing things have to be sharply challenged, and it has to be made clear there is no turning back to the old subsistence economy. From the start, development must proceed according to a clear time-table, specifying dates for the attainment of particular goals.

To make a real dent in the problem, agricultural cooperatives have to stand out as models to be respected and copied in the eyes of the surrounding countryside. Not so much on the score of greater visible well-being, as on the score of increased production. It is another mistake to try to accomplish both at the same time. The goal of increased productivity must have priority, so that all can see that by accomplishing this the other economic and social developments, including enhanced well-being, follow. At the same time, of course, since the very lowest living standards are themselves an obstacle to increased productivity, there must be a conscious effort to raise these first.

Another mistake, or a way that efforts of this kind can get side-tracked, is by attempts to revive one or another "old" type of village or community as vehicle for the reform measures envisaged. Such attempts to blend (or blur) the old with the new are impractical or utopian, for the representatives of the old order have neither the power nor the competence necessary to accomplish any really thorough social and economic reform.

One not unjustified criticism of the "community development approach" is that it is so slow to show results. An essential part of that approach is gradually to "instil" a feeling for progress in a hostile population, and unkind critics have spoken of "spoon-feeding." Again, we may observe that it is impractical to dress up technical progress in old-fashioned garb. No agricultural cooperative is going to succeed—not in the sense we give the term—so long as the land is left broken up into tiny holdings, or so long as most of it is given over to raising a whole variety of traditional crops for local consumption. Since the whole point is to create a commercially valuable surplus, the members of a cooperative must from the beginning work a suitably big holding, whether formed by equal shares of the best land possessed by each member or by their common clearing and working of land not previously cultivated. Only in this way is there some chance of producing results quickly. Such a cooperative has to be managed on a strict, business-like basis, if it is to compete successfully with the large plantations which are already commercially organized. At Riobamba, for example, the cooperative land covers 750 acres, of which each family works 25 acres. Purchases, sales, and the major agricultural investment (planting, harvesting, fertilizing, etc.) are handled on a cooperative basis.

More such experiments ought to be attempted. Crop yields and the quality of what is produced are often markedly superior to anything obtained by the traditional methods in the surrounding countryside. Centralized governmental services of research and experiment could do a great deal to cut down the expense and the time presently required for getting such projects underway. Food production for the internal market, organized on this basis, would attract food-processing and related industries which would themselves increase the national income.

As a means of introducing progress, this method is no doubt not the "ideal" one, from the strictly economic point of view. From that point of view, collective farms divided up strictly on the basis of optimum technical utilization appear the superior solution. This purely theoretical "ideal" fails to take account of the fact that man is not simply a tool of production, and yet there are a number of economically underdeveloped countries where the population in general, and the peasantry in particular, have reached so hopeless a low point of defeat and resignation that, as it seems to many, only the Marxist-type revolutionary solution can even begin to attack the problem.

One of the healthiest aspects of the cooperative experiments is that the results are apparent in dollars-and-cents terms. The peasants can see for themselves that they hold the key to progress, both individual and collective. They see that, although their material and moral poverty has in part come about through no fault of their own, still it can be almost entirely done away with, if only they will all individually co-ordinate their efforts with each other's.

Thus, for the lowest economic strata of the population, the cooperative movement constitutes an ideological movement. In combination with other ideologies, national and even universal, it can provide a practical instrument for overcoming the socio-cultural obstacles we have been describing.

POLITICAL FACTORS

The rapid growth of the technically underdeveloped countries demands certain basic political conditions for any enlightened program of reform to be drawn up and put into effect, with proper regard for the order in which projects are to be carried out. Among these are a strong central power supported by the citizens themselves and a governmental staff devoid of private interest and efficient, in the sense of being adapted to the actual needs of the country.

In most of the economically underdeveloped countries today, you have to look very hard indeed to find these absolutely essential conditions met even half-way. As has often been observed, there is a marked lack of anything like patriotism or national feeling, all power tends to be in the hands of a wealthy few and to be exercised primarily to their own profit, there are large numbers of governmental employees all concentrated in the capital—most often relatives of the wealthy class. Energies are dispersed to little practical effect, and there is frequently a quite unrealistic satisfaction with achievements more spectacular in themselves than of long-term benefit to the country as a whole. And this brief enumeration by no means exhausts the list of the specifically political bottlenecks to progress which parallels (and frequently reinforces) the list of socio-cultural bottlenecks enumerated above.

The Government Service. Both the countries which have quite recently attained independence and also those which did so decades or generations ago, suffer from the same persistent shortcomings, which are closely allied: the lower ranks of the government service are grossly overstaffed, and there is a terrible shortage of qualified leaders.

Hoselitz points out two principal causes for the poor quality in the lower ranks: illiteracy and contempt for manual labor.[53] In countries where few people can read and write, anyone with a primary school diploma is sure of a well-paid position, whether inside or outside the government. As more and more individuals become so qualified, the scramble for positions better paid and with more security than manual labor becomes quite hectic, and much use is made of family connections to obtain them.

As the administrative staffs of the former "colonial" powers leave, to go back to the mother country, and as new and complex problems arise which require efficient, delicate handling, the new governments find themselves in a difficult position, caught between pressures from the powers-that-be within their country and the inferior quality of the personnel on the government payroll. The ideal solution, in this situation—but of course it is utopian—would be "mechanization," that is, replacing personnel with machines to carry on administrative work. These shortcomings could be overcome, however, at least in part, if only the various government departments were headed by especially competent, experienced, and unselfish public servants. But this, alas, is rarely the case. Often they possess little or no training in the particular field where they are supposed to operate, and they are often under the thumb of a powerful minority or personally linked with business interests— that is, hostile to reform and identified with preservation of the status quo.

Hoselitz suggests some remedies for the situation, which we pass on here. Systems of recruiting must be revised. There should be on-the-job training in the lower ranks of the government service. Supervisory personnel should be drawn from portions of the population with qualifications other than just a few years of education in history, literature, or law. No institution is any better than the use which is made of it, and so it is especially important that the top supervisory staff in government should be given sufficient power and prestige to free them from outside pressures.

Poor Planning and Overcentralization. At a time when a good number of countries have still not attained political maturity, whether in terms of internal stability or of secure frontiers, the actual administration of these countries from the capital outwards is patterned wholly on that of the former colonial power.

This means that in the bigger countries, the regional administrators are cut off from the capital and act largely on their own, while in the smaller countries the traditional local authorities are losing their prestige and power. In either case, massive overcentralization keeps government policies remote from the hopes and preoccupations of the bulk of the citizens, and prevents establishment of a just balance between the development of the towns and that of the country. As Georges Balandier noted in *Le Tiers-Monde:*

The backward countries are reaching the threshold of material progress at a moment when large-scale political organization is badly needed. For the most part these countries are organized on a very small scale, and weakened by internal divisions. They have at the same time to create the structures of a national state or federation of states, and to modernize and industrialize their economies—two phases of development that occurred separately in European history, or at least not all at once.

In agricultural development, no less than in industrial development, there has to be an order of priorities. The scarcity of human and material resources makes adequate planning all the more urgent. Are we implying here that the governments of these countries are totally ignorant on this score? No—far from it. One of the first acts of a newly independent nation today is to draw up a magnificent five-year plan. Unfortunately such plans are too often as sketchy on the score of financing and the real possibilities of the region, as they are vague about how the plans are to be implemented. The goals emphasized often suffer from lack of economic realism, and depending on the country are to some lesser or greater degree promulgated for prestige purposes, with more than a hint of megalomania.

Gabriel Ardant notes that there are a number of levels to be taken account of, in elaborating a technique of planning.[54] The projects are selected by the central government. Regional and local authorities should be involved in carrying them out. A great number of the special problems that arise, relating to such matters as roads for transport, water supply and irrigation, the setting up of technical and research stations in the field, etc., must necessarily be handled by the central administration which alone possesses the requisite facilities, knowledge, and skills. It is left to the village communities, supervised by agricultural inspectors and advised by government agencies, to develop the agricultural techniques for carrying out that part of the program drawn up and assigned to them.

It is now that is most keenly felt the lack of authority and training on the part of the traditional public powers, the tribal chiefs, village headmen, etc. Thorner has inquired into the matter of whether, in the villages of India, the system of local government could not be reorganized around the former village *panchayats*.[55] He was led to conclude that in most Indian villages, these figures no longer possessed any authority and were unlikely to gain new authority. In places where they still amounted to anything, their functions were merely to bolster the caste system or, where this had itself disappeared, to bolster the power of the local landed proprietors. All of which obliges us to look more carefully into the matter of how political power is actually distributed in these countries.

Political Structures. As these countries gain independence, the regime that comes to power rarely is a democratic one, nor is it necessary that it should be. In the technically underdeveloped nations, government by the people is a utopian dream—for all that Westerners have always supposed, and still suppose, that they must demand otherwise.

However, the fact that the bulk of the citizens have no practice in formulating or in pressing their claims does encourage a governmental system organized for the profit of a minority. Rich, educated, and close to the machinery of power, this minority is very often much more concerned with keeping what it already has and adding to it, than with the over-all economic and social development of the country. And yet, on any long-term basis, its power and privileges will not last unless it espouses the cause of reform. As a class of discontented intellectuals grows up, and is drawn more and more to the extreme solution of popular revolution, the future of these oligarchic structures becomes increasingly precarious.

Moreover, the very scale of the difficulties to be overcome in these countries makes the need for national solidarity more and more apparent to individuals. Appeals to patriotic feeling could be effective in these young nations, and might go far to help speed up development. We have already seen how the traditional structures oppose progress in agriculture by their inertia. Might it not be possible, rather than trying to overcome that inertia through persuasion and compulsion, simply to put devotion to the country as a whole in the place of the primary social ties (family, tribe, village)?[56] Nationalism, in short, is an ideology appropriate to growth and development, though other ideological resources might also prove effective in some places—religious revivification or a cultural renaissance, for example.

However, the mass of the citizenry will not be fooled if it turns out that the sacrifices demanded in the name of patriotism and national solidarity turn out to fall solely on the shoulders of the poorest class. Little by little, the ruling classes must introduce the notion of an equality of rights and duties. That is the price of political stability, without which economic modernization will never be achieved.

FIRST PRIORITY: EDUCATION

We have tried to isolate a few of the political and socio-cultural characteristics presently blocking attempts to solve the problem of hunger. Some are very obviously and immediately involved, others more indirectly, but anyone who goes very deeply into the causes and consequences of underdevelopment must recognize the complexity of the problem and the manifold questions to be raised and answered. Fortunately, we have gotten rid of the illusion that it all comes down to purely economic, or purely technological, considerations. Today, international conferences devoted to the subject bring together economists, sociologists, doctors, anthropologists, and a variety of technical specialists in agriculture.

Still, foreign aid is going to be primarily financial and technological. It will be up to each of the countries undertaking a modernization program to see to it that this aid is intelligently used to the most productive ends.

On this score, the main obstacle, surely, to capital assistance will be the inability of the workers to make properly economic use of it. The lack of specialized training and experience in modern agriculture as in modern industry, illiteracy, and an educational system ill-adapted to the demands of the labor market—these are among the principal factors that prevent a backward country from "getting off the ground" with its plans for modernization.

In the more advanced countries there have been many studies of the important bearing higher education has upon individual and national incomes. Theodore Schultz maintains that a sizable part of the increase in the U.S. national income should be attributed to the country's willingness to spend money on education.[57]

It is our belief that the countries just developing should also put investment in education high on the list of things to be done, though it is neither necessary nor desirable that the Western system should be copied slavishly. Nor will better education in these countries simply have the effect of raising incomes. The political consequences will be no less great, for education opens the door to the control of power and even to its exercise.

Lastly, whether we like it or not, all the underdeveloped nations have gone on record as placing enormous hopes in education, as though it alone could raise them above their present poverty and obtain for them the well-being on which the West still holds a near-monopoly. More and more, technical assistance to the poorer countries is being oriented in this direction.

IMPLEMENTING TECHNICAL PROGRESS

There are two intellectual approaches to the study of underdevelopment, which between them attempt to circumscribe the problem. The first, operating at the level of attitudes and opinions, is attractive in that it makes underdevelopment seem a problem roughly the same for each country. It addresses itself to a complex of subjective reactions which have arisen out of experiences "in the order of existence."[58] The second approach, which attempts to give an account of social and economic reality in its formal aspect, is less easy of elaboration for it must take note of a variety of types of underdevelopment. We generally find it expressed in a number of different forms, in terms of structural types and criteria, for example, or of factors variously endogenous, exogenous, and relational.[59] This approach is complementary to the other, for example, in the sense that actual experience corresponds to some situation capable of being scientifically objectified—as in production reports, demographic structure, class make-up of the society, etc.

SITUATING THE PROBLEM

In this section of the book, we should like to put forward a hypothesis capable of explaining underdevelopment in both its aspects. To show the analytic value of the hypothesis, we shall bring to light a chain of economic and social processes which would seem to be serious factors that resist development. We hope that by this means we may lighten the task of those who, on the spot and in the field, are trying to find out "the how and the why" of all those "failures and half-successes which make such disappointing landmarks in the history of world economic growth."[60]

The Psycho-Social Approach. We shall first examine the way in which underdevelopment is conceived at the level of attitudes and opinions. Here we must work with all the historically defined reactions which are to be found in the more advanced countries as well as in the less advanced ones. These reactions are the expression of two groups different from each other in the face of the situation they find themselves in, which seems to them on the whole characterized by many inequalities. Among others, there are inequalities of numbers, of land available for exploitation and actually exploited, of standards of living, of capacity for coping with birth, hunger, and disease, of opportunities for social and economic advancement.[61] Awareness of these inequalities gives rise to more or less formally distinct attitudes on the part of the favored group no less than on the part of the less favored group.

In the more advanced countries, it is not at the level of the average man that such attitudes take shape. Though he may be well informed regarding contemporary problems, they hold little interest for him. It would be going much too far to claim for him any very clear concern with social justice on the international scale. His own attitude might be described as wavering between a more or less unconscious selfishness and a more or less reasoned altruism. At the level of organized groups, and at the governmental level, awareness of the need to act is made especially keen by fear lest the new countries fall under the influence of the rival bloc. As more and more African and Asian countries gain their independence, this fear gains ground. It is possible that this historical phenomenon goes a long way to account for the great interest shown these past few years in the problems of underdevelopment, and for the growing precision of the psycho-social approach under examination.

Reactions in the countries just now developing are more clear-cut still, with respect to opinions and attitudes alike. Here we must emphasize that, especially where populations as a whole are concerned, attitudes frequently tend to anticipate opinions, if not to form them. "The effect of demonstration," to which Nurske called attention, has set off a chain of imitative processes which in colonial days would have been limited to the individual plane, but which today are incorporated in government policies. And need we emphasize, too, that "The rich countries exert this kind of influence, simply because their own living standards have been raised and because they have at their disposal the vast means of modern communication to publicize the fact"?[62] Putting forward their own claims to a right of "initial well-being,"[63] as it has been called, seems perfectly normal to new nations still imbued with memories of the colonial past. Industrialization appears to them the only road to political power as a nation.[64] This perhaps explains the appeal of Communism, one of whose principles "seems to be . . . that every country . . . should have its own heavy industry, firmly based."[65] Awareness of the inequalities, and of how long they have gone on, together with growing doubts about the feasibility of imitating the advanced countries, tends to turn poverty into bitterness and rebellion. It is a state of mind that could lead some of these societies to turn their backs on the possibility of modernization and to break off contact with the rest of the world. This was what happened with the Quichuas in Peru and with the Araucans in Chile.[66] The psycho-social approach is essentially relational, and comes about through the interplay of many reciprocal attitudes. Policies elaborated to any important extent on the basis of this approach are constantly redefining its content.

It would be a mistake, however, to try to limit our approach (as some would like to do) to the purely quantitative elements of an actual situation, to the aspects which can readily be objectified: annual per capita income, birth and death rates, level of literacy, etc.

It is clear that scientific procedure would lose all its sense, if it were to be limited to the measurement of obvious factors and if it did not go on to seek out the most significant ones in order to supply an explanation. Yet there are strong temptations to do just this. Actually, measurement of the factors in question supplies a content for grasping the situation. At least to the degree—and whether rightly or wrongly—it is believed that the solution of the problem lies in the more advanced countries, we cannot do without the second approach.

The Socio-Economic Approach. Although the problem of underdevelopment appears roughly comparable from country to country when approached at the psycho-social level, this is by no means so immediately apparent when we approach it through study of the objectively real factors. From the point of view of economics alone, it must be recognized that there is an enormous diversity of situation.

The two main characteristics of the economic structures in the countries just developing are dependency and lack of articulation.[66]

As these are to be found with varying degrees of intensity in a given country, and as there is no strict correlation of them between countries, we cannot present any simple picture of the economic structures—the less so, since the extent to which economic relationships preponderate also varies from country to country. The complexity of the problem appears still greater when we take note of the way the political, the economic, and the cultural areas scarcely overlap. Neighboring countries like Venezuela and Brazil, for example, differ so greatly that we might almost ask whether the concept of "underdevelopment" can really be applied to both.

Much the same diversity appears when we turn to the political relations of these countries with the more highly developed countries. Besides the fact that no strict correlation can be established between political dependency (or former political dependency) and economic dependency, we are obliged to note that the political factor never was exactly reducible to the juridical terms of a colonial pact—any colonial pact. Present political relations are those that follow from a prior colonial status, and are perhaps best ascribable to the psycho-social level of attitudes and shows of dignity. What particularizes them is the import given situations and values by carefully worked-out policies, whether those of the colonial or ex-colonial powers or those of the new countries, for whom independence is often the cornerstone of a collective effort at modernization.[67]

A third factor making for diversity appears when we look into the class make-up of the just developing countries. The first conclusion to which one is drawn is that the concept of class simply cannot describe or explain the whole social structure in these countries. To gain an idea of just what degree of coherence obtains in economic relations, it is important to ask whether a social group exists that is capable of making so-called "collective advance payments,"[68] is capable, in other words, of filling the entrepreneur function. In this connection, one must beware of making the suggestions that first occur to him, until he has looked into just what that function consists of and what the real structures of the particular country are. Thus, before prescribing a solution for a country in which the State has a big role to play, one must make sure that an entrepreneur group exists to constitute the State and that it does not have other, more powerful means at its disposal than governmental ones, such as wealth, with which to promote the collective enterprise. One such group might be the political party in control. It would utilize the power of government to check the resistance factors and keep them from interfering in the economic system it has recognized or means to impose. The authoritarian character of such power is much more a function of the type of sovereignty which has been chosen, than of how the social structures are interrelated.

In short, there are such enormous differences between and among the social structures of Japan, China, parts of Black Africa, and Latin America, that it is dangerous indeed to sum up the problems under consideration in any single formula, let along to propose an omnivalent solution for any one of them.

It is from the socio-cultural point of view, most of all, that the countries in process of development defy comparison. There are important differences to be noted on the score of the degree of structural cohesion (the socio-cultural structure was greatly weakened in parts of Africa by the slave trade), on that of structural type (whether tribal community organization, semi-feudal organization, or pre-industrial system),[69] and on the score of length of time that particular cultural and social factors have been operative. A weakened social structure does not necessarily imply cultural decline.

HOW TO HOLD ON TO THE FACTORS FOR PROGRESS

Because we want to compare the problems faced by a number of countries called "underdeveloped," and to distinguish them from another set of countries called "developed," we are inclined to believe that even though the phenomenon of underdevelopment appears in extremely dissimilar forms, it can, nonetheless, be defined. The psycho-social approach, as we defined it, had its objective substratum in the recognition of a chain of inequalities. These had existed in the more advanced countries as the price of the industrial revolution, and more than one intellectual approach was devised to give them "form" and to predict their cumulative effects, yet they have tended to be felt more and more faintly within these same countries. Nonetheless, there is a tendency today to make it seem that they have become more acute as between countries, and especially between new countries and old ones. This opinion, to which the psycho-social approach to underdevelopment lends itself, threatens to bring our researches to a dead end. The inequalities which the proletariat bore during the industrial revolution are fundamentally different from those with respect to which the new countries today constitute the less favored group. This point can hardly be overemphasized, for the psycho-social approach in terms of which most policies are elaborated today leaves room for confusion between the two types of inequalities and thereby stirs up modes of activity which, far from remedying matters, frequently exacerbate further an already keen awareness of those inequalities.

We must here distinguish clearly between "holding on to" the results of progress, when it is a question of their distribution, and "holding on to" the factors for progress, the extremely diverse character of which we have been calling attention to. The latter is essentially a problem of propagation, of multiplying, spreading, diffusing, or disseminating these factors. The problem is not at all one of "sharing the wealth," but of "sharing prosperity." It implies a conversion of the systems and policies which would hinder propagation in this sense. This is an area which would be a proper sphere of action for the generosity of the more advanced countries—a generosity which should be both imaginative and innovationist. More fundamentally still, the problem is that of lifting the innumerable roadblocks to technical progress inside the underdeveloped countries themselves. On this score, assistance and cooperative measures will be very much to the point, although the investments required may bring little or no return especially as calculated on a short-term basis.

The problem of hunger, if not grasped in its widest context, could lead the advanced countries to adopt policies that are at face value highly charitable and satisfying to their consciences, and yet which would in the end merely push out of view a problem still harder to resolve. The prime means for lifting some of the road-blocks, and it is a means the advanced countries are eminently suited to supply, is to state the problem of underdevelopment in its real terms. This is hard for us to do, for our economic thinking has been shaped by "a narrow experience which is content (pedagogically) to pass off ignorance as knowledge so long as it is 'formally' correct, while the conflicts and the dead certainties which have worked themselves out in history mystify it (though not in any self-satisfied sense)."[70] It is hard for us to do, because there is "a close historical connection between colonialism and the rise of sociology."[71]

GETTING TWO DIFFERENT TECHNOLOGICAL ENVIRONMENTS IN TOUCH

As we search for an explanation for the phenomenon of under-development at the two levels, that of the psycho-social approach and that of the formal social and cultural approach, it is important to get rid of a number of prejudices that would persuade us that it is purely a growth phenomenon, of one or another structurally determined type such as we possess many models of.[72] The psycho-social approach has attempted to isolate, for example, the "changing attitudes" of people toward underdevelopment. However, we must at this stage of our analysis grasp how the approach itself is a social phenomenon of which our explanation must take account. Its relational aspect, like the diversity of the forms underdevelopment takes and the subsequent challenges to the factors for progress, finds its explanation, in the opinion of several writers, in the fact that "Underdevelopment is a notion, or rather a problem, which arises out of the interaction of societies at various levels of technological progress within a world where this last has been in the forefront of public concern since the industrial revolution."[73]

Creation. To grasp the full scope of this explanation, we must first call attention to the many determinisms that link the techno-logical factor with the socio-cultural system. We can then better bring out the phenomenon of progress and the necessity for its propagation. We can especially cast light on what an obstacle different technological levels are to the propagation of technical progress.

What we mean by "determinism," here, is "How particular facts are integrated within one or another of the many real frameworks or concrete worlds, which remain forever contingent."[74] Under the circumstances, these determinisms may be broken down into "Two highly distinct series of phenomenal chains, one of which proceeds upwards from technology to society, and expresses social changes in terms of technological changes; the other of which proceeds downwards from society to technology, expressing technological changes in terms of social changes."[75] A prerequisite to a study of these determinisms is the ability to distinguish clearly, at least at the analytic level, between the particular facts and the contingent framework within which they are to be integrated. Noting how far from clearly drawn the distinction is in current definitions,[76] Bernard concludes:

It makes no sense to study the social in terms of the technical, unless the relation of the instrumental to the social is clearly brought out, and unless the noninstrumental varieties of the technical are as-similated within the social itself.[77]

Downward Phase: The Collective Character of Innovation. Social changes cannot be accounted for as consequences of individual inventions of instrumental techniques. Only when a number of the latter are involved does there appear that phenomenon of mutation which is capable of transforming the socio-cultural system from top to bottom. Lewis Mumford considers that three such phenomena have appeared since the tenth century, constituting an eotechnic, a paleotechnic, and a neotechnic phase of industrial development.[78]

420 THE MEANS OF SUBSISTENCE

The wide gulf between the "developed" countries and those just setting out on their own development, would thus consist in the fact that the former are at the third phase while the latter are still at the first—or even at some yet more primitive phase—just when the latter's development becomes so especially urgent.

The obviously collective character of technological mutations[79] leads us to draw a basic distinction between invention and innovation. Invention is an individual act, or at least not necessarily a collective one, and it may be the result of a lucky find. In this connection, Dixon prefers the term "discovery,"[80] the conscious creation of something radically new. What innovation is, is the translation of the inventive idea into the material substructure, trying it out in association with other techniques within the social reality.

The creative imitation of those who come after is of the very greatest importance, yet not in the sense of little "bunches" of individual imitators gathering around individual inventors. What is striking are the new lines of communication opened up between social groups inside the fixed institutional framework, which lead to new groupings of inventions and innovations and bring about new relationships between old industries and new or revitalized ones.[81]

As it seems to us, the above distinction throws a good deal of light on the "upward" phase of determinisms. The collective character of innovation accounts for the circular, "autocumulative" aspect of social and technological transformations,[82] between which covariant relationships may be noted.[83] It also explains how "Technological progress produces consequences that vary with the institutional framework and the system of signification into which it is introduced."[84]

Upward Phase: Cultural Lag. And yet we must also emphasize that although "Instrumental techniques imply the whole of the psychological structure required for their exercise, they do not include it."[85] Actually, what it is important to show now, is how instrumental mutation sets off a whole complex of transformations, both in society's formal, socio-economic structure and in its psycho-social structure. As Marx noted long since, instrumental changes necessarily provoke changes in social relationships and, as a corollary, modify the social existence of the sociological units, i.e., their historical situation. At the same time, more slowly but at a deeper level, values and norms on the one hand, attitudes on the other, undergo development. Sometimes a considerable period may be required for the social reality to catch up with the transformations going on at the level of ideologies and institutions. The different rates of speed with which the various stages of development are reached—as also the different rhythms at which the various kinds of transformation proceed—have introduced the principle of temporal succession into sociology. Were it not for this "cultural lag," as it has been called,[86] human society would hardly be distinguishable from animal societies, that is, "A single biological organism, eternally reproducing the same archetype, once in a long while modified by some over-all mutation."[87] This very lack of synchronization in human social development may be what allows imbalances at one level to be assimilated before imbalances appear at some deeper level of reality. The imbalances offset one another, and societies are impelled onwards to some ultimately attainable degree of social coherence. We shall see in the case of the just developing countries that the developmental sequence is never the same, and how one source of the social imbalances and incoherences to be observed may lie in the very absence of "cultural lag."

Determinisms in the "downward" phase are much less readily apparent. Perhaps we could find an explanation for this in the fact that any technological stage is essentially contingent, may be subject to any number of temporary conditions. Such an approach would seem to agree with Mumford's views. In his explanation of how the paleotechnic phase of industrial development—represented by the steam engine, the rise of the textile trades, mining, and metallurgy—was related to the phenomenon of warfare, he stressed the regressive character of such mutations and went on to show

how the neotechnic phase could have built directly upon the earlier phase, in as much as Fourneyron had invented the turbine in 1832.[88]

Be that as it may, there is no evidence for the old saw "Necessity is the mother of invention." Quite to the contrary. As Harrison has shown, it is after a discovery or an invention has been made, and not before, that it is felt to be needed.[89] It is true that, as Leroi-Gourhan has written, human groups may find themselves gradually enriched by the successive small advances made possible by their tools in a particular stage of technological development, and that this may lead to a new period of intense association which "projects them literally into a new technological group."[90] However, there is no factor, and no group of factors, that can account adequately for such an embarkation upon a new technological phase.

Propagation. Technological progress has to be considered essentially as something borne along in a general economic development extending over a long period of time. It is not to be confused with narrowly economic progress brought about through increasing the number of goods and services. We call this economic development one of long-term expansion, because it presupposes alterations in the deployment of manpower and in the rates of production. It is not logically necessary, however, and constitutes an abstraction with relation to the contingent experience of the Industrial Revolution. At the same time, it is possible to show how and why this expansion occurs, from study both of the subjective ends and the objective reality. Here we have no intention of going into the matter, but we might perhaps be allowed to recall the important role played in long-term expansion by the way innovations are introduced into an economic structure characterized by developmental extremes and by environments equipped for propagation.

We shall go into greater length on the subject of the time element in long-term expansion. Apart from studies devoted to the crises which have developed in economic systems, and which serve mainly polemic purposes,[91] we have no sure indication of any approaching decline, although some significant slowdowns have been observed in some of the most advanced economies.

It might be useful to compare the lengths of time various economies have taken to advance beyond the paleotechnic phase. It took Europe's economy two centuries, that of the United States about half that, and it seems the U.S.S.R. has moved still faster. The fact that China has given herself twenty years to complete her industrial revolution and catch up with the technologically advanced countries, is a further indication of profound alteration in the time element as a measure of economic development. It would be tempting to account for it by the contingent character of the European Industrial Revolution, which would thus have made it possible for other economies to skip certain phases, such as the paleotechnic phase. However, such an explanation is contradicted by the efforts of the newer countries to equip themselves with a powerful heavy industry. Yet another explanation might be that propagation comes about more rapidly than creation. This at least partly accounts for the phenomenon. However, there are two further facts that force us to recognize the need for a radical change in our notions of the time element in economics: the growing perfection of the communications media and, correlative with this, the coming into being of new types of sovereignty.

The phenomenon of propagation employs totally new methods which have been necessitated by the lack of international economic integration. Instead of making use of the classic fluxes of international commerce, technological progress today tends to disseminate itself through the creation of "a coalition of new investments in the home country, linked with coalitions of new investments in foreign countries and overseas."[92] This new method of propagation upsets the traditional explanatory schemata by introducing the dimension of space into economic analysis.

Borrowings. Calling into question both the time factor and the space factor helps us to understand why it is that most of the new countries, instead of moving ahead rapidly as we should like them to, are subject to social imbalances that constitute serious resistance factors to technological progress. What we shall attempt to show, is that the special circumstances attending propagation in the new countries—namely those of intercultural contacts between dif-

ferent technological environments—*spontaneously* bring about
these imbalances, and that they are of a very different character
from anything the highly developed countries of today went
through in the past. We use the term "borrowings" to designate this
special type of propagation.

Downward Phase: The Need for "Foreign" Techniques. Instrumental techniques can be borrowed only with the help of technicians who understand their purpose and can keep the equipment
in functioning order. The gulf is so great between the eotechnic and
the neotechnic phases of technological development that skilled
technicians cannot be dispensed with. The essential characteristics
of such "borrowings" by the underdeveloped countries today are
(1) that there is no prior feeling that they are needed, and (2) no
understanding of what the borrowed equipment and skills are for.
This can be seen very clearly in countries where a small "modern-
ized" sector—whether native or foreign—exists alongside the traditional, technologically primitive, and economically inarticulate
society.

What makes borrowings so different from propagation is that
along with the technical equipment comes some larger or smaller
group of men "bound together in production relationships characteristic of the tools they bring with them."[93] These men have their
own values and are in no doubt about the merits of their own institutions. Now, we saw above how technological changes set off profound mutations within the socio-cultural system. So, with the arrival of the foreign technicians, very great differences begin to make
themselves felt on the score of social relations, values, and institutions, as well as that of status, attitudes, motives, and ideologies.
Since for both parties these differences are bound up with differences of a technological level, a whole set of imbalances grows up
which may go so far as to threaten a breakdown of economic relations. It may happen that the influencing group has a shattering
effect on the influenced group, although the former may assimilate
individuals for whom the experience was liberating and be able to
recast them in a new cultural pattern. Now, the effects of cultural

interchange need not be so shattering. Quite to the contrary, it is, as Elkin says,

Striking to note, even in the mid-twentieth century, that the same set of tools may be put to useful service within notably unlike social structures. . . .[94]

Indeed, it would seem that

The full effect of technological progress has been realized, only when the society on the receiving end has become sufficiently creative to make contributions to the society which exported its accomplishments.[95]

It is not for us to say *a priori* whether the final effect of technological borrowings is to turn one culture into the image of another, or merely to work a creative ordering within it. Only study of the extremely varied ways in which intercultural contacts work can tell us how and why there is the one result in a given case, the other result in another. What we mainly wish to bring out is that intercultural contacts between technologically dissimilar environments necessarily bring about imbalances and dislocations, although these may in part be due to the long-distance character of propagation today. They spring up all at once, moreover, not according to a previously familiar time-table of cultural lags and differently "phased" advances in the various parts of the social structure. In fact, when we compare the processes of socio-cultural change set in motion by propagation and by technological borrowings, respectively, we find that what most clearly and profoundly differentiates them is the almost total lack of "cultural lag" in the latter instance.

Why, then, under the circumstances, do not the underdeveloped peoples simply refuse the offered bait—these peoples whom "we may assume to be in balance with the conditions of their own culture, who understand nothing of the ultimate aims of machine civilization, yet who allow themselves to be tempted by ways of life they do not understand"?[96]

A good start towards an answer to the question might be to wonder whether these peoples, or for that matter all peoples, are necessarily "in balance with the conditions of their own culture." This may be the case in some societies, for example in that Burmese village culture described by Margaret Mead,[97] where no threat of sanctions was needed to enforce the law and where there were neither rich nor poor because everyone shared the wealth. And yet, we might recall also the observation of another anthropologist, Lévi-Strauss, to the effect that societies

which might appear most authentically archaic, are all of them full of teeth-shattering discords, wherever unmistakable events have left their marks.[98]

Social cohesiveness implies a minimum of deviant behavior-patterns. Could we be sure of the cohesiveness of all the societies involved in technical borrowings, we could agree that their peoples must be in balance with the conditions of their culture. However, as we have seen, these societies differ widely in their degree of cohesiveness and in the character of their social structures, and their cultures have developed at different rhythms than their social structures have. And we must acknowledge, too, that there have been many societies which men and women have been willing to turn their backs on forever, to quit for some new world, rather than to go on filling a role or occupying a status which for one reason or another (age, for example) made them feel left out of things.

That so many Africans have been moving to towns and signing contracts to work in labor camps must surely be due in part to a desire, on the part of some of them, to get out from under the occasionally tyrannical authority of their tribe or clan.

But in our opinion, the most comprehensive answer to the question asked above has been supplied in the following lines:

The Chinese coolie who took a job twenty-five years ago in a coal mine did not do so because he was interested in coal nor because he felt drawn to the values of industrial civilization, not even to its products. He did so because the job brought him cash wages which he could immediately convert into satisfactions as estimated within his own scale of values.[99]

Frankel adds his support to this view when he states that the Western employer should pay native workmen in a form immediately convertible into local exchanges.[100] The young native hires out in a modern enterprise to earn the money with which to pay his bride's purchase price. The Algerian family which allows a son to go to France for four or five years does so in the expectation he will come back with enough of a nest-egg to open a small stall in the village marketplace. Before they let him go, he must solemnly swear that he will send back money regularly and never forget where his home is: should he marry a French girl, he can never return, even if he wanted to. His wife will be considered a foreigner and he himself a traitor. His only recourse will be to settle in France or in one of the big Algerian towns.[101]

However, the first repercussions of cultural interchange can sometimes be deeply disturbing:

Japan supplies the most striking example. When the first American ships put in around the middle of the nineteenth century, the curiosity of the crowds quickly changed to apprehension. There were outbursts of anger, finally an incident, to which the ships replied with modern weapons. Deep feelings thus lay at the bottom of the social revolution which ended forever the age-old feudal structure of the Daimyos.[102]

Upward Phase: The Lack of "Cultural Lag." Now that we have explained how cultural interchange gets started, we must try to show how imbalances and incoherence arise spontaneously. People whose social relationships bring them into close contact with modern production are not slow to appreciate the specific goods it brings. For some time they look upon acquisition of them as a prestige factor in their own environment. This is the initial stage, when their own values remain as yet intact. But now the spatial character of propagation asserts itself, and new towns and cities spring up, constituting centers apart from the traditional environment, with new customs and ways of life. As the new centers become their new social environment, there is a fundamental transformation in people's values from the economic point of view. Wages, which had first been thought of as extra money, must now support them and their families. There is a shift in roles within the family itself. The wife ceases to be the important production factor she had been in the traditional society, and now it is she who looks around for ways of earning extra money. The exodus from the villages to work camps and to the towns is a serious threat to the family's stability. In the new population centers there are too few women, and prostitution spreads rapidly.

Ogburn, who has studied the effects of technical change on the socio-cultural system in our own societies, calls attention to an essential phenomenon: the gradual loss of control over individual behavior by the traditional community authorities, as a result of technological progress. This occurs, he said, within the family, within the village, and within the religious framework. It occurs in a still more aggravated form in the countries just embarking on their modernization programs. The time factor and the space factor to which we have referred accelerate this loss of control. The move to the new centers, far from the traditional community, does not just cut people off from it, but may subject them to laws and institutions deriving from an alien culture. It is an abrupt shift in time as well as in space, for there is no transition from the one pattern of authority to the other. Now the family is suddenly reduced to the mother-father-child relationship, and is no longer integrated within the broader clan structure. Individual wage labor replaces community subsistence labor. The only alternatives to the ancestral religion are Western religions or atheist materialism.[103] New roles and functions have to be learned, and new demands met, without any intervening period of adjustment. It is scarcely surprising if they perform poorly, for they have as yet but a superficial grasp of the values that rule the new relationships. Open conflicts may arise between traditional roles and those demanded by the new society, one example of which is the family parasitism which has sprung up in the cities of a number of new countries. In Africa, especially, workers are always asking for a raise because of the number of "brothers" they have to feed, or for a day off to go and greet them when they first arrive from the back country. We might mention once again that social imbalances and conflicts of this kind could certainly be lessened, or at least softened, if there were some way for the traditional authority groups to continue to fulfill their functions. There seem to be fewer such strains in certain agricultural societies where the only contact with a modern environment occurs about once or twice a year when crops are sold or bartered. It seems, also, that programs of the "Community Development" type tend to minimize such cultural disturbances.

In order to grasp the phenomenon as a whole, we shall now try to bring out the processes which complement the above, arising out of the psycho-social level. The "new" man's social situation may be said to be defined, in a general way, by his having been brought in touch with another culture. As such, it is not unlike that of the "marginal" man, who has been described as "belonging to two cultures, with neither of which he can fully identify." He has been emancipated, in the sense of not being bound to the behavior norms and value scales of either culture. He wavers between them, rarely sure of what he should be thinking, what he should be doing, and often he is viewed as an outcast by the two groups proper.[104]

Perhaps it would be more apt to speak of a marginal collectivity rather than of a marginal man. What brings about the lack of cultural lag at the psycho-social level, and the complementary processes at the formal, socio-economic level, is collective efforts to imitate the new and unfamiliar society. It is a collectively experienced social situation which gives rise to feelings of insecurity and the struggle for social survival, contradictory tendencies which leave the collectivity at the mercy of any ideological rationalization that may come along. Frequently, the foreign variety is preferred to the native variety, another instance of the lack of cultural lag. The danger in a poorly assimilated ideology is that it is likely to encourage violent expression of the troubles, the real reasons for which are not understood. Just how such an ideology takes hold depends, in the first instance, on the level at which representations of reality are formed, a matter which varies greatly from country to country with the degree of structural cohesiveness, openness to change, and susceptibility to cultural factors. Policies of the Western country involved, whether intended to or not, also play a considerable part in all this. In short, the consequences of intercultural contact are exactly proportionate to the nature of that contact and all that has gone into making it what it is. They include the psychosocial concept of development involved and all the divers elements which make up the formal, socio-economic reality of the situation.

Encounter between two very different technological environments represents a historical leap and thus may cut down the time required for a given progress to be realized, but only on the condition that the social dislocations which arise naturally are speedily adjusted. However, in the case of borrowings, there are none of those natural mechanisms of adjustment we find in the case of propagation, characterized by traditional group controls over individual behavior. Taken together, individual decisions have no chance of attaining some meaningful equilibrium, for no economic system exists to channel and guide them. Still, the social reality is not atomized to quite this point; a structure of social groups, eventually of classes, does take shape, within which jockeying for power goes on over a period of time and produces ups and downs. To bring our analysis to a conclusion, we must turn now to the level of macro-decisions, at which we shall find our best hope of a successful shortcut to the solution of these difficulties.

THE MEANING OF VALUES AND SITUATIONS

Actually, the problem is that of finding new groups which can play the part of the traditional groups, whose effectual control has been shattered by the factors of space and time. Moreover, they must be capable of more than just filling the functions of the old groups; they must be capable of giving new meaning to values and situations. This is the difference between propagation and borrowings, namely, that in the former new groups appear as the last stage in the process of social mutation, whereas in the latter they will appear as the first stage, supplying the motive power to all that follows.

Theirs is a complex task. The re-structuring of a hierarchy of values they are to bring about cannot be done with borrowed criteria. It must be soundly rooted in the psycho-social and the formal, socio-economic aspects of reality. A primary consideration for bringing together in a dynamic whole the factors of political independence and those of developmental modernization is that there should be a higher degree of integration within the countries than presently exists.[105] What has been preventing it, we know, have been such resistance factors as the frightful poverty of the peoples and the growing gulf between rich and poor, indeed, the growing gulf between the developed and the underdeveloped nations. Such resistance factors have been backed up, at the psycho-social level, by the chorus of conflicting ideologies. No sooner is a new nation's integration envisaged, than conflicts arise between government functions and the places where they are to be based, between the nation's own sovereignty and that which it should be accorded in terms of its place in the "developmental scale."[106] Moreover, such conflicts tend to spread and become conflicts of region against region or class against class, to the detriment of the nation's integration. One of the first values to be determined by the new groups, then, will be that touching the nation's sovereignty in *space*. Another and no less important determination of value will be that touching the collective future in *time*. There will have to be serious discussion of capitalist time[107] and also of native, traditional time, in order that out of the pros and cons a suitable measure of expectation may be arrived at. (This, in our opinion, is the sense of the Chinese twenty-year plan.) Still a third part of the new groups' task will be to convey meaningfully some sense of the cost progress entails, both in terms of human life and in terms of self-restraint.[108]

Nor will the new groups' functions stop here, for they dare not pass over a single aspect of value judgment.

Though the need for such groups is one of the fundamental problems of underdevelopment, it will not be enough to create them, nor enough that they should draw up an appropriate scale of values. What is also needed is that they be given authority. Nor can it be a solely economic authority, ultimate consequence of the strategic maneuvers of the economic powers-that-be. Actually, such maneuvers are not constant over a period of time, because the underlying structures are disjointed. But the chief reason why their authority cannot be solely economic in character is because the values to be drawn up and promulgated so as to gain acceptance by all go beyond the economic sphere. Economic creation has to be collective, has to involve the cooperation of many different groups if it is to be lasting and to surmount conditions of insecurity and uprootedness. Thus, the new groups must be essentially political, by no means identified solely with the new instrumental techniques that have brought about the social mutations requiring a fresh ordering of values.

The political bargaining out of which the new groups will be given authority often enough has the effect of weakening that authority and, thereby, of diminishing the coherence of the proposed scale of values. We have already said enough about how important the latter is. Indeed, without sufficient coherence the new order may have the effect of worsening conditions. The new authority must be strong if it is to persuade, or if need be to force, diverse groups to support an economic system which may well involve serious human costs, and wield them together into a single pattern of economic relationships.

Clearly, where political bargaining is concerned, foreign groups with their enormous economic and political power have an important influence to bring to bear. This is not the place to go into the matter of why the factors for progress are preserved when a country is launched upon a bipolar economic and commercial career. This will be the subject of another study.

What we want to emphasize most strongly is the primordial importance of the political factor:

An essential factor which necessarily has the tendency to strangulate whatever recommendations may be formulated by technicians. Here, the most positive approach is not to reflect upon what might be done if only one were backed up by unlimited authority, but to reflect upon what it is possible to do given the actual authority likely to be available. In most cases, this is very weak.[109]

The political factor should be kept essentially distinct from the enterprise factor. If the latter is to work in the national interest, it should be able to take its bearings within the frame of reference defined by the political groups. In this way collective projects and collective expectations will be fitted to "bring about increase, cumulatively and lastingly, in the nation's real over-all product."[110] There will be cases, it is true, where both functions will have to be assumed by government. However, the latter's assumption of the entrepreneur function is contingent upon highly unlike situations which we have tried to present to the reader.

In conclusion, technical changes spontaneously set off deep sociocultural changes which lead, in turn, to dislocations and disequilibrium. When the changes have been introduced through outright borrowing, the upsets they cause tend not to be readily assimilated. They should be guided at every stage by a conscious policy, backed up by substantial authority. In our opinion, this is our best hope of narrowing what has been the ever-widening gap between rich countries and poor countries.

NOTES

1. *Forward Appraisal of FAO Programs, 1959–64* (Rome: FAO, 1959), pp. 63–66.
2. *Ibid.*, pp. 37–43.

3. *Etude sur la situation économique de l'Europe* (Geneva: United Nations, 1956), p. 156.

4. M. R. Haswell, *Economics of Agriculture in a Savannah Village* (1953) quoted in *World Population and Resources: A Report by PEP* (London: Political & Economic Planning, 1955), pp. 33–34.

5. *Forward Appraisal* (FAO), p. 42.

6. *World Population and Resources* (PEP), p. 35.

7. FAO Doc. C.L. 1/4, Oct. 22, 1947, p. 2.

8. Cf. *Forward Appraisal* (FAO), p. 43.

9. Cf. *Ibid.*, p. 49.

10. Michel Cépède, "Démographie et Développement," *Progrès et Agriculture*, I (I.S.E.A., 1964).

11. *Le Mois d'ethnographie française* (March, 1950).

12. Cépède and Lengellé, *Economie alimentaire du globe* and *L'Economie de l'alimentation.*

13. Woytinsky, "World Resources in Relation to Population," *op. cit.*, p. 67.

14. *Population Growth and the Standard of Living in Under-Developed Countries* (New York: United Nations, 1950), p. 1.

15. Louis P. Aujoulat, *Aujourd'hui l'Afrique* (Tournai: Casterman, 1960), p. 398.

16. Cf. *Commerce des produits de base et développement économique* (New York: United Nations, 1953), pp. 8, 12.

17. *Mesures à prendre pour le développement économique des pays insuffisamment développés* (New York: United Nations, 1951).

18. H. Simonet, *La formation du capital dans les pays sous-développés et l'assistance financière étrangère* (Brussels: Institut Solvay, 1959), pp. 54–55.

19. *Le "Tiers-Monde,"* p. 80.

20. *Population Growth and the Standard of Living in Under-Developed Countries* (New York: United Nations, 1954), p. 10.

21. Georges Balandier in *Le "Tiers-Monde,"* p. 80.

22. *Ibid.*

23. T. Stark, *Justice dans le Monde* (Louvain), I, 3 (March, 1960), 366.

24. W. Banning, "Rencontres de cultures, réflexions d'un Occidental," *Justice dans le Monde*, III (Sept. 1961), 5 ff.

25. D. P. Mukerji, "Les Vues de Mahatma Gandhi sur les machines et le progrès technique," *Bulletin International des Sciences Sociales* (UNESCO), VI, 3 (1954), 458.

26. Balandier, *op. cit.*, pp. 129 ff.

27. Banning, *op. cit.*, p. 13.

28. Paul Kwang-Tsien Shih, "L'Asie de l'Asie et le monde moderne," *Justice dans le Monde*, III (Sept. 1961), 19 ff.

29. Balandier, *op. cit.*, p. 290.

30. Georges Balandier, "Structures sociales traditionnelles et changements

économiques," *Revue de l'Institut de Sociologie Solvay* (Brussels), no. 1 (1959), p. 30.

31. Balandier, *op. cit.*, pp. 28, 33.

32. *Ibid.*, pp. 23, 33.

33. Aujoulat, *op. cit.*, p. 115.

34. *Ibid.*

35. Balandier, *op. cit.*, p. 38.

36. Paul Kwang-Tsien Shih, *op. cit.*

39. Two especially successful efforts along these lines are described in the following FERES publications (Fédération internationale des institutions de Recherches socio-religieuses): C. Torres and B. Corredor, *Las Escuelas radiofonicas de Sutatenza* (Friburg: FERES, 1961), and O. Dominguez, *El Campesino chileno y la Acción Católica rural* (Friburg: FERES, 1961).

40. "Rapports de l'Occident avec le reste du Monde," *Prospective* (Paris: Presses Universitaires), no. 3 (April, 1959), p. 65.

41. "Three Sociological Aspects of Economic Development," *Economic Review of Latin America* (Bogota) Aug. 1955, p. 57.

42. R. Firth, "La monnaie, le travail et l'évolution sociale dans les systèmes économiques de la région indo-pacifique," *Bulletin International des Sciences Sociales* (UNESCO), VI, 3 (1954).

43. Margaret Mead (ed.), *Cultural Patterns and Technical Change* (New York: Mentor Books, 1955), p. 197.

44. *Ibid.*, p. 196.

45. P. T. Bauer and B. S. Yamey, *The Economics of Under-Developed Countries* (Cambridge: Cambridge U. Press, 1957), p. 231.

46. On this topic, see S. Torres and B. Corredor, *Transformación en el Mundo rural Latino-americano* (Friburg: FERES, 1961).

47. Consult in this connection, *La Réforme agraire: Les défauts de la structure agraire qui entravent le développement économique* (New York: United Nations, 1951).

48. J. Martens, "Le petit agriculteur et l'artisan indien face au marché de l'argent et des capitaux," *Revue du Centre catholique international de coopération* (Sept. 1961), p. 11.

49. Paris, Presses Universitaires, 1959.

50. Cf. *Le progrès social par l'aménagement des collectivités* (New York: United Nations, 1955), p. 6.

51. L. J. Lebret, *Suicide ou survie de l'Occident* (Paris: Editions Ouvrières, 1958), p. 265.

52. For a discussion of such conditions, see *Le progrès social par l'Action Coopérative* (New York: United Nations, 1954), pp. 18–20.

53. B. F. Hoselitz, "Le recrutement des employés dans les pays insuffisamment développés," *Bulletin International des Sciences Sociales* (UNESCO), VI, 3 (1954).

54. *Le Monde en friche, op. cit.*, pp. 125 ff.

55. Daniel Thorner, "The Village Panchayat as Vehicle of Change," *Economic Development and Cultural Change,* II (Oct. 1953).

56. Hoselitz, *op. cit.,* p. 494.

57. Theodore W. Schultz, "Investment in Human Capital," *The American Economic Review* (March 1961).

58. S. Bernard, *Les conséquences sociales du progrès technique: Méthodologie* (Brussels: Institut Solvay, 1956), p. 66.

59. Georges Balandier, "La mise en rapport des sociétés différentes et le problème du sous-développement" in *Le "Tiers-Monde,"* pp. 119 ff.

60. S. Bernard, "S. Herbert Frankel et sa philosophie du sous-développement," *Revue de L'Institut de Sociologie Solvay,* no. 3 (1955), p. 528.

61. Lebret, *op. cit.,* pp. 23–154.

62. Gunnar Myrdal, *Une économie internationale* (Paris: Presses Universitaires, 1958), p. 231. An I.S.E.A. publication.

63. *Ibid.,* pp. 229 ff.

64. H. Janne and S. Bernard, "Analyse critique des concepts relatifs aux implications sociales du progrès technique" in *Changements techniques économiques et sociaux* (Paris: UNESCO, 1958), p. 75.

65. Myrdal, *op. cit.,* p. 206.

66. Janne and Bernard, *op. cit.,* p. 76.

66. François Perroux, "Qu'est-ce que le développement?" *Etudes* (Jan./March, 1961), pp. 16–33.

67. Myrdal, *op. cit.,* p. 226.

68. François Perroux, *Théorie générale du progrès économique: I. Les composantes: 1. La Création* (Paris, 1957). An I.S.E.A. publication.

69. Y. Lacoste, *Les pays sous-développés* (Paris: Presses Universitaire), p. 78.

70. François Perroux, "Une distinction utile à la politique des pays à croissance retardée: points de développement et foyers de progrès" in *Développement, Croissance, Progrès* (Paris, 1959), p. 9. I.S.E.A. Cahier 94, series F, no. 12.

71. Myrdal, *op. cit.,* pp. 241–44.

72. Cf. S. Herbert Frankel, *The Economic Impact on Under-Developed Societies* (Oxford: Basil Blackwell, 1953), p. 71.

73. Janne and Bernard, *op. cit.,* p. 71.

74. Georges Gurvitch, *Déterminismes sociaux et liberté humaine* (Paris: Presses Universitaires, 1955), p. 40.

75. Janne and Bernard, *op. cit.,* p. 33.

76. Cf. Friedman, Lasswell, Frankel, MacIver, Merton.

77. Janne and Bernard, *op. cit.,* p. 37.

78. Lewis Mumford, *Technics and Civilization* (New York: Harcourt, 1934).

79. François Perroux has tried to bring this out in contradistinction to Schumpeter's formula, in the instance of both the European and the American industrial revolutions (*La Création*).

The Process of Food Production   437

80. Melville J. Hershkovits, *Les bases de l'anthropologie culturelle* (Paris: Payot, 1952), p. 193.
81. Perroux, *La Création,* p. 15.
82. Janne and Bernard, *op. cit.,* p. 56.
83. Gurvitch, *op. cit.,* pp. 64 ff.
84. H. Janne, "Notes critiques relatives à la sociologies de la technique," *Revue de l'Institut de Sociologie Solvay,* no. 4 (1952), p. 603.
85. Janne and Bernard, *op. cit.,* p. 42.
86. W. F. Ogburn, *Social Change* (New York: B. W. Huebsch, 1922).
87. Janne and Bernard, *op. cit.,* p. 62.
88. Mumford, *op. cit.*
89. Hershkovits, *op. cit.,* p. 126.
90. A. Leroi-Gourhan, *Milieu et techniques* (Paris: Albin Michel, 1945), p. 407.
91. François Perroux, *La coexistence pacifique* (Paris: Presses Universitaires, 1958), vol. 1, p. 179.
92. Janne and Bernard, *op. cit.,* p. 44.
93. *Ibid.*
94. "Les conséquences sociales du progrès technique," *Bulletin International des Sciences Sociales* (UNESCO), IV, 2 (1952), 343 ff.
95. G. Balandier and C. Moraze, "L'apport synthétique de l'anthropologie et de l'histoire" in *Changements techniques économiques et sociaux,* p. 331.
96. Janne and Bernard, *op. cit.,* p. 44.
97. Mead (ed.), *op. cit.,* pp. 23–57.
98. Claude Lévi-Strauss, *Anthropologie structurelle* (Paris: Plon, 1958), p. 116.
99. Janne and Bernard, *op. cit.,* p. 44.
100. Frankel, *op. cit.*
101. Saadia and Lakhdar, "L'aliénation colonialiste et la résistance de la famille algérienne," *Les Temps Modernes* (July, 1961), pp. 52–80.
102. Balandier and Moraze, *op. cit.,* p. 322.
103. M. Bennabi has brought out how serious, and in his opinion well-founded, are the resistances aroused in this connection: *La Vocation de l'Islam* (1954), p. 164.
104. Cf. S. Gillin, *The Ways of Man* (New York: Appleton-Century-Crofts, 1956), p. 566.
105. Myrdal, *op. cit.,* pp. 235–313.
106. François Perroux, *La coexistence pacifique,* vol. II.
107. Perroux, *op. cit.,* p. 23. (See n. 70, above.)
108. Perroux, *op. cit.,* pp. 33 ff. (See n. 68, above.)
109. Bernard, *op. cit.,* p. 707.
110. Perroux, *op. cit.,* p. 16. (See n. 66, above.)

PART III
CONCLUSIONS

Chapter 8

Fewer People or Enhanced Subsistence?

WITHOUT QUESTION, whether or not the world is to stay at peace for the next fifty years will be conditioned by whether or not we solve the problem of hunger. The 3 billion world population today will by the year 2000 have climbed to 5 or 6 billion. If all the nations, rich and poor alike, do not join forces to develop the existing and potential resources of the planet now, there will be a steady increase in the proportion of undernourished within the total population. While the well-fed nations are absorbing a 20 per cent rate of population growth, the ill-fed nations of the world will be multiplying their present totals by 4 or 5. It is very hard to see how a comparative few of the world's peoples can go on consuming 80 per cent of the world's food production and keeping to themselves the privileges of material wealth, technical progress, and education.

Study of world population growth and the factors that account for it has made us clearly aware of the size, urgency, and complexity of the problem before us. It scarcely seems realistic, indeed, it seems to us illusory, that the present trend toward rapid doubling of the world population can be slowed down, let alone checked, solely by measures affecting the birth rate.

For a long time to come, the successful campaigns of the World Health Organization against contagious diseases and infant mortality will continue to make themselves felt, not just in falling death rates and rising life expectancy figures, but also in fertility and birth rates. There was a rapid doubling of the population in northern Iran after malaria was stamped out. It goes without saying, surely, that advances in medicine and public health will continue to spread, and that there can be no turning back of the clock in the name of "natural selection" or some allegedly "eugenicist" policy.

A number of individuals have advocated (and their words have influenced demographic policy in more and more of the underdeveloped countries) that the most recent scientific discoveries be applied to measures for lowering birth rates and encouraging planned parenthood. A great deal of research has gone forward in this spirit towards perfecting a sterilizing pill. The thinking seems to be that, since it is impossible to keep food production apace with the needs of a steadily growing population, then all we can do is to bring down the volume of population to the scale of existing means of subsistence. This strikes us as evading the issue, an alibi of the type men invent for themselves rather than face a problem squarely, when to do so would involve them in sweeping reforms requiring courage and daring. We shall come back to this point. For the moment we may observe that reproduction is subject to biological laws, not all the workings of which are as yet perfectly understood, and we might perhaps be endangering the future of the race when we rashly break them. Moreover, study of the cultural and social factors touching natality has shown them to be far more powerful determinants than the biological factors, their extreme diversity proof of mankind's ever-growing freedom and powers of control over the numbers of its progeny. The failure of populationist policies in a few countries during the interwar years is very much a case in point. But is it true that the earth can no longer feed her inhabitants? Is it quite certain that the entire arable surface of the planet has been made the most of, that every latest technical advance in clearing and conserving the land is already in use on every continent? That we have an economic system capable, not just of linking areas of production with those of real human needs, but of supplying actual and potential producers with the greatest possible incentives for intensive cultivation of their lands? We need scarcely mention again all those obstacles and resistances to such an order of things which have already been detailed in these pages.

The solution Europe found to the problem of hunger in the nineteenth century can scarcely serve as a basis for expecting things to go the same way in the rest of the world over the next half century. The vastly different scale of the two phenomena and the speed of the present population explosion suggest a quite contrary conclusion. At the same time, willingness to set aside some of the obstacles and refusal to be taken in by some of the alibis would, in our view, represent a first step towards recognizing the problem of hunger for what it is and its causes for what they are. Honest investigation of the planet's physical resources and of present-day technical knowledge and skills leads us to the conviction that these increasing numbers of people *can* be fed. Indeed, in the opinion of agronomists and other scientific specialists *today,* present agricultural production could be tripled.

Since the physical and technical solutions exist, is it not within the capacity of mankind so to readjust its behavior as to make their practical application to the problem a reality—another step forward in human progress?

The two brief chapters which follow are meant to show how, although much of the planet has been plundered by the men who inhabit it, and although other parts of it remain an undeveloped wasteland, still it yet provides them with the means for overcoming these limiting factors upon the multiplying of their species.

Chapter 9

What Can Be Done

WHEN IT COMES to increasing planetary food production, what can be done through expanding physical resources is, of course, much more limited than what can be done through utilizing technical knowledge and skills. There is only so much of the earth's surface available, and beyond a certain point man has little influence over climate, topography, and altitude. On the other hand, technical advances open up enormous possibilities. Applied science is able to make more and more out of less and less. Technical advances are morally neutral, however, and can be employed for the destruction of the species just as readily as for betterment of the human condition. Thus, for example, the way production rates kept rising in the industrial countries throughout the nineteenth century was one kind of progress; another was the way timber reserves were squandered without a thought for the future over the same period.

Unquestionably, the cultivable areas of the earth's surface are still far from having been all made use of. As we saw in an earlier chapter, only half of the 17 billion acres in this category are at present under cultivation; of these only 3.2 billion are being put to agricultural use and 5.7 billion serving as grazing land. Moreover, of the land actually used to grow crops, much of it still produces very meager yields, and much of it is given over to raising crops unsuited either to the soil or to the needs of the populations working it. In this connection, a number of past mistakes are not to be repeated under any conditions, including wholesale clearing of land without preliminary study of the soils, which may be too new or insufficiently prepared to be cultivable. The Amazon basin seems to many the ideal prototype of virgin lands sure to produce the highest yields from the moment they are cleared and planted, but here the relative youthfulness of the terrain suggests caution.

One type of agriculture should be banished from the earth, in the name of human wisdom and foresight, the type we have called "extractive" agriculture, which in an earlier chapter we compared to the exhaustion of mineral wealth. It is utterly useless to keep clearing new land if every year several million acres have to be abandoned because they are exhausted and there are no funds for their conservation. As we noted above, it is far less alarming that Algeria has 1,000 more human beings every day, than that there are also 250 fewer cultivable acres. In this connection the hunger-ridden Algerian people are far less to be blamed than are those "advanced" countries whose system of setting prices on agricultural products makes impossible a fair return on capital investment in the land.

The planet has indeed been plundered, and large parts of it do in fact just lie there, an undeveloped wasteland; two realities which cannot be reconciled with attempts to solve the problem of hunger —attempts, nonetheless, which could succeed.

There is a much broader range of opportunity for achieving results through the application of technical advances. Agronomists are unanimous that agricultural production could be sizably increased, solely by re-arranging existing production factors and by adopting a few simple instrumental techniques which have long been known. For example, greater use of the water buffalo in parts of Asia would not just spare the rice farmer at planting and harvest times, but would permit him to work a bigger field and thus to produce more rice.

While we do not want to treat mechanization as any panacea, still through it many farmers can double and triple their yields. What keeps more of them from adopting progressive farming methods is fear of bringing prices down by swamping the markets.

Further, by no means have all the new research findings as yet been applied in practice. Dr. M. Y. Nuttonson, head of the American Institute of Crop Ecology, quoted in a chapter on "World Resources in Relation to Population" by W. S. Woytinsky,[1] gives a long list of laboratory discoveries which have not as yet been utilized on an international scale. He begins by noting that American food production could be increased several times over by borrowing methods of intensive agriculture from highly populated countries like Japan. He notes, too, that the reason many of the techniques developed in the U.S. Department of Agriculture field stations have not been taken up by farmers is solely an economic one: they are afraid of overproduction on the domestic market and the foreign markets lack purchasing power. He cites experiments where plants have been grown in a nutritive solution over gravel, speaks of the possibility of crops being grown in the sea, and of how the Scottish firths (or fjords) could be "fertilized" so as to increase the yield of fisheries. Lastly, he speaks of how the increasing use of plastic and chemical fibers for clothing would release for food crops a great deal of land presently given over to the raising of plant fibers. This would, of course, involve the use of nonrenewable materials. There are other possibilities, however. Egon Glesinger has pointed out that an acre of resinous trees, properly tended, can produce many times the fiber an acre of cotton does, and without destroying the soil.[2]

One major cause of hunger in most of the underdeveloped countries is the need they find themselves in to give over more and more land to raising crops for export, in order to obtain the credits with which to purchase the equipment they need—equipment whose price is always rising while the price of the raw materials exported is always going down. One step in the right direction taken by Cuba in the course of her agrarian reform was to turn back some of the land to its primary mission of feeding the Cubans. Over the years, more and more acreage had been given over to the export sugar crop, while the population at home was constantly growing.

Lastly, it is only to the degree his problems become urgent that man finds solutions for them. Was not that abrupt increase in the output of American agriculture, during World War II, a case in point? Dare we suppose that measures taken under the pressure of wartime necessity, and by government decision, could not also be taken under the pressure of hunger?

It remains a fact that this stupendous task of getting the most out of the world's food resources would in large part be undertaken by populations which were, at least initially, seriously weakened by undernourishment. Poverty creates a vicious circle: development is held back by malnutrition and undernourishment, while these last cannot be remedied for lack of development.

Some such method of instituting and financing stockpiles of food in the rich countries as was discussed above (see pp. 309–331) could serve to get the initial phase of development going, on condition that it served as an investment in production and was, as such, part of an autonomous plan of over-all development. Although solving the problem of hunger is an absolute prerequisite to the modernization of agriculture, still increased agricultural production will, in the countries that are suffering from hunger, set off a sequence of economic factors.

An economic circuit will gradually come into being, linking the mass of wage-earners in the towns and in industry—encouraged by increased agricultural productivity to move into other sectors of the economy—with the agricultural population who, once they have built up a commercially valuable surplus, will be in a position to make further improvements in farming methods.

Once the technical aspect of the problem of enhancing the means of subsistence has been solved, then all that will be needed will be (given an adequate economic structure) to bring the doubled or tripled supply into line with the true demand for foodstuffs. This last may be very different from the "real" demand at the market price, dear to Keynesian economists. As we have already noted, "real" demand may find its level under conditions of underemployment, both of men and of resources.

It is surely obvious that not every country nor every continent is going to succeed in feeding its entire population. Necessarily some parts of the world will always produce surpluses and other parts will fall short. "To enjoy a diet sufficient in animal products (i.e., calculated in original calories), yet without cutting down on available vegetable products, Africa, South America, and Asia would have to triple their agricultural production."[3] That will not, of course, happen overnight. It will thus be up to the generosity of the highly developed countries in the meantime to make up the nutritional deficit.

It seems to us that the only true, the only realistic approach to solving the problem of hunger is this one, in terms of a world-wide increase in agricultural production.

The world's enormous potentialities show how false it is to accuse Creation of avarice. Even without speculating on how by the year 2000 scientific research will have altered our ways of thinking about the problem, mankind today possesses the physical and technical resources needed to satisfy its nutritional needs.

Attempts to adjust the numbers of people to the means of subsistence do not just insult human dignity, they constitute an evasion of the problem, rather than a solution, the effects of which could only take longer to be felt. They would mean an appalling step backwards in man's long struggle to gain mastery over the created world.

Nor is it enough to affirm that the earth is capable of feeding her inhabitants. This capacity has to be realized.

The obstacles to solution of our problem are to be met with, alas, in man's own behavior, in his institutions, and in his governments. We are not so naive as to suppose that these obstacles will be surmounted quickly. There is weighty resistance and much self-deception. Just what the obstacles are, and why international solidarity alone can overcome them, are discussed in the following chapter.

NOTES

1. In Philip M. Hauser (ed.), *Population and World Politics,* pp. 60–62.
2. Egon Glesinger, *The Coming Age of Wood.*
3. Georges Balandier, "Les Pays en voie de développement," *Analyse sociologique et politique.* Les cours de Droit (Paris, 1960–61), fasc. 1.

Chapter 10

Obstacles and Alibis

EVERY DAY that passes makes clearer the mounting need for a world-wide solution to the problem of hunger, and greater willingness to recognize it. FAO is a good example of the growing sense of urgency among the developed countries, as are plans for disposing of surplus food stocks, and other efforts by other international organizations to draw up and put into effect a long-term policy for meeting world needs. Through good years and bad, after experiencing a succession of advances and retreats, men have finally come around to admitting the concept of the interdependence of nations as a remedy for their ills. However, as often as not the concept remains very much in the abstract.

The cultural obstacles to the development of agriculture in the countries just developing have been described at length. There is superstition and the weight of age-old customs and habits to be overcome (including food habits); people are confined in rigid class and caste divisions; there is apathy, resignation, inertia on the part of the peasant masses in the face of all suggestions for economic and technical change. These factors represent continuing hazards for government staffs eager to promote their countries' development as rapidly as possible. The only true solution, as we have seen, is for the peasants to be initiated on a grand scale into the mysteries of a market economy, to be instructed in modern production techniques, and to be integrated within the political structure of their nation. In this connection, and despite its excesses, the Cuban revolution might serve as a case in point: at least it has courageously addressed itself to solving these *fundamental* problems.

Genuine enough when we meet them in the peasantry of an undeveloped country, these socio-cultural obstacles frequently take on the character of alibis when put forward by those who hold political power in these countries. Members of a privileged minority, they may be tempted to put off the settling of accounts, to delay the inception of indispensable reforms, and seek rather to deal with the population explosion by distributing birth-control devices and providing instruction in their use. There are no more urgent measures, however, for the solution of our problem than (1) agrarian reform, and (2) the democratizing of political programs. As it seems to us, the fact that a minority of landowners underexploits a major part of a country's land, or the fact there is no legislation to protect farmers and give them some measure of security, is quite as serious a matter for a country's future as the fact that the masses are slow to adopt modern production techniques. The growing inequality of income between the various population strata in these just developing countries is another obstacle to be overcome.

Obstacles and alibis of the same type are to be met with in the developed countries. Nobody can any longer maintain that a capitalist economy accountable to nothing save the laws of supply and demand, can help solve the problem of multiplying subsistence. The paradoxical situation of food surpluses in a world where a majority of mankind suffers from endemic hunger, is evidence that speaks for itself. If economic laws are such that they cannot solve the world's most urgent problem, then before blaming this state of affairs on too many mouths to feed, perhaps those laws should be changed. The primordial task of the economy is to serve human needs, not to seek out ever greater profits, or—at the least—the pursuit of profit ought not to prevent the satisfaction of needs. In the nineteenth century the so-called "natural" laws of the labor market were unable to furnish wage-earners adequate remuneration; today the principle of "adjusting" food production to prices on the world market is just as incapable of serving as a criterion in drawing up a world-wide agricultural policy. What happens is that production is stabilized at the point where supply is in accord with "real" demand (see pp. 317–331, above)—the fraction of demand which is backed up by adequate purchasing power—not with the actually existing demand for foodstuffs. We have seen earlier how this creates an unnatural market situation and aggravates existing problems.

Without doubt, this false explanation of market tendencies is still influencing production policy in the countries with sizable agricultural surpluses. The U.S. Soil Bank's action in setting aside 4 per cent of the country's farmlands between 1956 and 1959[1] (an area six times that of Belgium's land under cultivation) derives in part from an attempt to adapt supply to demand (demand of this artificial type described). To build up surpluses for the purpose of distributing them to the starving countries will unquestionably make great demands on the generosity of the developed countries. However, in the long run such a policy will bring greater returns than the policy which has hitherto been followed, if it does have the effect of helping to modernize the economies of the just developing countries on an autonomous basis. The final effect would be to put purchasing power behind a demand which has lacked it until now. It is not often enough recalled in the highly industrialized nations, that there is a 40 per cent difference in productivity between a worker who is well fed and one who is not. The investments in food recommended by FAO are quite as stimulating to production as are policies of financial aid and technical assistance.

A genuine transformation of some of our economic beliefs, from the bottom up, ought to be one of the primary objectives to be realized by the wealthy countries. A saner conception of economics is very much in order. To a considerable extent, this will consist in practicing on the international scale what they already practice at home, within their own borders: redistribution of income in view of greater justice and to encourage new enterprise, re-allocation of costs in line with individual capacities to pay. The current trend is very much in this direction, but intentions too often get sidetracked by selfish political, economic, and even racial considerations. Besides avarice in individuals, there is such a thing as class avarice, national avarice, and even avarice on the continental scale. It is very disquieting to compare the different degrees of urgency with which problems are posed in the developed countries and in those just developing. In the latter, to a considerable extent, sheer survival is the issue. In the former, the dominant consideration is how to create greater demand for more and more goods of the luxury type. Are we here raising the question of the obligation the more advanced countries are in, even at the expense of their own continuing expansion, to assist the economically backward countries in getting their modernization programs "off the ground," even safely underway? It might be so. . . .

However, the first duty of the more privileged peoples is to *allow* the development of their retarded brothers. There are still far too many political and economic obstacles to their autonomous advancement. Moreover, much of the generous aid they have received is, in effect, prevented from being as useful as it might be by the obstacles we are speaking of. The 1958 recession cost the underdeveloped countries more than the total loans granted them by the International Bank for Reconstruction and Development over the preceding years.

In the last chapter we saw that the problem of hunger can be solved through joint action to increase the means of subsistence. Moreover, this is the only solution which does not mean a step backward.

It is, then, up to mankind to solve the problem in this sense, and to get rid of the obstacles and alibis that stand in the way. Delay will only enlarge the dimensions of the problem, making its solution more hazardous and more complicated.

Since it is in their own agricultural and industrial techniques that men will find the answer to their population growth and the problems of hunger in the world, it is up to them to find within themselves the genius necessary to redress the balance between population and the means of subsistence in a positive, rather than a negative, manner.

Their responsibility is great, in as much as it cannot be disposed of as arising out of supernatural or physical causes.

To say that a problem has been solved once it has been correctly put, is only partly true. And yet to have accomplished even that much is to have made a good start, to have advanced at least a bit of the way.

NOTE

1. J. Stassart, "Les surplus agricoles et l'avenir de l'agriculture," *Annales de l'Economie Collective*, 49, 1 (Jan./March, 1961), p. 26.

Chapter 11

General Conclusions

IT IS TODAY manifest that, by applying what the science of agronomy has so far learned to the wealth (both existing and renewable) that nature puts at our disposal, mankind can provide itself with the highest dietary level as yet known. It can do this, moreover, without touching the capital of nature's wealth—actually increasing the latter in the process. To feed 5 billion human beings, it would suffice to draw from the soil of lands recognized capable of being cultivated (some 17.5 billion acres) just half of what a Far Eastern peasant, or one-third of what a Western European peasant, produced per acre, prior to 1938.[1] Obviously, it is not availability of land which is the limiting factor in food production.

Agronomic advances teach us that the world's arid zones could become important areas of agricultural production. Besides limiting factors—some of them introduced by human misuse of the land—these zones hold what are theoretically "the greatest agricultural potentials in the world."[2] In the Sahara, for example, although "the most serious limiting factor on agricultural productivity" will always be "the scarcity of water and a certain scarcity of soils of the type which can be cultivated, properly speaking, by the conventional techniques," yet on the other hand there is

Almost continuous brilliant sunshine every day of the year (equal to 4000–4200 kilowatt hours per square meter per year), and tempera-

454

tures notably favorable to the growth of the most productive plant species, thanks to the great daily variations.[3]

Agronomists have been making great strides in finding ways to utilize those elements of nature's wealth which hitherto constituted limiting factors on agricultural productivity. Already, the 13 per cent of the world's cultivated land which has only become so thanks to irrigation, supplies 25 per cent of the world's food. At Chouard's project in Béni-Abbès, the weight of the crops harvested per cubic meter of water used is generally three times or more that of the yield in the nearby palm grove.

Under the circumstances, we have no right to accuse nature and nature's Creator of "parsimony" with regard to us.

We have already observed that far more often the limiting factor on productivity is human labor. The proportion of units of the latter to the number of consumers is frequently inadequate to satisfy the primary, and especially the nutritional, needs of the consumers.

There are at present some 1.7 billion persons inhabiting the rural regions of the world. Were we to ask them to supply the world's present population with the 10,000 original or vegetable calories which the best fed among us consume, then they would each of them have to produce a bit more than each rural-dweller in northwest Europe was producing before World War II. That is, four and a half times more than the rural-dweller in the Far East was producing in the same period.

It is not an impossible thing to ask, but it does represent a much more sizable advance in the productivity of cultivable land than we should be asking.[4]

We have seen how this limiting factor, too, can be overcome, though not without difficulties it is true. The room for progress, however, is so great in this connection that, if we really wanted to do so, we could raise enough food to supply some billions of people with the subsistence required for optimum levels of consumption.

Now, at the present time, two-thirds of mankind suffers from hunger, while in the most advanced parts of the world farmers are being discouraged from producing . . . what some dare refer to as "surplus" food. How are we to explain this situation? As simply the result of ignorance and error? And though ignorance and error can never excuse anything, neither do they fully account for this situation. Is it, then, an economic problem with which we are dealing?

To define it in Aristotle's terms, the economic problem would be due to ignorance and errors that prevent "the head of the family," who is responsible for "care of the human household," from so administering nature's bounty as to provide mankind with its subsistence. It is not an insoluble problem, though it has not as yet been solved everywhere.

Our contemporaries, however, think of as "economic"—as the Stagirite did not—matters he put rather under the heading of the science of gaining wealth, his term for which was "chrematistics" (*Politics* 1256-Ae) and which he associated with the appearance of exchange.

So long as the exchange is a "natural" one, i.e., bears upon products and services that can satisfy the particular needs of the parties to the contract, it is hard to see what grounds there would be for forbidding production of what helps satisfy primary needs. No doubt inequalities of wealth might, in periods of scarcity when everyone is relatively poor, bring about nutritional discrimination and encourage the production of luxury goods at the expense of primary needs. However, the tendency would not go far so long as the chrematistic impulse remained "natural." Commerce cannot develop unchecked in pursuit of unlimited wealth until money appears on the scene, that *lucrum in infinitum* so frequently condemned by medieval thinkers and in particular by St. Thomas Aquinas (*Summa theologica,* IIa–IIae, "On Justice").

Nor need the introduction of money as a medium of exchange of itself, ipso facto, lead to pursuit of *lucrum in infinitum*. The distinction to draw is the one Karl Marx made between "simple circulation" in the cycle "goods–money–goods" and "capitalist circulation" in the cycle "money–goods–money." It is at the moment goods become mere commodities, i.e., pretext for the accumulation of riches, that the chrematistic impulse begins to go beyond all bounds.

Now with the transformation of goods into commodities, all that counts is their "exchange value," i.e., what they cost or what they will bring. Capitalism, according to Marx, has brought about an "alienation" of their use value. Moreover, when Marx maintained that it was only the labor which had gone into them that could give sense to the equation x lbs. of steel $= y$ bus. of wheat, he was drawing a conclusion that goes back to Aristotle and which had, before Marx, been stated by William Petty. Far from claiming any originality for his point of view, Marx made rather a point of its traditional lineage. He gives one other example of "alienation." Capitalism, which has turned things into "merchandise" and usefulness into "value," similarly transformed the concrete, living labor of the old-fashioned craftsman into abstract labor, a quantum, qualitatively indeterminate but measurable now in terms of "the time socially necessary to produce a commodity."[5]

With organization according to the "money–goods–money" cycle, commerce recognizes no further restraint upon the accumulation of wealth. "Exchange value" and "unit of labor" cease to be based upon any perceptible human reality. Should scarcity become a necessary condition for endowing a commodity with value, then scarcity will be brought about to the limit of what consumers will stand for—their needs subordinated to "exchange value" on the commodity market. At the same time, whatever a given commodity's usefulness in the satisfaction of human needs, the producer risks not getting a just return for his labor, sometimes not even repayment for the expenses he has incurred.

There have been a number of consequences to unchecked profit-seeking. First of all, the old moderating restraints have been swept away, such as the notion of a just price and just wages, and the sense of extreme need as constituting an exception to all rules. These at least provided a modicum of justice in economic relations. In addition, there have been concerted efforts to adjust production to purchasing power; there is more money to be made supplying luxury goods for those who can buy them, than there is in satisfying the primary needs of the multitude.

Simonde de Sismondi was one of the first to demonstrate how a "general overproduction" might come about, through "permanent underconsumption of basic products on the part of the poor who, becoming ever poorer, must consume less and less." He went on to observe:

The personal consumption of a millionaire factory owner who has working for him 1,000 men whom he pays the lowest possible wages, is much less valuable to the nation than the consumption of 100 manufacturers who are much less wealthy and who employ but ten workmen apiece, who are much less poor.[6]

Moreover, it has become more profitable to produce less. That is, the "extensive" type of agriculture yields higher returns than the "intensive" type. (See above, p. 260.) To the landowner who keeps a weather eye on the market in farm properties, preference may well be given to the prospective tenant who practices the former type of agriculture.

Sismondi also observed that a well-farmed property which brings in an annual net return of 1,000 crowns on an annual rental of 100 crowns, might be turned over to pasture land and as such bring the landlord 110 crowns in rent. What do you suppose the landlord will do?

He will get rid of his wine-grower or market-gardener and will earn 10 crowns more than he did. The nation, however, will have lost 890. All the capital that went into making the property so successfully productive will lie idle and bring no return. Those who tilled its soil will now be without work and thus without income.[7]

It is true that as distinctions have grown up between capitalist and entrepreneur, and as more and more impersonal ways of accumulating wealth have been devised, economic processes have become rather more complicated than they seemed in Sismondi's day. However, can we say that there has been any slowing down in the consequences of economic exploitation, or that the pursuit of wealth has found its natural limits? It scarcely seems so. As jobs get more and more specialized and as each production factor is linked with some ever more abstract and dehumanized profit, all sense of ethical bounds disappears. Between them the *dolus bonus* and cant phrases like "normal business procedure" cover as with a veil of modesty the sharpest practices at the expense of justice, to say nothing of charity.

He to whom it has been given as a duty "to administer the goods of the poor" is under obligation to invest money advantageously, although Aristotle long since recognized of money that "it bears no offspring." If rich men have forgotten their duty in the ordinary sense, with respect to the goods of the poor, this seems the more justified to them for the fact that they can scarcely be said to administer their own goods anymore—or what they suppose to be their own.

Under the circumstances questions as to which is the more just of two prices or two wages, with both parties to the dispute possessing "equal" rights, can only be decided by force. Government controls of one sort or another become more and more necessary if the world's wealth is to secure the common weal and, above all, if it is to procure satisfaction of the primary needs of the multitude.

Contempt for whatever "doesn't cost anything," meanwhile, encourages the squandering of goods not presently scarce, i.e., which have no "exchange value" at the moment.

The final effect of all this poor management of the common welfare is to discourage production of goods to satisfy the primary needs of the greatest number, by raising the specter of "overproduction" in the markets which handle them solely with respect for that fraction of the current demand which is solidly backed by purchasing power. On this pretext, natural wealth indispensable to future food production in the years to come is destroyed.

The only variety of conservatism that wins out in such an economic system is the variety which tends to protect the gains of a privileged few, which limits production by practices of "economic Malthusianism" so as to underwrite scarcity, and which would rather see population itself limited by "Neo-Malthusian" practices than risk compromising its own gains by the alternative course of a healthy economic expansionism.

Both forms of Malthusianism, though ostensibly at odds with one another in their declared aims, derive from the same spiritual despair so far as mankind's future is concerned.

The fact that, were scarcity to disappear, the social suprastructures would be threatened, is sufficient to alarm the privileged groups in today's society. This is not hard to understand. The masses of human beings who suffer from scarcity and from the "alienation" which proceeds from it, are less likely to be frightened at the prospect of a leap into the unknown. All the more important, then, that it should be a leap from prehistory into history, not into a period of further scarcity and excessive exploitation, both of men and the land.

The responsibility which weighs upon mankind and upon each of us who constitutes it is a heavy one. Though it seems less self-evident to all than that other responsibility which weighs upon a comparatively few men only in the atomic age, yet it is of the same order of magnitude, and perhaps for the very reason it is harder to discern is also the harder to bear.

How can we hesitate to do what must be done, when we know that there can be no going back, and when we have a right to believe that humanity has not reached this point—has not been led to it by Providence—only to end here and now, catastrophically, as we stand on the very threshold of better times?[8]

Instead of giving in to the sordid calculations of the despairing Malthusians, let us take heart, have faith in youth and in the future, and remember that we are bidden to take dominion over the earth.

Let us boldly envisage the prospect of a planet on which ten billion or more human beings shall live better than we live. . . . In any case, neither the one Malthusianism nor the other leads anywhere, whereas until now humanity has escaped the very gravest perils thanks to those few of its members who have recognized that "It is not wisdom to be only wise."

NOTES

1. Michel Cépède, "Nourrir les Hommes" in *Encyclopédie Française* (Paris: 1960), IX, pp. 9–54.
2. P. Chouard, "Mise au point de cultures hydroponiques au Sahara," *Académie d'Agriculture de France,* session of Dec. 20, 1961.
3. *Ibid.*
4. Cépède, *op. cit.*
5. Pierre Vilar, "Marx, marxisme" in *Dictionnaire des Sciences économiques* (Paris, 1960), V, pp. 714 ff.
6. Sismondi, *Nouveaux Principes d'Economie Politique.*
7. *Ibid.*
8. Michel Cépède, "L'homme et le sol," *L'Agro,* no. 26 (Oct./Nov. 1959).